Revision f PHYSICS *GCSE*
• *with answers* •

KEN FOULDS
is Senior Teacher at Seaham Comprehensive School, Co. Durham

JOHN WATTS
is Head of Science and Physics
at Kimberworth Comprehensive School, Rotherham

Y

Authors' acknowledgements

I should like to thank the teaching staff of Brightlingsea Secondary School, Essex in the late 1960s, especially Mr Norton and Mr Rice, for having faith in my abilities and encouraging me to extend my education, and also my parents for supporting me. The interest and support shown during the writing of this book by my colleagues at Kimberworth Comprehensive School, Rotherham has been greatly appreciated. However, most thanks must go to Chris and Caroline for their never-ending patience and encouragement. I should also like to thank the editorial staff at John Murray and Jane Roth for all their hard work and support.
John Watts B.Sc. (Hons.)

I should like to thank my family and friends for their encouragement and support, and the staff at John Murray and Jane Roth for their hard work, during the production of this book.
Ken Foulds M.Sc.

The Examination Boards

This book was written to cover all GCSE Physics syllabuses. The authors and publishers are grateful to the following examination boards for kind permission to reproduce past examination questions. The answers supplied are written by the authors. The examination boards have not approved the answers and bear no responsibility for the accuracy or method of working given. Students should be aware that the answers may not necessarily constitute the only possible ones.

Northern Examinations and Assessment Board (NEAB), Devas Street, Manchester, M15 6EX

Southern Examination Group (SEG), Stag Hill House, Guildford, Surrey, GU2 5XJ

Midland Examining Group (MEG), Syndicate Buildings, 1 Hills Road, Cambridge, CB1 2EU

London Examinations, a division of EDEXCEL Foundation (London), Stewart House, 32 Russell Square, London, WC1B 5DN

Photo acknowledgements

The publishers are grateful to the following for permission to reproduce copyright photographs:
p.67 David Hoffman, p.104 Andrew Lambert, p.110 H.R. Wallingford.

© Ken Foulds and John Watts 1999

First published in 1999 by
John Murray (Publishers) Ltd
50 Albemarle Street
London W1X 4BD

Illustrations by Eric Apsey and Anthony Warne
Layouts by Fiona Webb

Typeset in 11/13pt Garamond Book by Wearset, Boldon, Tyne and Wear
Printed and bound in Great Britain by St Edmundsbury Press, Bury St Edmunds

A catalogue entry for this title is available from the British Library.

ISBN 0 7195 7634 2

Contents

Introduction

During the last few years, you have gained a great deal of important knowledge and understanding from the National Curriculum – Science (Physics). You have probably forgotten some of the work. This work must be revised for your examinations.

Unfortunately, revision is hard work and it is easy to avoid. Some of the most common ways are shown in the cartoons below.

First, get organised!

Plan

It is always a good idea to plan your revision. The plan below is an example of a revision timetable. Each box represents up to 2 or 3 hours of work. Make up something like this for your own revision, and stick it on your wall.

Study/Revision planner	Mon	Tues	Wed	Thurs	Fri	Sat	Sun
1 Plan all your revision before you begin it.	15 March Section 1 1.1–1.4	16 Section 1 1.5–1.7	17 Section 1 1.8–1.10	18 Section 1 1.11–1.14	19 Try some exam questions	20 Section 2 2.1–2.4	21 Day off
2 Each box represents up to 2 or 3 hours work.	22 Section 2 2.5–2.7	23 Section 2 2.8–2.11	24 Try some exam questions	25 etc.	26	27	28
3 Try to keep to your plan, but don't be afraid to change it.	29	30	31	1 April	2	3	4
	5	6	7	8	9	10	11

Be an active learner

Try to be an active learner. Rather than just reading through notes, make sure that you write or draw or underline as you read through them. Make summaries and answer questions. Use revision summaries like the one shown below.

fossil fuels

coal, oil, natural gas

dead organisms, crushed, changed over millions of years

non - renewable

renewable energy sources

can be used over and over

wind, solar, tides, hydro - electricity

Example of a revision summary

Next, use this book!

This book has been written to help you prepare for your GCSE Physics examination – whether as separate Science: Physics, or as the Physics component of a Double Award (Coordinated) course.

This book will be of most use to you as you come to the end of your course, especially when you are ready to start with your revision. Of course this book can be useful in other ways, such as when you are preparing for tests or school examinations during your GCSE course.

Your teacher will suggest which level you should aim for, foundation or higher. Also, it is very important for you to obtain a checklist of the topics that you need to study from your teacher.

1 This book has been written in six sections. Read through carefully and make sure you understand the ideas. Do the quick questions as you go along. If you cannot answer a question, re-read the text and try again. If you still cannot answer, ask your teacher for help. Answers are given on pages 170–186.

2 To help draw attention to the more important words, the first time scientific terms are used they are printed in **bold**. These words and phrases are included in a glossary on pages 167–169. This glossary can be used as a self-test or as a simple reference section.

3 Examination practice questions are given at the end of each section so you can test your knowledge and understanding of the work covered. The level of each question (foundation or higher) is indicated. Some questions are from recent GCSE Science: Physics papers. Check your answers with those at the end of the book. See your teacher about anything you still do not understand.

4 Try to read and re-read the relevant topics as often as you can so that you become familiar with the ideas and learn them more effectively.

1.1 Static electricity

Some materials, when they are polished, become charged with static (stationary) electricity. To understand static electricity you need to know something about the structure of atoms - the small particles from which every substance is made. The basic structure of an atom is shown below.

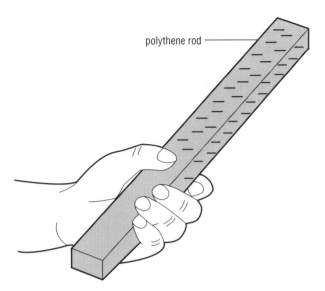

Figure 1.1.2a Polythene becomes negatively charged when rubbed with a cloth

If, on the other hand, the atoms in a material lose electrons, they are left with more protons than electrons. The material then has excess positive charge - it is described as being positively charged (Figure 1.1.2b).

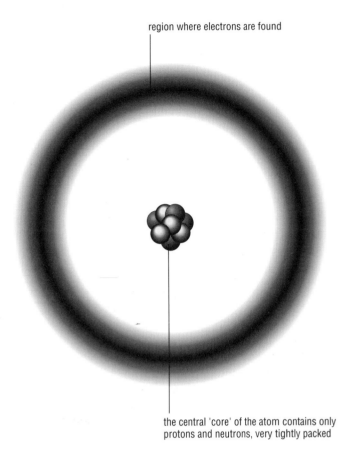

region where electrons are found

the central 'core' of the atom contains only protons and neutrons, very tightly packed

Figure 1.1.1 The smallest particles – the electrons – orbit the nucleus

The **neutrons** are uncharged particles. The **protons** are positively charged and the **electrons** are negatively charged. The negative charge on an electron is equal in size to the positive charge on a proton.

An atom contains equal numbers of protons and electrons. The negative charge on the electrons is therefore 'balanced' by the positive charge on the protons so an atom is uncharged overall.

Charging materials

Materials become electrically charged when the number of electrons in the atoms changes. If a material gains electrons there will be more electrons than protons. There is then an excess negative charge on the material - it is described as being negatively charged (Figure 1.1.2a).

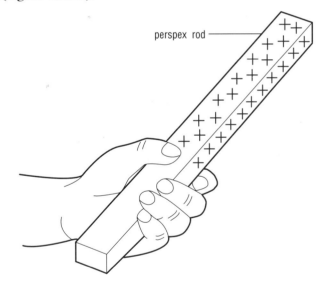

Figure 1.1.2b Perspex becomes positively charged when rubbed with a cloth

It is the transfer of electrons that causes the material to become charged. The number of protons and neutrons remains unchanged throughout.

Materials can become charged by friction. When a polythene rod is rubbed with a cloth, for example, some electrons are 'pulled off' the atoms in the cloth and are transferred to the rod. As a result the polythene becomes negatively charged (because it has gained electrons) and the cloth is left positively charged (because it has lost electrons).

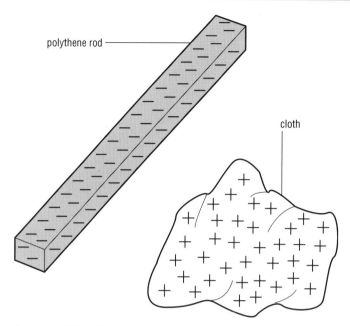

Figure 1.1.3 The cloth is left with excess positive charge

The effect on uncharged materials

A charged material will attract small pieces of paper. Paper is a good enough conductor to allow electrons to move inside it. When, for example, a negatively charged rod is brought close to the paper the negative charge on the rod repels the negatively charged electrons to one end of the paper. That leaves excess positive charge on the surface of the paper nearest the rod. The negatively charged rod then attracts the paper.

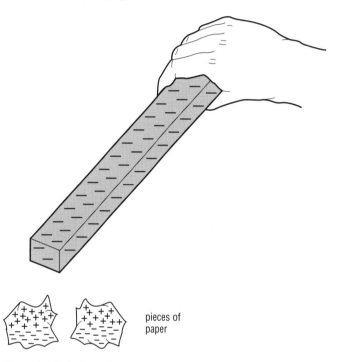

pieces of paper

Figure 1.1.4 A charged object will attract small uncharged objects

Perspex, on the other hand, becomes positively charged when it is rubbed with a cloth. In this case the cloth pulls electrons from the atoms in the perspex. As a result the cloth becomes negatively charged.

Note that rubbing the materials does not 'make' charge – it simply transfers the charged particles, which are already there, from one material to another. It is the overall balance in the number of charged particles that is important.

Charged objects can exert forces. A positively charged perspex rod, for example, will pull (attract) a negatively charged polythene rod. A negatively charged polythene rod, on the other hand, will repel (push away) a similarly charged rod. The general rule is: *like (the same) charges repel and unlike (different) charges attract.*

Conductors and insulators

In some materials some of the electrons are only loosely attached to the atoms and can flow through the material. These materials are described as **conductors**. All metals are good conductors. Carbon (in the form of graphite), although a non-metal, is also a good conductor.

Materials through which electrons cannot pass are called **insulators**. Most non-metals are insulators.

If we try to charge a metal rod by holding it and polishing it, any excess charge that is generated is immediately cancelled out by the transfer (through the metallic conductor) of electrons between the rod, ourselves and the earth. Metals can only be charged if they are insulated from the earth. The insulating material prevents the transfer of charge between the rod and the earth.

When the rod is removed the charges on the paper become evenly distributed once again. For similar reasons, dust is attracted to charged objects in the home, such as your TV screen.

Quick Questions

1 What will happen when:
   a) a charged polythene rod is brought close to another charged polythene rod?
   b) a charged perspex rod is brought close to some small uncharged pieces of polystyrene?
   c) a negatively charged rod is brought close to a positively charged rod?
2 A perspex rod is polished with a cloth and becomes positively charged.
   a) Explain, in terms of the transfer of charge, why the perspex becomes charged.
   b) The cloth also becomes charged. What will be the charge on the cloth and how does it become charged?

1.2 Charge on the move

The dome of a Van de Graaff generator is charged because of friction between the rubber belt (an insulator) and the air and between the belt and the plastic roller. The (concentrated) charge spreads evenly across the metal dome and remains there because the dome is insulated from the earth.

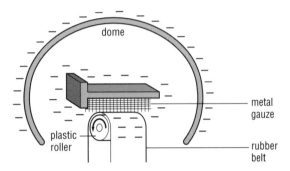

Figure 1.2.1 Inside a van de Graaff generator dome

If a second metal sphere (connected to earth) is placed near the dome, sparks jump the gap between the two spheres. The sparks are caused by **ionisation** of the air around the dome. The strong negative charge on the dome attracts the positive nuclei of molecules in the air. Negative electrons are repelled. If the charge on the dome is sufficiently concentrated some electrons may be separated from their parent molecules, leaving positively charged particles called **ions**. The electrons may join up with other molecules, creating negatively charged ions.

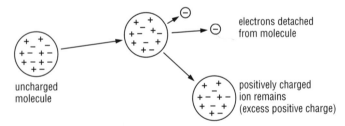

Figure 1.2.2 Ionisation of o ne particle

Once a positively charged ion is formed it will be rapidly attracted towards the dome, colliding with other molecules in the air as it goes. The collisions are strong enough to free electrons from other molecules, creating even more ions. The spark we see is a sudden rush of ions colliding at such high speeds that they emit light (and sound).

If the dome of the generator is connected to earth by a conducting wire, the charge passes (as fast as it is produced) through the wire to earth (rather than building up on the dome as static charge). By connecting a sensitive galvanometer in the wire, we can see that an electric current is flowing between the generator and earth. The **electric current** is the flow of charged particles through the wire.

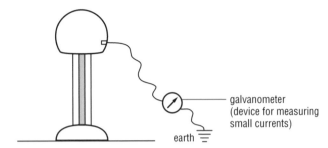

Figure 1.2.3 The charge flows to earth

Potential and potential difference

Regions which have a high concentration of static charge are said to have a 'high potential'. The greater the concentration of charge, the greater the potential. The earth is so vast that any excess electrons spread themselves out so that we can regard the earth as having zero potential. When the dome of the van de Graaff generator is connected to earth, there is a difference in potential between the two points – we say that there is a **potential difference** between the dome and earth. Charge flows from the point of higher potential to the point of lower potential – in this case electrons flow from the dome to earth. An electric current flows between two points only when there is a potential difference between the points.

Lightning conductors

Huge amounts of charge can build up on thunderclouds (created by friction between moving particles within the clouds). Eventually the charge becomes so concentrated (creating a very high potential difference) that a spark (the lightning) jumps between the clouds and the ground.

Lightning can cause severe damage if it strikes buildings. To reduce the risk, many buildings are fitted with lightning conductors – strips of copper connecting the ground to the highest point on the building.

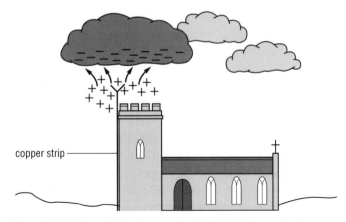

Figure 1.2.4 Some of the charge around the lightning conductor cancels some of the opposite charge in the thundercloud

The lightning conductor works in two ways:

- The conductor itself can become charged as negative ions in the cloud repel electrons in the conductor. At the point of the conductor, positive ions in the air stream upwards. These may cancel out some of the negative charge on the cloud. The potential difference between the cloud and the conductor (connected to earth) is reduced, so reducing the chance of a lightning strike.
- If lightning does strike then it will strike the highest point – the lightning conductor. The copper strip provides a good conducting path through which the charge flows directly to earth. Without the conductor the lightning may pass through the building itself, causing damage.

Using electrostatics

Electrostatic effects are used in many ways, notably in crop sprayers, where the static charge ensures that an even spray is produced.

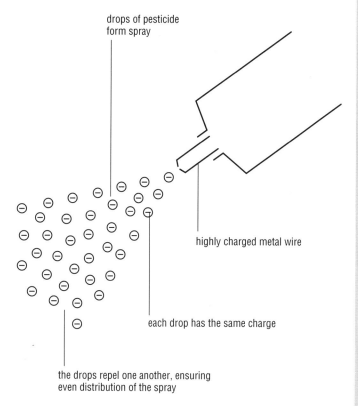

drops of pesticide form spray

highly charged metal wire

each drop has the same charge

the drops repel one another, ensuring even distribution of the spray

Figure 1.2.5 The principle of a crop spray gun

The same principle is used in:

- Paint spray guns, where the static charge ensures an even distribution of the droplets of paint.
- Dust extraction units, especially those fitted to power station chimneys to reduce atmospheric pollution by the waste products – the charged waste particles are attracted to large collecting plates rather than being released into the atmosphere.

Quick Questions

1 Describe two ways in which a lightning conductor works.
2 **a)** Explain how electrostatic charge is created in:
  i) a van de Graaff generator;
  ii) a thundercloud.
  b) The diagram below shows a wig placed on the dome of an uncharged van de Graaff generator. When the dome is charged, the strands of hair rise and separate. Copy the diagram and draw charges on the picture to show why this happens.

Figure 1.2.6

3 Sort the following materials into **a)** those which are electrical conductors and **b)** those which are insulators: copper, glass, polythene, iron, carbon, plastic, aluminium, steel.

4

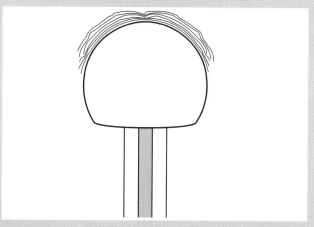

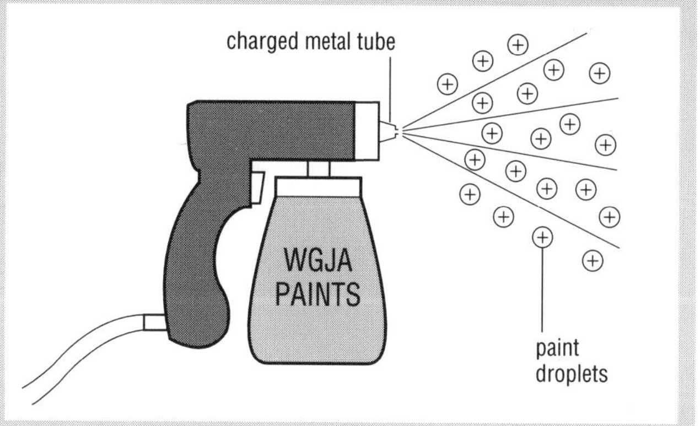

charged metal tube

WGJA PAINTS

paint droplets

Figure 1.2.7

  a) Why does the paint spread out after leaving the nozzle of the paint sprayer above?
  b) If the droplets of paint have a positive charge, what type of charge should be on the metal tube?
5 When aircraft are refuelled, liquid fuel is pumped quickly through a pipe from a tanker.
  a) How can this be dangerous?
  b) A metal conductor is connected between the tanker and the aircraft. How does this make the situation safer?

1.3 Safety in the home

Most electrical appliances are connected to the socket via a plug. Plugs are generally made from insulating materials such as plastic or rubber. This prevents electricity flowing through the plug and then through you! The cables must be connected correctly inside the plug.

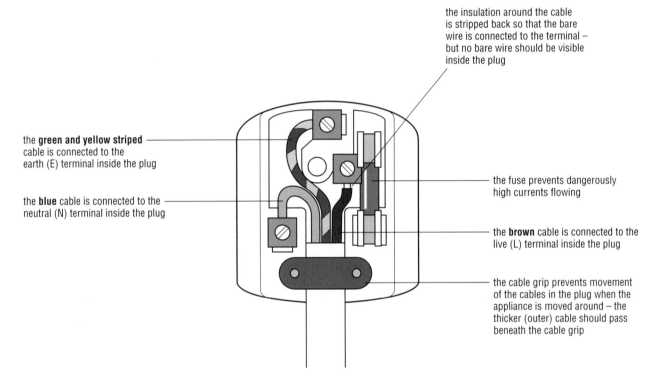

the insulation around the cable is stripped back so that the bare wire is connected to the terminal – but no bare wire should be visible inside the plug

the **green and yellow striped** cable is connected to the earth (E) terminal inside the plug

the **blue** cable is connected to the neutral (N) terminal inside the plug

the fuse prevents dangerously high currents flowing

the **brown** cable is connected to the live (L) terminal inside the plug

the cable grip prevents movement of the cables in the plug when the appliance is moved around – the thicker (outer) cable should pass beneath the cable grip

Figure 1.3.1 Connections in a standard three-pin plug

The earth wire

Sometimes a fault develops in an appliance. Without an earth wire, parts of the appliance (such as the metal case) could become live - they would be at a high potential. If you were to touch any live part you would get an electric shock as current flowed between the appliance and earth - through you!

The earth wire is there to protect you. Any metal parts on the outside of the appliance are connected, via the earth wire, to the ground around your house. That ensures that all those metal parts will be at zero potential. If a fault develops, such as a live wire working loose and touching the metal parts of the appliance, current would flow through the circuit formed by the live and earth wires, melting and breaking the thin wire in the fuse. Everything would then be disconnected from the live terminal.

Some appliances, such as hairdriers and electric drills, are 'double insulated'. They have an outer plastic body and are designed so there can be no contact between any external metal parts and the electrical parts inside. No earth connection is needed for these appliances.

Fuses

Current must pass through the fuse in the plug when an appliance is used. If too much current flows, without a fuse the appliance or the cables could overheat, possibly causing a fire. The fuse protects the appliance by limiting the current that can flow.

The fuse is a thin strand of metal inside a glass or ceramic tube.

circuit symbol

Figure 1.3.2 Cartridge fuse

If the current is too big the fuse wire melts and breaks the circuit, cutting off the current. The wire inside a fuse melts when a certain current flows through it. A 3 amp fuse, for example, will melt when the current reaches 3 amps (or thereabouts). A 13 amp fuse will melt when the current is larger than 13 amps. At one time you could buy fuses of many different values. It is now generally accepted that the standard sizes are 3 A and 13 A.

Calculating which fuse is needed

To calculate which fuse you should fit into a plug you need to know the power of the appliance (usually found on a label on the outer case) and the mains voltage. You can then calculate the maximum current that will flow through the appliance:

$$\text{current (amps)} = \frac{\text{power (watts)}}{\text{voltage of supply (volts)}}$$

Worked example

A kettle has a power rating of 1200 watts and operates on a 230 V supply. Which fuse should be fitted to the plug?

Current (amps) = power (watts)/voltage of supply (volts)

         = 1200/230

         = 5.2 A

Generally you should choose a fuse which has a higher current rating than the value of the current you have calculated. Here a 13 A fuse would be fitted to the plug.

Fuse boxes and circuit breakers

Older houses have (in addition to fuses inside the plugs) a fuse box in the consumer unit. The fuse box contains a bank of fuse wires of different thicknesses, which protect all of the circuits around the home.

Modern houses are more likely to have circuit breakers in the consumer unit rather than separate fuses. Each circuit (such as the lighting circuit) in the home is protected by one circuit breaker.

The circuit breakers are electromagnetic devices which immediately break the circuit by separating two contacts if the current exceeds a safe value. They operate much faster than standard fuses and so are much safer. Also, once the fault has been located, it is easier to reset a circuit breaker (by simply pressing a button) than to replace a fuse.

Quick Questions

1 Each of the plugs shown below has at least one fault.

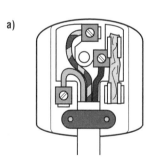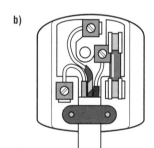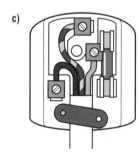

Figure 1.3.3

Identify the fault(s) in each one and say what should be done to correct it/them.

2 Calculate the current flowing through each of the following appliances and say which fuse (3 A or 13 A) should be fitted in the plug. Assume each one operates on the mains supply of 230 volts.

  a) A bedside lamp with a 60 watt bulb.

  b) A 650 watt microwave oven.

  c) A 2000 watt washing machine.

  d) A 30 watt hi-fi.

3 A 5 A fuse contains a length of fuse wire connected between the metal capped ends of the fuse cartridge. Explain what happens when a current of 8 A suddenly flows through the fuse.

4 **a)** Why do most plugs have plastic or rubber outer covers?

  b) Why are the terminals inside the plug made from steel or brass?

  c) Why should you never handle a plug with wet hands?

1.4 Current electricity

Electrical appliances only work when current flows through them. The electric circuit provides a route through which the current can flow. Current flows continuously through a complete circuit, transferring energy from the power supply to the appliance.

An electric current may be **direct current (d.c.)** or **alternating current (a.c.)**. Cells and batteries supply direct current, which flows continuously around the circuit in the same direction.

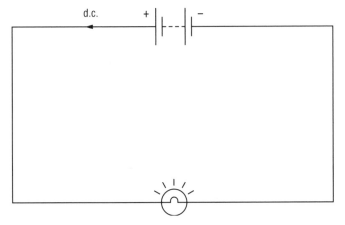

Figure 1.4.1 Direct current flows one way

On diagrams such as this the current is always shown flowing from the positive terminal of the supply to the negative terminal, although in reality electrons in a metal wire flow from negative to positive.

The mains electricity in the UK is an alternating current driven by a 230 volt, 50 Hz supply. Alternating current oscillates (pulses to-and-fro) in the circuit. The frequency of the a.c. supply dictates how often the current changes direction.

The term '50 Hz' (50 **hertz** – note the unit of frequency) indicates that the current has 50 cycles each second and changes direction 100 times each second.

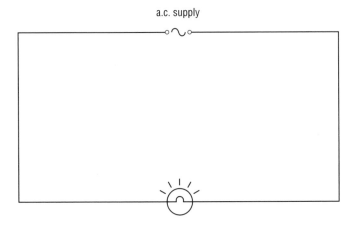

Figure 1.4.2 Alternating current oscillates but still transfers energy

Some power supplies may supply either a.c. or d.c.

Circuit symbols

Electric circuits are drawn using circuit diagrams. The components in circuit diagrams are represented by symbols. The most commonly used symbols are shown below.

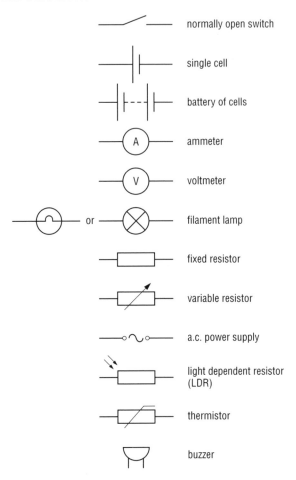

normally open switch

single cell

battery of cells

ammeter

voltmeter

filament lamp

fixed resistor

variable resistor

a.c. power supply

light dependent resistor (LDR)

thermistor

buzzer

Figure 1.4.3 Common circuit symbols

The conducting material (such as connecting wire) used to connect circuits is always shown as a straight line.

Series circuits

The components in very simple circuits are connected end-to-end in a single loop – we say they are connected in series.

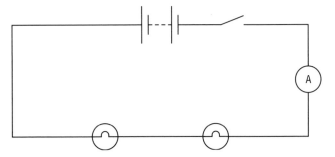

Figure 1.4.4 A simple series circuit

Series circuits have significant disadvantages:

- Everything must be on or everything must be off – the components cannot be controlled independently of one another.
- If one component fails, the circuit is broken and nothing will work.

Parallel circuits

The components in most practical circuits are connected in parallel. They are connected in several parallel loops. The lights and sockets in your home are connected in this way. Most lights on vehicles are also connected in parallel.

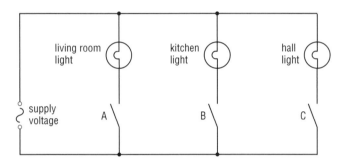

Figure 1.4.5 Downstairs lighting circuit of a house, simplified

The advantages of **parallel circuits** are:

- Each component or device can be operated independently - one can be on whilst others are off.
- If one device fails, the others will continue to work.

Switches

Most switches are simple mechanical devices which 'break' the circuit (open a break or gap through which current cannot pass) or 'make' the circuit (close the break to complete the circuit).

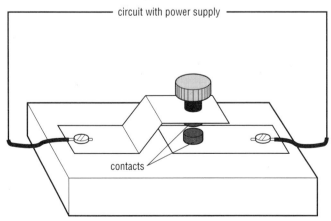

Figure 1.4.6a In this position there is an air gap between the two contacts of the switch. Because air is an insulator, the circuit is broken and no current flows

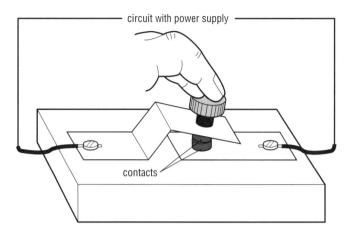

Figure 1.4.6b When the switch is pressed the two metal contacts meet, forming a complete circuit through which current can flow

An electric current will only flow through a complete circuit.

Quick Questions

1 Name each of the components shown by the symbols below.

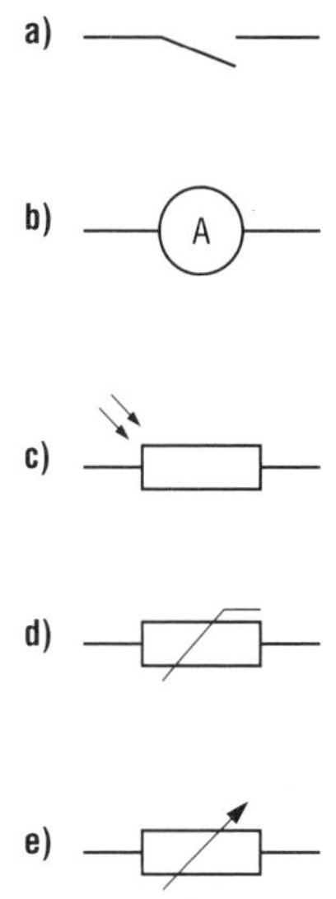

a) ————
b) —(A)—
c) (LDR symbol)
d) (thermistor symbol)
e) (variable resistor symbol)

Figure 1.4.7

2 Describe two advantages that parallel circuits have over series circuits.

3 a) Draw circuit diagrams showing:
    i) two 6 V bulbs in series with a 6 V battery;
    ii) two 6 V bulbs in parallel with a 6 V battery.
  b) In which of the circuits will the bulbs be brighter? Why?
  c) Draw circuit (ii) again, adding switches so that you could have:
    both bulbs off
    or one bulb on
    or both bulbs on.

1.5 Current, charge and resistance

The atoms of all materials contain electrons which are normally strongly bound to the nucleus. In metals, such as the copper used in connecting wire, some of the electrons are free to move within the metal. They move randomly, passing from atom to atom. They are known as **free electrons**.

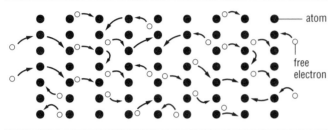

Figure 1.5.1 Normally the free electrons move around randomly from atom to atom

One terminal of a d.c. power supply is at a high electric potential. The other terminal is at a lower potential. When the ends of a conductor are connected to the supply, the potential difference between the terminals drives the electrons through the conductor.

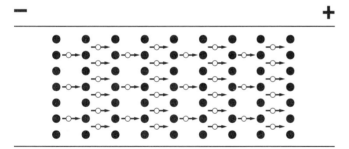

Figure 1.5.2 When the conductor is connected to a power supply, the potential difference created between the ends forces the free electrons to drift in the same direction

The flow of the electrons through the conductor is the electric current.

Measuring current in a circuit

The size of the current flowing through a circuit is measured using an **ammeter**. Ammeters are connected in series with everything else in the circuit. The units of current are **amperes**, often abbreviated to amps (A). A smaller unit, the milliamp (mA), may be used for smaller currents.
1 milliamp = 0.001 A (1/1000 A).

In any series circuit the current has the same value at all points.

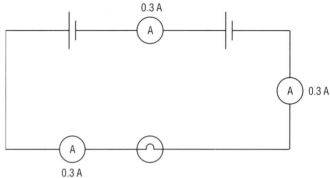

Figure 1.5.3 Current values in a series circuit

In a parallel circuit the current divides wherever the circuit branches.

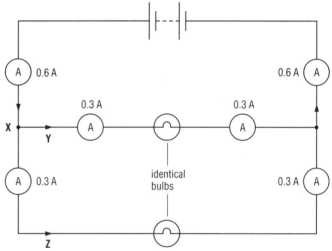

Figure 1.5.4 Current values in a parallel circuit

In the parallel circuit shown above the current divides at point X. Since the two bulbs are the same, half flows through branch Y and half flows through branch Z.

In any parallel circuit:

- The sum of the currents flowing through each branch is equal to the current leaving and returning to the supply.
- The amount of current flowing through each branch is determined by the resistance of the devices in that branch (see page 17) – the higher the resistance, the lower the current.

Charge

There may be several million electrons flowing past any point in a circuit each second. Each electron carries a small amount of (negative) electrical charge. The current can therefore be thought of as a flow of charge around the circuit.

The amount of charge passing any point in a circuit depends on:

- The current that is flowing – the bigger the current, the more charge is transferred in a given time.
- The time for which the current flows – the longer the time for which the current flows, the more charge is transferred.

The quantity of charge that is transferred by an electric current is measured in units called **coulombs (C)**, and is calculated using the equation:

charge (coulombs) = current (amps) × time (seconds)

or:

$$Q = I \times t \quad \text{where } Q = \text{charge (C)}$$
$$I = \text{current (A)}$$
$$t = \text{time (s)}$$

Resistance

Each part of a circuit (such as the connecting wires, bulbs, buzzers) tries to resist the flow of current – we say they provide a **resistance** to the flow of current. The value of the resistance is measured in units called **ohms (Ω)**.

The resistance of good conductors, such as copper wire, is so small that it can normally be ignored. Insulators, on the other hand, have extremely large resistances – so large that under normal circumstances current cannot flow through them. In between there is a range of materials which offer resistances from a few ohms to several million ohms.

The value of the current flowing through a circuit depends on:

- The voltage of the supply.
- The resistance of the components in the circuit (the combined resistance of all the parts).

The diagrams show what happens to the current in a circuit as the voltage of the supply changes (but the resistance is constant).

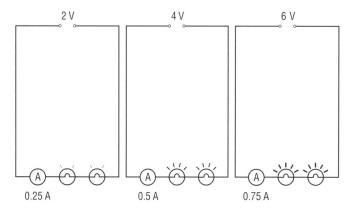

0.25 A   0.5 A   0.75 A

Figure 1.5.5 The current increases as the supply voltage increases

You can see that as the voltage of the supply increases, the current also increases. The bulbs become brighter.

Increasing the number of components in the circuit increases the resistance. The illustrations below show what happens to the current as the resistance in a circuit increases (but note that the supply voltage is constant).

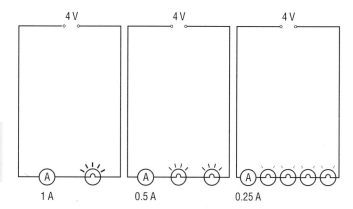

1 A   0.5 A   0.25 A

Figure 1.5.6 The current decreases as the number of bulbs increases

You can see that as the resistance increases the current decreases.

In general:

- The bigger the supply voltage, the bigger the current.
- The bigger the resistance, the smaller the current.

What affects the resistance of a conductor?

The resistance of a metallic conductor (such as wire) depends on:

- The material from which it is made. Some types of wire have a higher resistance per metre than others.
- The length of the conductor. The longer the wire, the bigger the resistance. Resistance is directly proportional to the length.
- The temperature of the conductor. The resistance of most wires increases as the temperature increases.
- The diameter of the wire. The resistance decreases as the diameter of the wire increases. Resistance is inversely proportional to the cross-sectional area.

Knowing the **resistivity** (a constant which represents the resistance of a one metre length of the material with an area of 1 m²) we can calculate the resistance of a wire made from it by using the equation:

$$\text{resistance } (\Omega) = \frac{\text{resistivity } (\Omega \text{ m}) \times \text{length (m)}}{\text{cross-sectional area (m}^2)}$$

Fixed resistors

Electronic circuits (such as those in a TV, personal stereo, etc.) use resistors to control the flow and distribution of current through the circuit. The resistors are made from a mixture of carbon and some other material and can have a range of values from less than 1 ohm up to millions of ohms.

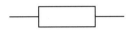

Figure 1.5.7 Circuit symbol for a fixed resistor

Calculating the resistance in a circuit

When resistors (and other components) are connected in series the total resistance is the sum of the resistances, as shown below.

Figure 1.5.8 Resistances in series

Total resistance $= R_1 + R_2$
$$= 10 + 20$$
$$= 30 \text{ ohms}$$

For resistors connected in series:

$$R_{total} = R_1 + R_2 + R_3 \text{ etc.}$$

where R_1, R_2 and R_3 are the values of individual resistors.

When the components are connected in parallel, a different equation must be used:

$$\frac{1}{R_{total}} = \frac{1}{R_1} + \frac{1}{R_2} + \frac{1}{R_3} \text{ etc.}$$

Where there are only two resistors in parallel, this equation can be simplified to:

$$\text{combined value of the resistors} = \frac{\text{product}}{\text{sum}}$$

or

$$R_{total} = \frac{R_1 \times R_2}{R_1 + R_2}$$

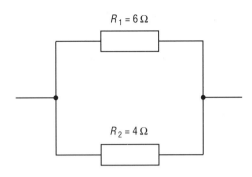

Figure 1.5.9

If, for example, the values of R_1 and R_2 were 6 Ω and 4 Ω as in the circuit above then the resistance they would provide in combination would be:

$$\text{Resistance} = \frac{\text{product}}{\text{sum}} = \frac{6 \times 4}{6 + 4} = \frac{24}{10} = 2.4 \ \Omega$$

Note that the resistance provided by the combination is less than the value of either of the individual resistors.

Variable resistors

Variable resistors allow us to vary the current through a circuit by varying the resistance in the circuit. They may be used to control:

- The brightness of your house lights.
- The temperature of an iron.
- The loudness of your TV or hi-fi.

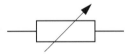

Figure 1.5.10 Circuit symbol for a variable resistor

Increasing the resistance decreases the current, which changes the way the devices in the circuit work. Assuming a constant supply voltage:

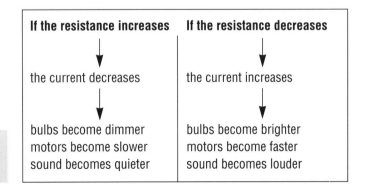

If the resistance increases	If the resistance decreases
↓	↓
the current decreases	the current increases
↓	↓
bulbs become dimmer motors become slower sound becomes quieter	bulbs become brighter motors become faster sound becomes louder

Quick Questions

1 What will be the value of the current shown on the ammeters in each of these circuits?

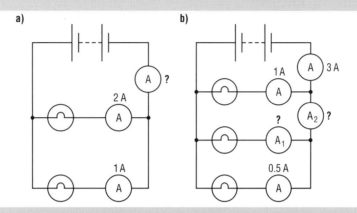

Figure 1.5.11

2 Calculate the charge transferred by a current of 4 amps flowing for 10 seconds.

3 If it takes 5 seconds for a charge of 30 coulombs to be transferred, calculate the current which must be flowing through the circuit.

4 A battery charger supplies a current of 2 amps when connected to a car battery. If the battery is charged for 12 hours, how much charge is transferred to the battery by the current?

5 A length of resistance wire is connected in the circuit in Figure 1.5.12.

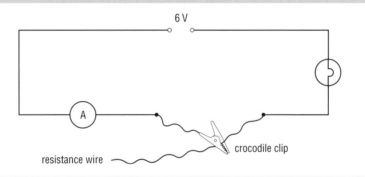

Figure 1.5.12

What would happen to **a)** the brightness of the bulb and **b)** the reading on the ammeter if:
  i) a longer length of the same wire was used?
  ii) a thicker wire of the same length was used?
  iii) the same length of the same wire was used with a bigger supply voltage?

6 A piece of copper wire has a resistance of 20 ohms. What would the resistance be if:
  a) its length was halved?
  b) the same length of copper wire, with half the cross-sectional area, was chosen?

7 Calculate the value of the combined resistance in each of these circuits.

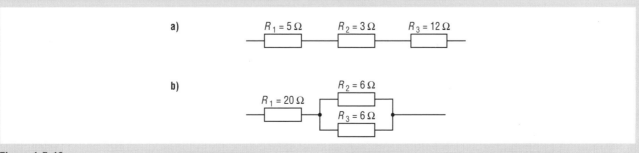

Figure 1.5.13

1.6 Work, voltage and potential difference

A power supply must do work to make the devices in a circuit work. The **voltage** (or **potential difference** across the terminals) of the supply is an indication of the amount of work done on each coulomb of charge that passes through it.

A 1 **volt** cell, for example, does 1 **joule** of work on each **coulomb** of charge flowing through it. The work done by the supply is transferred to the current as **electrical (potential) energy**. The current then transfers this energy to the devices in the circuit.

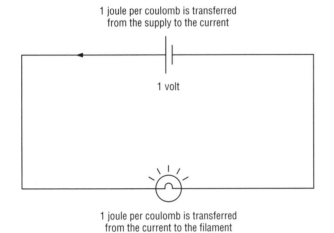

1 joule per coulomb is transferred from the supply to the current

1 volt

1 joule per coulomb is transferred from the current to the filament

Figure 1.6.1 All of the energy transferred to the current by the supply is transferred to the devices in the circuit

Sometimes several cells may be connected in series to provide a higher voltage (and higher current through the circuit). The total voltage across the cells is the sum of the voltages of the individual cells.

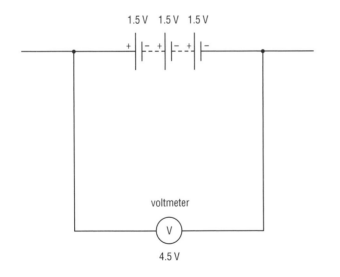

1.5 V   1.5 V   1.5 V

voltmeter

4.5 V

Figure 1.6.2 The voltage across this battery of cells is 1.5 + 1.5 + 1.5 = 4.5 volts (4.5 V)

At other times several cells may be connected in parallel.

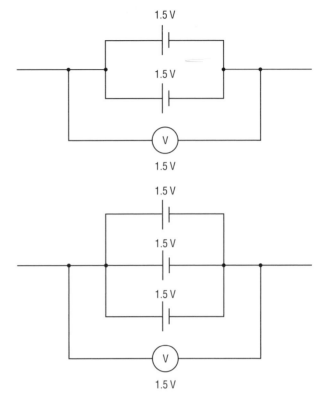

1.5 V

1.5 V

1.5 V

1.5 V

1.5 V

1.5 V

Figure 1.6.3 The total voltage across these cells (regardless of how many are connected) = 1.5 V

The total voltage of two or more identical cells connected in parallel is the same as the voltage across each individual cell.

Potential difference

Potential difference (p.d.) is a measure of the energy gained or lost by each coulomb of electricity passing between two points. In the circuit below, the voltage or potential difference across the battery is 3 volts. The battery transfers 3 joules of energy to each coulomb. Each coulomb then transfers 3 joules of energy to the bulb as it passes through it. We say that there is a potential difference of 3 volts across the bulb.

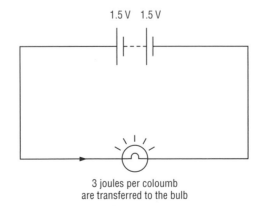

1.5 V   1.5 V

3 joules per coloumb are transferred to the bulb

Figure 1.6.4 The potential difference across the bulb = 3 V

Measuring potential difference

The potential difference across any component is measured using a **voltmeter** connected in parallel (across the ends of the component).

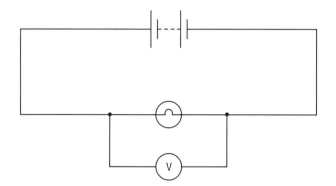

Figure 1.6.5 The voltmeter measures the potential difference across the bulb

Where several components are connected in series, there is a clear relationship between the potential difference across the supply and the potential difference across the components, as shown in the diagram below.

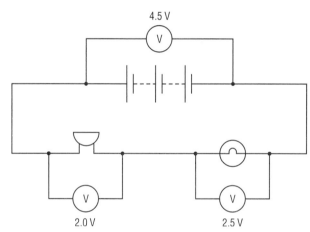

Figure 1.6.6 Potential differences in a series circuit

We can say that, for a series circuit:

$$\begin{array}{c} \text{the potential difference} \\ \text{across the supply} \end{array} = \begin{array}{c} \text{the sum of the potential differences} \\ \text{across all of the devices in the circuit} \end{array}$$

The potential difference across each component depends on the resistance of the component. The bigger the resistance, the bigger the potential difference.

Where components are connected in parallel there is a different relationship between the potential difference across the supply and the potential difference across each component. The relationship is shown in the circuit in Figure 1.6.7.

When appliances are connected in parallel:

$$\begin{array}{c} \text{the potential difference} \\ \text{across each device} \end{array} = \begin{array}{c} \text{the potential difference} \\ \text{across the power supply} \end{array}$$

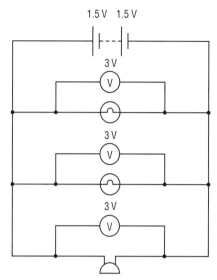

Figure 1.6.7 Potential differences in a parallel circuit

The sockets connected into the ring main of your home are all connected in parallel. No matter how many devices are connected, each one will benefit from the 230 V mains supply voltage.

Quick Questions

1 Four 1.5 V batteries, connected in series, are used to power two electric circuits each containing four 1.5 V bulbs. What is the potential difference across each bulb if:
   a) all four bulbs are connected in series?
   b) all four bulbs are connected in parallel?
2 In each of the circuits below the voltage of the battery is indicated. All the bulbs are identical. What will be the readings on the voltmeters in each circuit?

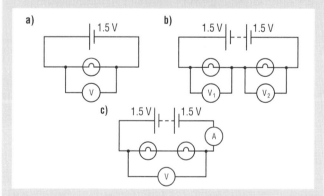

Figure 1.6.8

3 Fill in the missing words:
   Ammeters measure ……… ……… and are always connected in electric circuits in ……… . Voltmeters are connected in ……… with the component whose ……… difference is required.
4 Calculate the potential difference across a component in a circuit if 3 coulombs of charge transfer 36 joules of energy to the component.

1.7 Ohm's Law

The potential difference across a metallic conductor and the current flowing through it are connected by a simple relationship which can be shown using the circuit below.

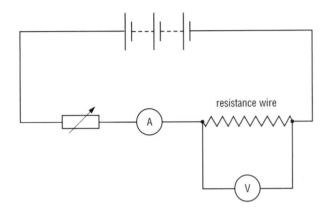

Figure 1.7.1 Measuring the potential difference across and current through a length of resistance wire

The current flowing through the circuit is controlled using the variable resistor (or rheostat). A clear relationship can be seen if a graph of potential difference (across the resistance wire) against current is drawn:

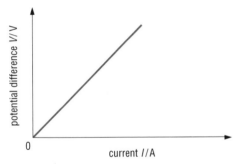

Figure 1.7.2 Potential difference plotted against current for the resistance wire

The straight line shows that the current is directly proportional to the potential difference. This relationship is known as **Ohm's Law** and states that *the current flowing through a metallic conductor is directly proportional to the potential difference across the conductor, provided that the temperature of the conductor remains constant.*

The gradient of the graph (V/I) is a constant, and represents the resistance of the component. The relationship is often written in the form:

$$R = \frac{V}{I}$$

where R = resistance of the conductor (Ω)
V = potential difference across the conductor (V)
I = current flowing through the conductor (A)

This equation may be applied to complete circuits, or to individual components within a circuit. Consider how we might calculate the current flowing through the following series circuit. Under these circumstances R represents the total resistance in the circuit.

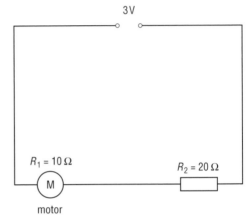

Figure 1.7.3 The current in this circuit can be calculated

Rearranging the equation:

$$I = \frac{V}{R}$$

Total resistance in the circuit = 10 + 20 = 30 Ω. Potential difference across the components = 3 V (equal to the potential difference across the supply). So:

$I = V/R = 3/30 = 0.1$ A

Current flowing = 0.1 amps.

The same equation can be used to calculate the potential difference across either of the components in the circuit. Rearranging the equation:

$$V = I \times R$$

Under these circumstances R represents the resistance of the component in question. Call these $R_1 = 10\ \Omega$ and $R_2 = 20\ \Omega$. V_1 is then the potential difference across R_1 and can be calculated using $V_1 = I \times R_1$, where I = current flowing = 0.1 A. So:

$V_1 = 0.1 \times 10 = 1$ V

Potential difference across R_1 = 1 V.

Because the potential difference across the cell is 3 V, the potential difference across R_2 must therefore be 2 V (i.e. potential difference across cell minus potential difference across R_1).

Calculating the current in parallel circuits

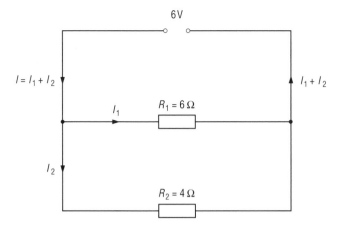

Figure 1.7.4 The current through each branch can be calculated

The potential difference across the ends of each branch in the circuit above will be 6 V, equal to the potential difference across the supply.

To calculate the current through R_1:

current (I_1) = potential difference (V)/resistance (R_1)
$$= 6/6 = 1.0 \text{ A}$$

and the current through R_2:

current (I_2) = potential difference (V)/resistance (R_2)
$$= 6/4 = 1.5 \text{ A}$$

Note that the current before and after the branch in the circuit will be 2.5 A, equal to the sum of the currents through each of the branches.

Temperature and resistance

The temperature of a conductor may significantly affect the value of its resistance. That, in turn, will affect the current flowing through the conductor. This can be seen if we consider a graph of V against I for a filament bulb. (Remember that the slope of the graph represents the resistance of the wire.)

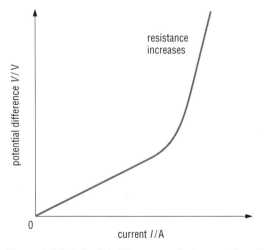

Figure 1.7.5 Potential difference against current for a filament bulb

You can see that for low voltages the filament seems to obey Ohm's Law – the graph is a straight line – and the resistance of the filament remains constant. At higher voltages, however, the temperature of the filament changes considerably (by as much as 1000 °C), and the graph shows that the resistance increases (the graph has a steeper gradient). In general, the higher the temperature, the greater the resistance.

Quick Questions
• •

1 **a)** Draw circuits with:
      i) one cell, one switch and three bulbs connected in series;
      ii) three identical bulbs connected in parallel with each other and a cell.
   b) If in each circuit a current of 0.6 A is drawn from the cell, indicate on your diagrams the current through each bulb.

2 The potential difference across a component is 12 V. A current of 2 A flows through the component. Calculate the resistance of the component.

3 Study the voltage/current graphs shown below.

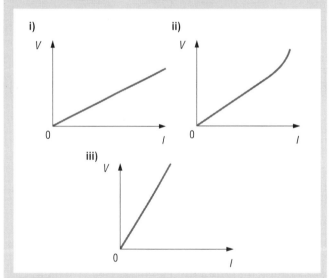

Figure 1.7.6

   a) Which line shows the conductor with the greatest resistance?
   b) Which line shows the conductor with the least resistance?
   c) What can you say about the temperatures of the three conductors?
   d) Which graph is likely to be for a filament lamp?

4 **a)** When a light bulb 'blows', what has actually happened?
   b) Using your knowledge of current and resistance, explain why most bulbs 'blow' when they are switched on rather than after they have been on for a while.

1.8 Heating effect

In any circuit, energy is transferred to the devices in the circuit by the current.

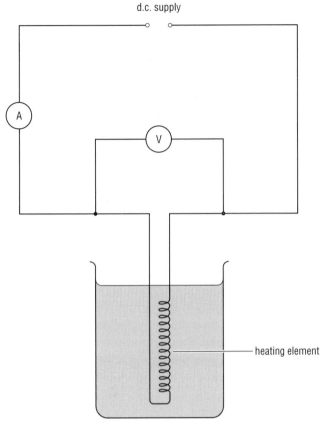

d.c. supply

heating element

Figure 1.8.1 The energy transferred depends on the voltage and the current

The potential difference across the heater in the circuit above is an indication of the amount of energy transferred by each coulomb of charge as it passes through it. The bigger the potential difference, the more energy is transferred per coulomb.

The current transfers energy from the supply to the heater. Increasing the current – the rate of flow of charge – therefore increases the rate at which energy is transferred.

The amount of energy transferred by the heater therefore depends on the current, the voltage, and the time for which the current flows. These are related by the equation:

$$\frac{\text{energy}}{\text{(joules)}} = \frac{\text{current}}{\text{(amps)}} \times \frac{\text{potential difference}}{\text{(volts)}} \times \frac{\text{time}}{\text{(seconds)}}$$

or:

$$\text{energy} = I \times V \times t \quad \text{where} \quad \begin{aligned} I &= \text{current (A)} \\ V &= \text{potential difference (V)} \\ t &= \text{time (s)} \end{aligned}$$

Power

Power is the rate at which a device transforms energy:

$$\text{power (watts)} = \frac{\text{energy transferred (joules)}}{\text{time taken (seconds)}}$$

Substituting energy $= IVt$ in this equation, we get:

$$\text{power} = \frac{IVt}{t} = IV$$

or:

$$\frac{\text{power}}{\text{(watts)}} = \frac{\text{current}}{\text{(amps)}} \times \frac{\text{potential difference across device}}{\text{(volts)}}$$

Other versions of these equations

Rearranging $R = \dfrac{V}{I}$,

$$I = \frac{V}{R} \quad \text{and} \quad V = IR$$

Substituting these in the equation

$$\text{energy} = IVt$$

we can deduce other forms of the equation which may be more appropriate under different circumstances:

$$\text{energy transferred} = IVt = \frac{V}{R} \times V \times t = \frac{V^2 t}{R}$$

or $\quad \text{energy transferred} = IVt = I \times IR \times t = I^2Rt$

These equations can be used to determine further relationships between power, potential difference and current:

$$\text{power} = \frac{\text{energy transferred}}{\text{time}}$$

so $\quad \text{power} = \dfrac{V^2 t}{Rt} = \dfrac{V^2}{R}$

or $\quad \text{power} = \dfrac{I^2Rt}{t} = I^2R$

Worked example

230 V ~   50 Hz

1200 W

Figure 1.8.2 Informatiion label on an electric kettle

The information on this label tells us that the kettle is designed to operate from a 230 volt supply, and has a power rating of 1200 watts. Calculate the resistance of the heating coil, and the current through it when the kettle is switched on.

Power = V^2/R

so $\quad R = V^2/\text{power}$

$\quad\quad = (230)^2/1200$

$\quad\quad = 44\ \Omega$

The resistance of the coil is 44 ohms.

To calculate the current through the circuit:

Power = I^2R

so $\quad I^2 = \text{power}/R$

$\quad\quad = 1200/44 = 27.3$

so $\quad I = \sqrt{27.3} = 5.2\ \text{A}$

The current through the coil will be 5.2 amps when the kettle is switched on.

Quick Questions

1 State three quantities, and their units, that affect the amount of energy transferred by an electrical device.
2 Find the resistance of a 2.3 kW device which is operating on a 230 V supply.
3 Find the current flowing through a 100 W bulb operating on a 230 V supply.
4 An energy-saving 12 W bulb is able to emit the same amount of light as a 60 W bulb.
   a) Calculate the current which flows through each bulb when connected to a 230 V supply.
   b) Suggest why the 12 W bulb is able to emit the same amount of light as the 60 W bulb.
5 Study the labels of the three electrical devices below.

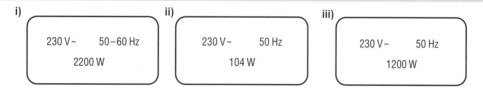

   i)   ii)   iii)

  230 V ~   50–60 Hz   230 V ~   50 Hz   230 V ~   50 Hz

        2200 W   104 W   1200 W

Figure 1.8.3

  a) Which device uses the most power?
  b) Which is the cheapest to run?
  c) Which uses the least current?
  d) Without any calculations, what can you say about the resistances of devices **i** and **ii**?
  e) Calculate the resistance of device **i**.
6 Compare the energy use of some common appliances that make use of the heating effect of a current, by completing the table below. (Be careful with units.)

Appliance	Power /W	Time for which it is used	Amount of energy transferred /J
Hairdrier	1500	5 minutes	
Kettle	1200	3 minutes	
Toaster	800		96 000
Iron		15 minutes	990 000

1.9 Electronic circuits

Potential divider circuits

Many electronic circuits use the principle of a series circuit containing two resistors as a 'potential divider'.

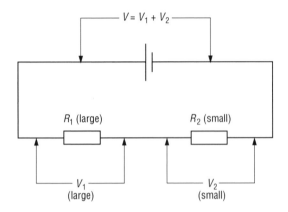

Figure 1.9.1 Potential divider circuit

In circuits such as this the sum of the potential differences across the resistors is equal to the potential difference across the input (the power supply). Here R_1 is larger than R_2, so the p.d. across R_1 will be greater than the p.d. across R_2.

Thermistor circuits

If one of the resistors is replaced with a **thermistor** (a temperature dependent resistor), then we can have a temperature sensing circuit. A thermistor has a large resistance when it is cold but a small resistance when it is hot. When the thermistor is cold, R_1 will be much larger than R_2, so V_1 will be much bigger than V_2. In fact, V_2 will be almost 0 V.

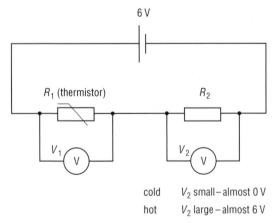

Figure 1.9.2 Temperature sensing circuit

When it is hot, R_1 will be smaller than R_2, so V_1 will be smaller than V_2. V_2 may be almost 6 V. The value of V_2 therefore depends on the temperature of the thermistor. The circuit therefore responds to changes in the voltage across the thermistor brought about by changes in temperature.

LDR circuits

A similar circuit could be constructed by replacing the thermistor with a **light dependent resistor (LDR)**. An LDR has a very large resistance in the dark but a much smaller resistance in the light. R_2 has a resistance somewhere between the two values of R_1. In the dark, R_1 is much larger than R_2, so V_1 will be much larger than V_2. Because of the high resistance of the LDR, the actual value of V_2 will be almost 0 V.

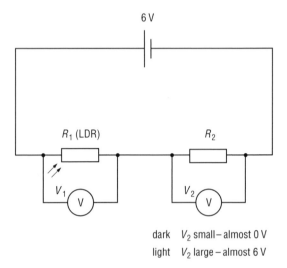

Figure 1.9.3 Light sensing circuit

In full light, R_1 is much smaller than R_2, so the value of V_1 will be much smaller than V_2. The value of V_2 will be close to 6 V. It will change from nearly 6 V to 0 V as the LDR is moved from light to dark. The value of V_2 depends on the amount of light falling on the LDR – in other words the circuit responds to changes in light levels.

For all such potential divider circuits:

$$V_1 = V \times \frac{R_1}{R_1 + R_2} \quad \text{and} \quad V_2 = V \times \frac{R_2}{R_1 + R_2}$$

V_1 and V_2 are often described as output voltages. The voltage V of the supply is described as the input voltage.

Electronic systems

Simple electronic systems consist of three sections:

- The INPUT section – which contains sensors which detect changes in the environment.
- The PROCESSOR section – which decides what action is needed in response to the input.
- The OUTPUT section – which is controlled by the processor.

The simple system outlined in Figure 1.9.4 is designed to sound a buzzer if dampness is detected.

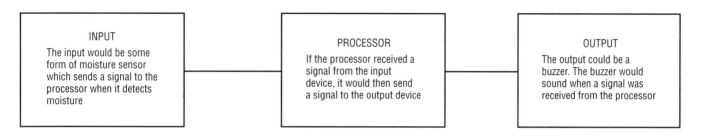

Figure 1.9.4 A simple electronic system

Input devices in electronic systems include mechanical switches, pressure sensitive switches, tilt switches, moisture sensors, temperature sensors and light sensors.

Output devices include lamps, buzzers, motors and magnetic relays.

Processors can be made using **logic gates**. Logic gates are digital systems. A digital system is one in which the input and output voltages cannot have any value, but must be either HIGH (logic state 1) or LOW (logic state 0). Logic gates are called gates because they 'open' and give a high output (1) only when a particular combination of 1's and 0's is present at their inputs. Three common logic gates are NOT, AND and OR, shown below left.

The easiest way to summarise how logic gates work is to use a **truth table**. A truth table shows the various output states for all combinations of the inputs. Truth tables for the NOT, AND and OR gates are shown below.

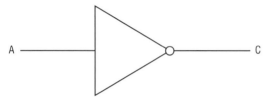

for the output (C) to be HIGH (1) the input (A) must NOT be high – it must be LOW (0)

Figure 1.9.5 The NOT gate

Table 1.9.1 Truth table for a NOT gate

Input	Output
A	C
0	1
1	0

Table 1.9.2 Truth table for an AND gate

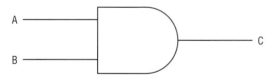

for the output (C) to be HIGH (1) the first input (A) AND the second input (B) must be HIGH (1)

Figure 1.9.6 The AND gate

Inputs		Output
A	B	C
0	0	0
1	0	0
0	1	0
1	1	1

Table 1.9.3 Truth table for an OR gate

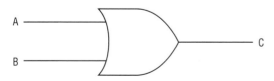

for the output (C) to be HIGH (1) the first input (A) OR the second input (B) OR both inputs must be HIGH (1)

Figure 1.9.7 The OR gate

Inputs		Output
A	B	C
0	0	0
1	0	1
0	1	1
1	1	1

Using logic gates

Logic gates are used as part of the processing section of an electronic system. Imagine, for example, the system shown in Figure 1.9.8. Using this system, the door would open only when the shop is open *and* when someone steps on the mat at the entrance.

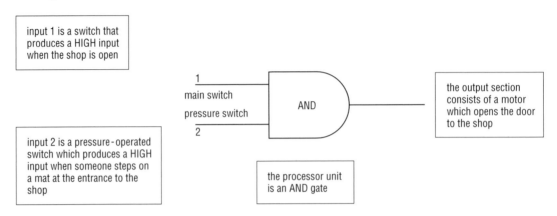

Figure 1.9.8 System operating automatic doors to a shop

The transistor

A **transistor** can work as an electronic switch. It has three terminals called the base, the emitter and the collector.

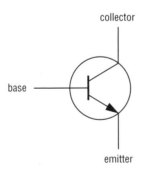

Figure 1.9.9 The transistor symbol and its connections

When no current flows into the base of the transistor, no collector current flows. Under these circumstances the transistor is 'off' (just as a normal switch would be off). When a small current flows into the base of the transistor, the collector current is much bigger than the base current (the transistor is now 'on').

Transistors are often used to control a second circuit in response to, for example, changing light levels or temperatures. In these circumstances the output stage of the system is an electromagnetic **relay** (see page 27). The relay is operated by the output from the transistor circuit. Figure 1.9.10 shows a circuit that acts as a light dependent switch.

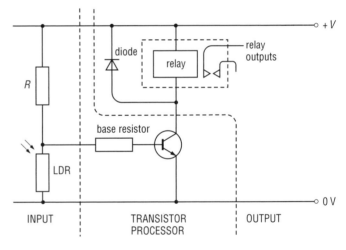

Figure 1.9.10 A transistor switching circuit

- When it is dark the LDR has a larger resistance than the resistor R, so the p.d. across the LDR is much greater than the p.d. across R. The base is therefore at a low potential and the transistor is off. The relay is also off, so no current flows in the secondary circuit.
- When it is light the resistance of the LDR becomes small. The p.d. across the LDR therefore decreases and the p.d. across the resistor R increases. The base potential becomes high and the transistor switches on. The relay then operates and current flows through the secondary circuit.

The diode shown in the circuit allows current to flow in one direction only. It is included in circuits such as this to prevent current flowing back through the transistor from collector to emitter, damaging the transistor.

A transistor can also work as an amplifier. The circuit in Figure 1.9.11 shows a transistor acting to amplify the input voltage from a crystal microphone.

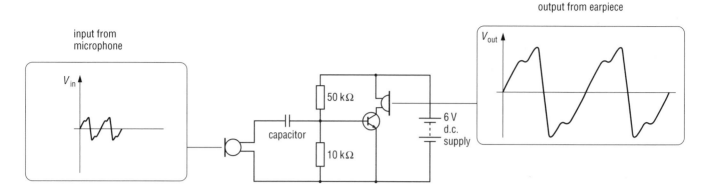

Figure 1.9.11 A transistor as a voltage amplifier

The capacitor (because it blocks d.c.) prevents current from the battery passing through the 50 kΩ resistor and the microphone.

Capacitors

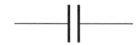

Figure 1.9.12 Circuit symbol for a capacitor

Capacitors are circuit components that can store electric charge. When direct current flows into an uncharged capacitor, charge is stored and the potential difference across the capacitor increases to some maximum value determined by the value of its 'capacitance'.

Capacitance is measured in units called farads:

$$\text{capacitance (farads)} = \frac{\text{charge on the capacitor (coulombs)}}{\text{potential across the capacitor (volts)}}$$

If a conductor is connected across a charged capacitor, a current flows through the conductor and the potential difference across the capacitor decreases.

The time taken to charge or discharge a capacitor depends on:

• The resistance of the charging/discharging circuit – the greater the resistance, the longer it takes the capacitor to charge or discharge.
• The capacitance of the capacitor – the greater the capacitance, the more charge it can store, so charging and discharging take longer.

Capacitors can be used in the input circuits of electronic systems to create time delay switches.

Quick Questions

1 Name the three sections of a simple electronic system and then list three devices that could function in each section.
2 **a)** How does the resistance of an LDR change as the light becomes brighter?
  b) How does the resistance of a thermistor change as its temperature rises?
3 Complete a truth table for the system below.

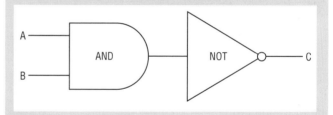

Figure 1.9.13

4 **a)** Name the three connections to a transistor.
  b) State two functions of a transistor.
  c) What is a diode and how should one be used with a transistor?
5 Show the arrangement of logic gates needed in this system to switch on a greenhouse heater automatically when it is cold and dark.

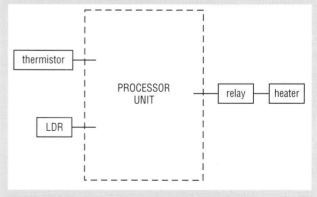

Figure 1.9.14

1.10 Magnets

Some objects have the ability to attract other objects containing iron or steel. They are called magnets. Some magnets retain their magnetic properties for several months or years. We call them permanent magnets. They are normally made from steel (which is an alloy of iron mixed with small amounts of carbon). Only two elements, other than iron – cobalt and nickel – are magnetic. Good quality magnets are often made from alloys containing mixtures of these metals.

Temporary magnets, such as electromagnets, are made from 'soft' iron. (The term 'soft' means the material is magnetised easily but also quickly loses its magnetism.)

The properties of magnets

The places where the magnetism is at its strongest on a magnet are called the poles. One pole is a north (N) pole. The other is a south (S) pole. The position of the poles varies from magnet to magnet.

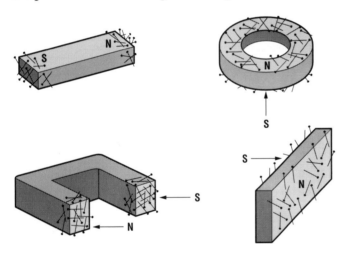

Figure 1.10.1 Small steel objects are attracted to a magnet

If a bar-shaped magnet is hung from fine thread, in such a way that it can turn freely, it comes to rest with its poles lined up with the North and South (magnetic) poles of the earth.

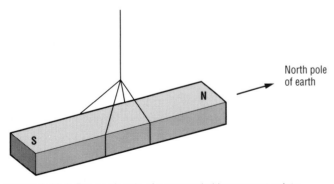

Figure 1.10.2 The north pole of a suspended bar magnet points towards North

The end of the magnet that points towards the North pole of the earth is the north pole of the magnet (originally described as the 'north-seeking' pole). The opposite end is the south pole. The actual positions of the poles are just inside the ends of the magnet.

Forces between magnets

If two magnets are brought close together they can exert forces on one another. The magnets may push away (repel) or pull together (attract). The general rule is: *same poles repel* (i.e. north repels another north pole, south repels another south pole) and *different poles attract* (i.e. a north pole is attracted to the south pole of another magnet).

Testing magnetic poles

The needle of a direction-finding compass is a permanent magnet, with a north and a south pole. Smaller compasses, called plotting compasses, are often used in magnetism experiments.

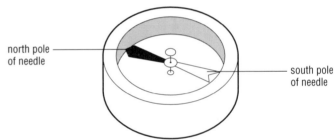

Figure 1.10.3 A plotting compass

The needle of a plotting compass is small so it is easily deflected by the presence of other magnetic poles. To identify the poles of a permanent magnet the plotting compass is placed close to one end.

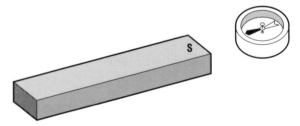

Figure 1.10.4 A plotting compass needle points towards a magnetic south pole

- If the north pole of the plotting compass points towards the end of the magnet, then that end is a magnetic south pole (different poles attract).
- If the south pole of the plotting compass is drawn towards the end of the magnet, then that end is a magnetic north pole.

Magnetic fields

The magnetic forces exerted by a magnet can be detected (depending on the strength of the magnet) several centimetres from the magnet – we say the forces act 'at a distance' from the magnet. The region around the magnet in which the magnetic forces act is called the **magnetic field**.

In the magnetic field a force will act on any other magnet or magnetic material. The direction of the magnetic field at any point is the direction in which the magnetic force would act on a north pole placed at that point.

The magnetic field can be represented by a pattern of distinct lines (called the magnetic field lines). The arrows show the direction of the magnetic field and are always shown pointing away from the north pole and towards the south pole.

A magnetic field can be mapped in several ways, including using iron filings or small plotting compasses. The magnetic field patterns for two bar magnets close together are shown below.

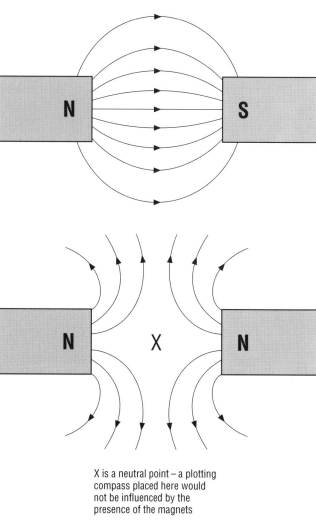

X is a neutral point – a plotting compass placed here would not be influenced by the presence of the magnets

Figure 1.10.6 Magnetic field patterns between two permanent magnets

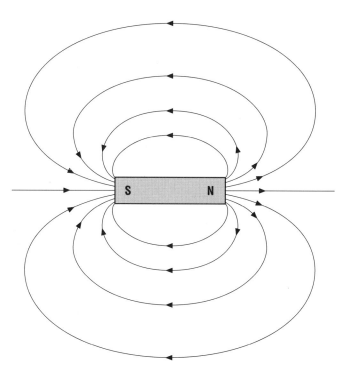

Figure 1.10.5 Magnetic field pattern due to a permanent bar magnet

Note that:

- The pattern on each side is symmetrical.
- The magnetic field lines seem to come together at the poles (but not right at the ends).
- The direction of the magnetic field lines is shown by small arrows – always going from the north pole towards the south pole.
- The lines are most concentrated around the poles. Those further away from the magnet are much further apart, showing that the magnetic force gets weaker as you move further from the magnet.

Quick Questions

1 Name the three magnetic elements.
2 Fill in the missing words:
   Like poles will .... when placed next to each other.
   Unlike poles will .... when placed next to each other.
   A north pole placed next to a .... will repel.
3 Draw the field pattern between:
   a) two south poles;
   b) two north poles;
   c) a north and a south pole.
4 Three unmarked materials are freely suspended from pieces of cotton. You are told one is a magnet, one is a piece of soft iron and the third is a piece of non-magnetic material. Using only a bar magnet, how could you identify each material?

1.11 Magnetism and electricity

When an electric current flows through a wire or cable, a magnetic field forms around the wire. The magnetic field pattern around a long straight wire is a series of concentric rings.

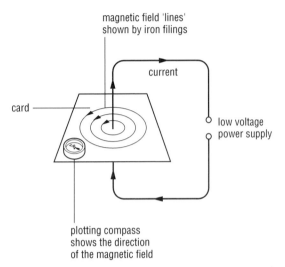

Figure 1.11.1 Demonstrating the magnetic field around a long straight current-carrying wire

The magnetic field direction can be found using the *right hand grip rule*:

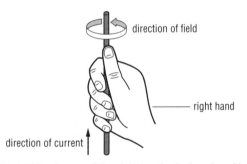

Figure 1.11.2 If the fingers of the right hand grip the wire with the thumb pointing in the direction of the current, then the curl of the fingers shows the direction of the magnetic field

The magnetic field can be made stronger if the wire is formed into a coil, called a solenoid. The pattern of the magnetic field around a solenoid is similar to that around a permanent magnet.

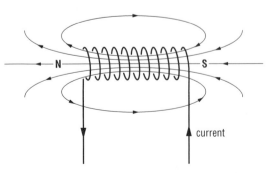

Figure 1.11.3 Magnetic field pattern due to a current-carrying solenoid

The ends of the solenoid behave as if they were magnetic north and south poles. The polarity of the solenoid (which end is north and which is south) can be deduced using a rule similar to the right hand grip rule just described:

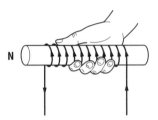

Figure 1.11.4 If the right hand grips the coil in such a way that the fingers point in the direction in which current is flowing, then the outstretched thumb points towards the north pole

Reversing the current through the solenoid reverses the polarity of the ends.

The magnetic field strength can be increased considerably (at least one thousand times) if the wire is wrapped around a piece of soft iron.

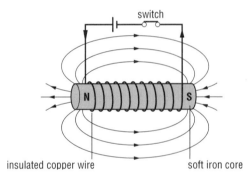

Figure 1.11.5 A simple electromagnet

When current flows through the coil, the soft iron becomes magnetised. The bar then behaves as a strong magnet, with north and south poles, and with a similar magnetic field pattern.

When the current is switched off, the soft iron loses its magnetism. Magnets such as this, which can be controlled by the flow of electric current, are called **electromagnets**. They are often used in places where strong magnets are needed, or where permanent magnets would be unsuitable.

The strength and polarity of electromagnets

Electromagnets are versatile because they are easily controlled. The strength of an electromagnet can be varied by:

- Changing the number of coils of wire – the more coils, the stronger the magnet.
- Changing the current – the larger the current, the stronger the magnet.

The polarity of electromagnets depends on the direction in which the current flows through the coil. Reversing the current reverses the polarity of the magnet. The rule illustrated in Figure 1.11.4 for a solenoid can be used to identify the poles, or the method described below may be used.

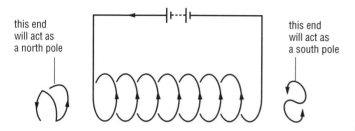

Figure 1.11.6 The polarity of an electromagnet

Looking at the coil from the end:

- If the current flows clockwise through the coil, then that end is a south pole.
- If the current flows anti-clockwise through the coil, then that end is a north pole.

Electromagnetic relays

Electromagnetic **relays** are used in situations where we need a low power circuit to control a higher power circuit. Mechanical robots used in the motor industry need very high currents. They are controlled by microprocessors which use very small currents – far too small to operate the robotic machinery. An electromagnetic relay allows the low power circuit to control the high power robot circuit.

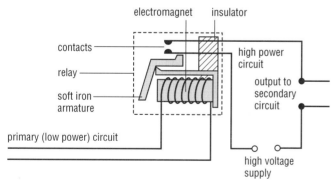

Figure 1.11.7 A relay circuit

- When current flows through the primary coil of the relay, the core acts as an electromagnet, drawing the armature towards it. The armature operates the lever which closes the contacts, completing the secondary circuit. A high current can then flow in that circuit.
- When the primary circuit is switched off, the soft iron core loses its magnetism and the lever falls back to its original position. The contacts open once again, breaking the secondary circuit.

The loudspeaker

In a loudspeaker an alternating current from the amplifier passes to the coil which surrounds the permanent magnet.

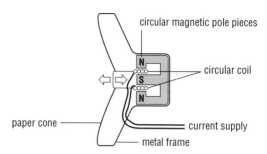

Figure 1.11.8 The principle of a loudspeaker

As the current flows through the coil, an alternating magnetic field is produced around the coil. This alternating magnetic field interacts with the magnetic field of the permanent magnet. The coil will be drawn towards, or pushed away from, the permanent magnet, depending on the nature of its magnetic field. As the coil vibrates, it causes the paper cone to vibrate at the same frequency. Sound is produced as the air molecules are made to vibrate by the cone. Electrical energy has been transformed into sound energy by the loudspeaker.

Quick Questions

1 a) Draw the pattern of the magnetic field in and around the solenoid below. Include arrows to indicate the field direction.

Figure 1.11.9

   b) Draw the magnetic field lines around a wire, assuming the current in it is flowing towards you.
2 Describe two ways of increasing the strength of an electromagnet.
3 What is the main difference between the magnetic field pattern for a bar magnet and that for a solenoid?
4 The diagram below shows a circuit breaker, often used in a power pack.
   a) What is the purpose of a circuit breaker?
   b) Explain how the circuit breaker works.

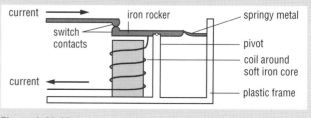

Figure 1.11.10

1.12 Motors

When a current flows through a long straight conductor placed between the poles of a large magnet, a force acts which makes the wire move to one side – the wire 'kicks'.

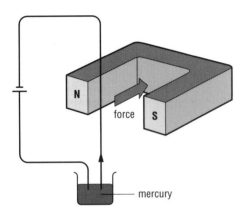

Figure 1.12.1 Demonstrating the motor effect

The direction of the force (and, therefore, the direction in which the wire moves) depends on:

* The direction of the current.
* The direction of the magnetic field.

Reversing either the current or the magnetic field reverses the direction in which the force acts on the wire. The direction in which the force acts can be predicted using the *left hand motor rule* (Figure 1.12.2).

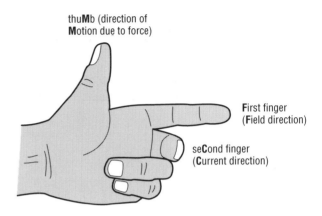

Figure 1.12.2 If the thumb and first two fingers of the left hand are held at right angles to one another, the direction of the force is shown by the thumb

The size of the force depends on:

* The magnetic field strength.
* The size of the current flowing through the wire.

Increasing either the magnetic field strength or the current increases the force on the wire.

The electric motor

The effect described above is the principle behind an electric motor. Figure 1.12.3 shows the parts of a simple motor.

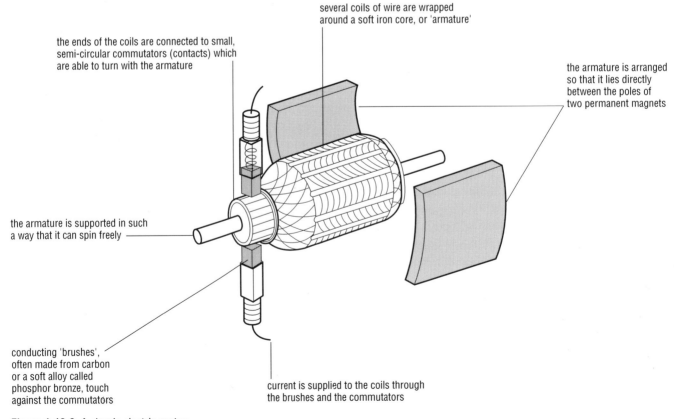

Figure 1.12.3 A simple electric motor

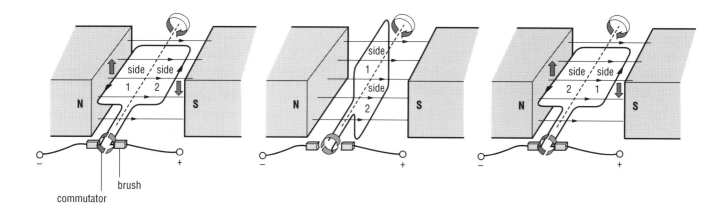

Figure 1.12.4a As current flows through the coil, a force acts on each side of the coil. Because the current flows in opposite directions in each side of the coil, the force on side 1 acts in the opposite direction to the force on side 2. The two forces form a couple – a turning effect – which makes the coil rotate. The largest couple acts when the coil is moving at right angles to the magnetic field

Figure 1.12.4b As the coil moves through the vertical position it is moving parallel to the magnetic field. The commutator segments have rotated with the coil and are no longer in contact with the brushes. No current flows in the coil. No force acts on the coil in this position but its momentum carries it forward

Figure 1.12.4c The coil rotates further and side 1 is now on the right, with its commutator segment touching the right hand (positive) brush, so it has a downward force acting on it. Similarly, side 2 has an upward force on it. Thus the couple always acts in the same direction as earlier (clockwise) and the coil spins

As current flows, forces act on each coil (because they lie within a magnetic field) forming a turning couple.

A simplified stage-by-stage diagram, Figure 1.12.4 a–c above, helps you to understand how the forces on each coil contribute to the rotation of the armature and coils.

The size of the turning couple on the armature of a motor depends on:

- The magnetic field strength.
- The current through the coils.
- The number of coils on the armature.

The greater the couple, the faster the motor turns.

Practical d.c. motors

Practical motors have several separate coils of wire wrapped around the armature, each with its own pair of commutator segments. Each coil contributes to the movement of the motor, producing more efficient and effective running – there is always a couple acting on the armature because some of the coils are always cutting through the magnetic field. Carbon or phosphor bronze 'brushes' make contact with the commutator segments as they rotate. The brushes tend to wear out with time (much more quickly than the harder copper of the commutators) and must be replaced.

Quick Questions

1. Write down three ways of increasing the speed of an electric motor.
2. Write down two ways of reversing the direction of an electric motor.
3. The diagram below shows a wire placed in a magnetic field. A current flows in the direction of the arrow.

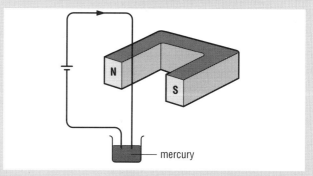

Figure 1.12.5

Which rule is used to find the direction in which the wire will move?

Use the rule to find the direction in which the wire will move.

4. a) Why is carbon or phosphor bronze used for the brushes in an electric motor and not a harder material?
   b) Why is the commutator an essential part of a motor?

1.13 Electromagnetic induction

When a loop of wire is moved at right angles through a magnetic field, a potential difference is created across the ends of wire and a small current flows. A galvanometer (a very sensitive current-measuring device) can be used to detect the current.

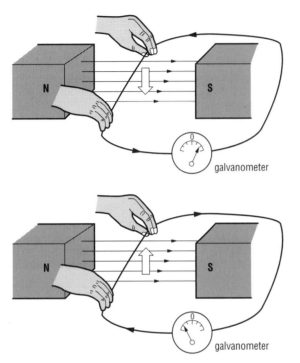

Figure 1.13.1 A small potential difference is induced across the ends of a wire as it cuts through magnetic field lines. This produces a small current if the wire forms part of a loop

The current is called an **induced current**, and the effect is called **electromagnetic induction**.

The direction in which the current flows depends on:

* The direction in which the wire moves through the magnetic field – if the wire is moved in the opposite direction, the flow of current is reversed.
* The direction of the magnetic field – reversing the magnetic field (by reversing the position of the poles) reverses the direction of the current.

Note that if the wire is stationary in the magnetic field, no potential difference is induced and no current flows – the wire must move in such a way that it cuts through the lines of the magnetic field for induced current to flow. For similar reasons no current will flow if the wire is moved parallel to the magnetic field lines.

The size of the induced current can be increased by:

* Moving the wire faster.
* Using stronger magnets to produce a stronger magnetic field.

* Increasing the amount of wire passing through the magnetic field, by creating several loops and moving them through the magnetic field together.

The same effect can be seen if a magnet is moved in such a way that the magnetic field cuts through the wire. It is much more easily seen (because the induced current is bigger) if the wire is formed into a coil. As the magnet is moved into and out of the coil, an induced current flows first in one direction, then the other. Again, if there is no motion there is no induced current.

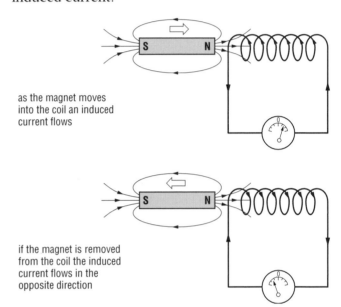

as the magnet moves into the coil an induced current flows

if the magnet is removed from the coil the induced current flows in the opposite direction

Figure 1.13.2 Current is also induced if the magnetic field moves relative to a stationary conductor

Direction of the induced current

The direction of the induced current in a straight conductor can be found using the *right hand generator rule*.

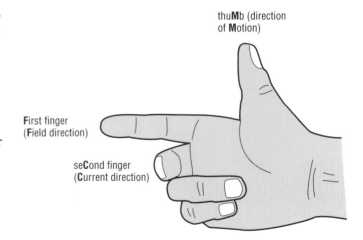

Figure 1.13.3 If the thumb and first two fingers of the right hand are held at right angles to one another, the direction of the induced current is shown by the second finger

Notice the similarities between this and the left hand motor rule – the fingers and thumb represent the same factors.

The direction in which induced current flows through a coil can be found using Lenz's Law, which states that *an induced current always flows in such a direction as to oppose the change which is causing it*.

Consider how this applies to the situation in Figure 1.13.4. As the magnet moves into the coil, an induced current flows through the coil in such a way that the magnetic field generated around the coil opposes the magnetic field of the permanent magnet.

In this example the induced current through the coil flows in such a direction as to create a north pole at the end closest to the magnet (to oppose the north pole of the permanent magnet). The current must therefore flow anti-clockwise at that end (see Figure 1.11.6, page 27). This can be verified by the right hand grip rule, as shown in the diagram below.

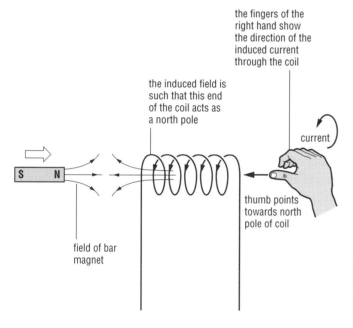

Figure 1.13.4 The induced field opposes the field of the permanent magnet

Power generation

The generators in electricity generating stations use the ideas above to generate the electricity needed by our homes and industry. The basic structure of a generating station is shown in Figure 1.13.5. The turbines are driven at high speed by high pressure steam from the boilers. The turbines then turn the large electromagnet. As the electromagnet turns, its magnetic field cuts through the coils on each side. A large induced (alternating) voltage is generated in the coils.

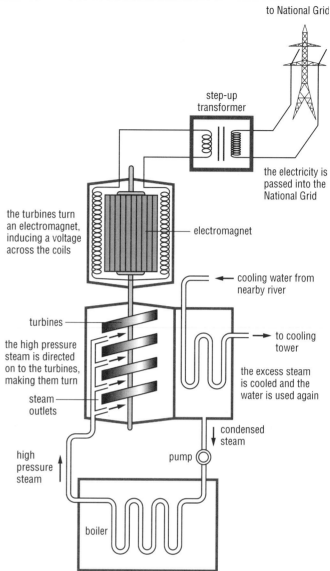

Figure 1.13.5 Generating electricity at a thermal power station

Quick Questions

1 Describe three ways of increasing the induced current through a solenoid when a bar magnet is inserted.

2 Find the current direction through the solenoid shown below.

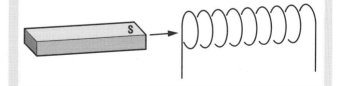

Figure 1.13.6

3 Electromagnetic induction has its most important application in electrical generators. How many different energy sources can you name which are used in generating (power) stations? (Pages 142–143 may help you here.)

1.14 Transformers and generators

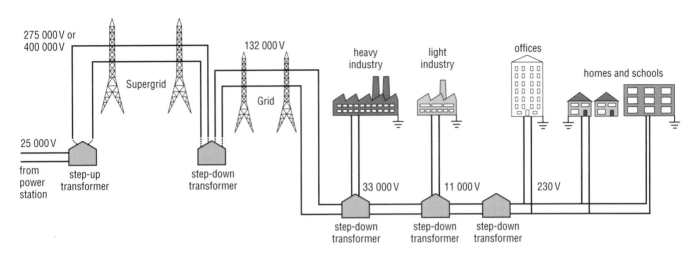

Figure 1.14.1 Voltages in the National Grid

Electricity generating stations produce power at 25 000 volts. This voltage is increased to about 400 000 volts before entering the National Grid. Increasing the voltage reduces energy losses in the cables (by reducing the current, so reducing the heating effect).

The voltage is changed by a **transformer**. Throughout the National Grid, transformers increase or decrease the voltage. Before the electricity enters our homes, a transformer reduces the voltage to a safer level of 230 V – the 'mains voltage'.

A transformer consists of two coils, each of several thousand turns, wrapped around a soft iron core. As an alternating current flows through the primary coil, an alternating current is induced in the secondary coil.

How the transformer works

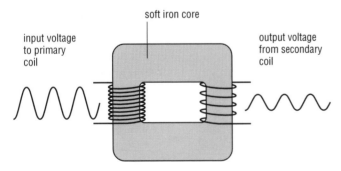

Figure 1.14.2 The principle of a transformer

The alternating current (at 50 Hz) through the primary coil generates an alternating magnetic field. The alternating magnetic field cuts through the secondary coil, generating an induced, alternating voltage with the same frequency (50 Hz) across the secondary coil. The current from the secondary coil is therefore an alternating current.

If a transformer was 100% efficient (i.e. there were no energy losses), we could say that:

> power input to transformer = power output from transformer

or, because power = current × voltage,

input current × input voltage = output current × output voltage

$$I_{in} \times V_{in} = I_{out} \times V_{out}$$

The output voltage depends on the number of turns on the primary and secondary coils. Assuming no energy is lost, we can say that:

$$\frac{\text{secondary voltage}}{\text{primary voltage}} = \frac{\text{number of turns on secondary coil}}{\text{number of turns on primary coil}}$$

Imagine, for example, that we have a transformer with 960 turns on the primary coil and 16 turns on the secondary coil, and that the primary coil is connected to a 240 V a.c. supply. Then we can calculate the output from the secondary coil using the equation above:

$$\frac{\text{secondary voltage}}{240} = \frac{16}{960}$$

$$\text{secondary voltage} = \frac{16 \times 240}{960}$$

$$= 4\,\text{V}$$

In reality, transformers are not 100% efficient. There are always some energy losses due to:

- Heat loss as current flows through the coils.
- Magnetisation and demagnetisation of the core. Using soft iron for the core reduces these losses to a minimum.

1 line long both cols

- Eddy currents – the core is a conductor, so as the magnetic field builds up and decreases, small currents are generated in the core. These heat the core, and energy is lost. To reduce the eddy currents, the core is made from thin layers of soft iron, glued together with an insulating material between the strips. This creates a laminated (layered) core which cuts down the energy losses.

The generator

Dynamos and generators convert kinetic energy into electrical energy. A simple generator consists of a coil (wound on an armature) which rotates in the magnetic field produced by magnets situated on each side. As the coil rotates it cuts through the magnetic field, generating an induced current through the coil and then through the rest of the circuit.

Generators can produce either direct current (d.c.) or alternating current (a.c.). The main difference between the two types of generator is in the shape and structure of the commutator section. An a.c. generator is similar in construction to an electric motor, the key difference being that the commutator consists of two full rings connected to the ends of the coil. See Figure 1.14.3a. These rotate with the coil and make permanent contact with the brushes, which conduct the current into the rest of the circuit. The potential difference (across the ends of the coil) generated at each stage of one rotation is shown in the graph, Figure 1.14.3b.

- As sides AB and CD of the coil move through the vertical position the coil moves parallel to the magnetic field. Because the coils are not cutting through the magnetic field, no potential difference is induced across the ends and no current flows.
- As AB and CD move towards the horizontal position they increasingly cut through the magnetic field and so the potential difference across the ends of the coil increases. When the coils are in the horizontal position the potential difference is at its maximum.
- As AB and CD begin to move towards the vertical position once more, the potential difference decreases, becoming zero when the coils are vertical once again.
- As the coil passes through the vertical position, CB and AD are now moving in the opposite direction to that in which they were moving in diagram 1. The potential difference across the ends of the coil, and the direction of the current, is reversed. The potential difference increases as the coil moves back into the horizontal position.

An alternating potential difference is therefore generated across the ends of the coil, which drives an alternating current through the coil. The frequency of the alternating current depends on the speed of rotation of the generator. If the generator rotates ten times per second, the alternating current has a frequency of 10 Hz.

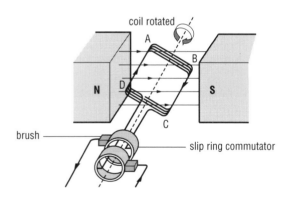

Figure 1.14.3a A simplified a.c. generator

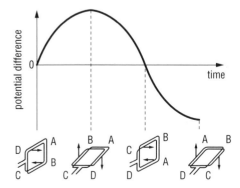

Figure 1.14.3b Alternating output from the coil

Section One: Examination Practice Questions

Foundation Level

1. **(a)** Use the following words to answer the questions below:

iron copper carbon nickel steel zinc cobalt plastic

(Each material can be used more than once.)
   (i)   Which three elements are magnetic?
   (ii) Which material is magnetic but is not an element?
   (iii) Which material is an electrical insulator?
   (iv) Which material is used to make the brushes for simple electric motors?
   (v)   Which material is often used for the commutator in an electric motor?
   (vi) Which material is used to make the core in electromagnets and transformers?

(b) The diagram shows a magnet hanging from a fine thread. A second piece of material (which may also
   be a magnet) is brought close to the suspended magnet. Copy and complete the table below
   describing what will happen in each case.

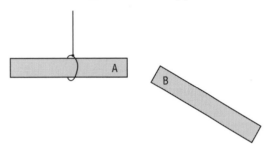

A	B	Effect
North pole	South pole	
North pole	North pole	
South pole	South pole	
North pole	Iron	

2. This diagram shows a copper wire suspended
between two permanent magnets.

(a) What will happen to the wire when the
   switch is closed?
(b) What will happen if the battery connections
   are reversed?
(c) What will then happen if the magnetic poles
   are reversed, with the same battery
   connections as in part (b)?

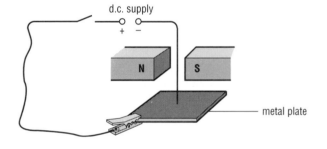

3. **(a)** Nicola rubs a plastic comb with a dry duster. She then puts the comb near to her hair. What will
   happen?
(b) She then puts the comb near to some small pieces of paper on a table. What will happen?
(c) When Nicola rubbed the comb it became charged.
   (i)   There are two types of charge; what are they?
   (ii) Which of the following particles are responsible for the comb becoming charged?

   neutrons protons electrons

   (iii) If the comb was found to be positively charged, what can you say about the charge on the duster?
(d) Two pieces of polythene were charged. One of them was then placed on a watch glass as shown
   below.
   What will happen when the second piece of charged polythene is moved close to the one on the
   watch glass?

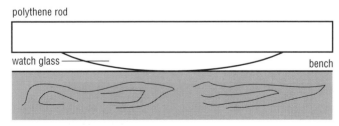

(e) The rod on the watch glass is replaced with a charged acetate rod. Acetate gains the opposite charge to polythene when polished with a duster. What will happen when the charged polythene rod is brought close to the acetate rod?

(f) Some paint sprays use electrostatics to produce an even spray.

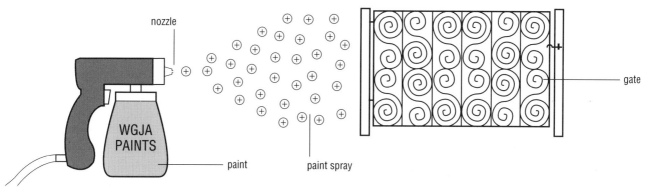

(i)   The paint droplets become charged by friction. Where will this take place?

(ii) The droplets of paint spread out as they are sprayed. Why does this happen?

(iii) The gate is also charged but is given an opposite charge to the paint spray. How will that help?

4. (a) For each of the circuits below, say whether bulbs A and B are on or off.

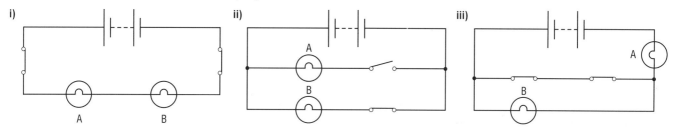

(b) Draw a circuit showing a single cell, switch and two bulbs connected in series.

(c) Draw a circuit with two bulbs connected in parallel with a cell. Include a switch for each bulb.

(d) What advantages do parallel circuits have over series circuits?

5. Wayne needs to measure the current through a circuit containing two lamps. He connects the circuit and draws it, as shown below.

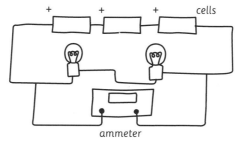

(a) Wayne has made a mistake in the circuit. What is it?

(b) Draw the circuit he should have used, using the correct circuit symbols.

(c) He then decides to measure the potential difference (voltage) across the two lamps. On your circuit diagram draw what he should do.

(d) Rose built this circuit. Complete the table, saying what happens when the switches are closed.

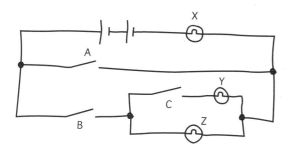

What she does	Bulbs which light
Switch A closed	
Switch B closed	
Switches B and C closed	
Switches A, B and C closed	

6. **(a)** Which letter on this diagram of a 3 pin plug shows:
    (i) the live pin?
    (ii) the neutral pin?
    (iii) the earth pin?

    (b) What is the purpose of the earth wire in the connection to an appliance?

    (c) What is the purpose of the fuse inside a plug?

    (d) The diagram below shows the inside of a 3 pin plug and the connections to an electric heater.

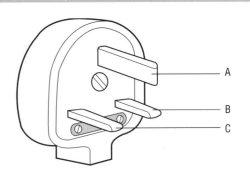

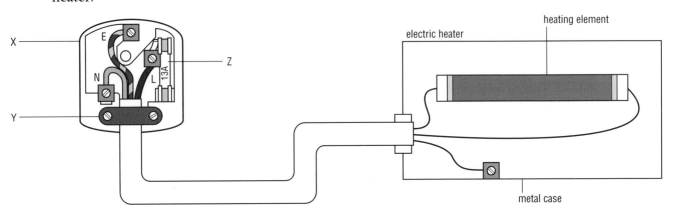

    (i) Name the parts labelled Y and Z.
    (ii) Name one material from which X could be made.
    (iii) What are the colour(s) of the live, neutral and earth wires?
    (iv) Which wire should be connected to the metal case of the electric fire?

7. This diagram shows the circuit inside an electric fan heater.

    (a) Which switches need to be on if you require:
    (i) slow cold air?
    (ii) slow hot air?
    (iii) fast cold air?
    (iv) fast hot air?

    (b) The 5 A fuse is essential for safety.
    (i) What is inside the case of the fuse?
    (ii) Describe carefully what happens if a fault occurs resulting in a current greater than 5 A.

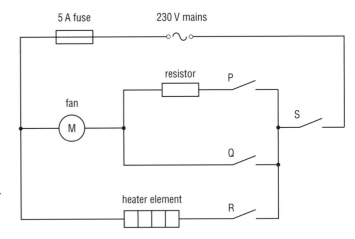

8. The labels below are from five electrical appliances.

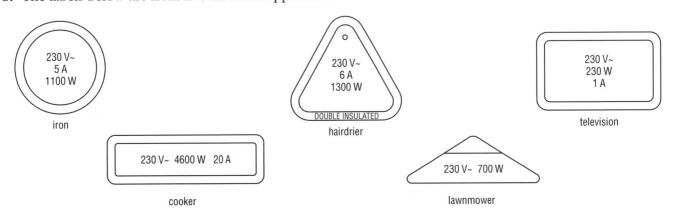

(a) The abbreviations A, V and W are units of measurement. What units do these letters represent?

(b) Which appliance is most powerful?

(c) Which will be the cheapest to use per hour?

(d) Which does not need an earth wire?

(e) Which draws the biggest current when used?

(f) Why does a cooker not normally use the current shown?

(g) A cooker is not plugged into a normal 13 A ring main household socket. It has its own fused circuit. Why does it need a separate circuit?

(h) Calculate the actual current used by the hairdrier.

(i) Should the hairdrier plug be fitted with a 3 A or a 13 A fuse?

(j) Say why your answers to parts (h) and (i) are different.

(k) Assuming 1 kWh of electricity costs 7p, calculate the cost of using:
 (i) the iron for 1 hour;
 (ii) the television for 4 hours;
 (iii) the hairdrier for 15 minutes.

(l) Calculate the current needed to operate the lawnmower.

(m) All of the appliances shown need an a.c. mains supply.
 (i) What do the letters a.c. mean?
 (ii) A battery is a d.c. supply. What do the letters d.c. mean?
 (iii) The diagrams below show traces on a cathode ray oscilloscope (CRO).

A
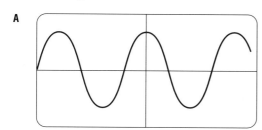
B
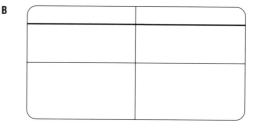

 Which shows a.c. and which d.c.?
 (iv) Explain the main difference between current flow in a.c. and d.c. circuits.

9. Consider the circuit below.

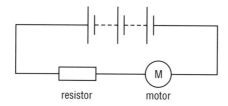

resistor   motor

(a) What would happen to the speed of the motor if the resistor was replaced with one of higher resistance?

(b) Caroline wants to find the value of the resistor. She knows she will need to use a voltmeter and an ammeter in the circuit. Copy the circuit diagram. Draw in where Caroline should put the meters, using the correct symbols.

(c) She finds the voltage is 5 units and the current is 2 units.
 (i) What are the units of voltage?
 (ii) What are the units of current?

(d) Calculate the value of the resistance. Include the correct unit.

(e) In the circuit below, the component marked X is a variable resistor.

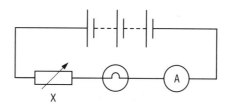

X

Complete the gaps in the passage below.

As the resistance of X is increased the brightness of the bulb .... and the reading on the ammeter .... To obtain a larger current through the circuit we need to .... the resistance of X.
If the voltage of the supply was increased, but the resistance stayed the same, the size of the current would .... Under these circumstances the brightness of the bulb would ....

(f) Caroline builds another circuit as shown below.

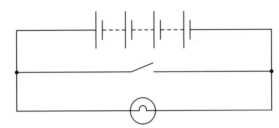

She finds the bulb goes out when the switch is closed. Use your knowledge of current and resistance to explain why.

10. Look at the five circuits below, in which all the batteries and bulbs are identical.

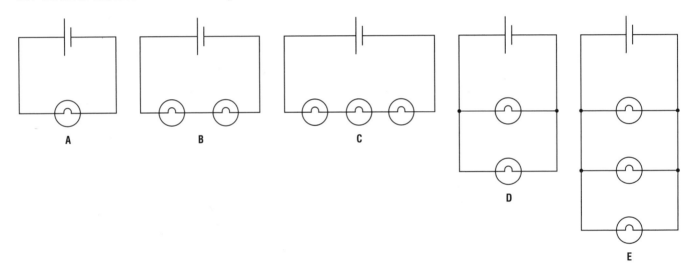

(a) Which are parallel circuits?
(b) If the current through circuit **A** is 0.5 A, what is the current drawn from the batteries in each of the other four circuits?

11. The diagram below shows a coil of wire connected to a very sensitive ammeter (galvanometer). The galvanometer has a centre-zero scale. Next to the coil is a bar magnet which Laura moves into the coil in the direction shown by the arrow.

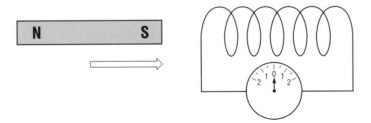

(a) What would Laura notice on the galvanometer as the magnet was moving?
(b) The magnet is held steady inside the coil. What would be the reading on the galvanometer?
(c) The magnet is then removed from the same end of the coil. What would she notice now?
(d) Describe three ways in which the induced current through the circuit could be increased.
(e) Describe two ways in which the current could be reversed.

12. The diagram below shows an electricity generating station.

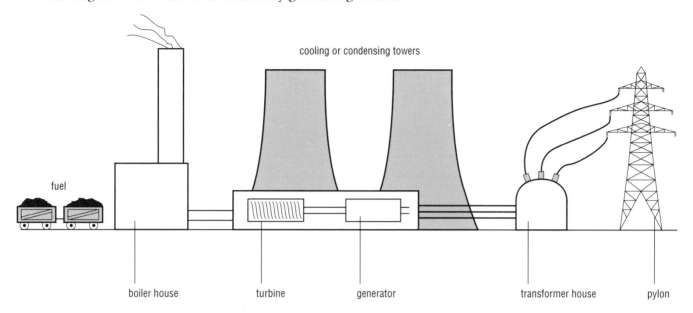

cooling or condensing towers

fuel

boiler house   turbine   generator   transformer house   pylon

   (a) Name three fuels which could be used to heat the water in the boiler.

   (b) Write energy transfer diagrams for the changes that take place in (i) the boiler system , (ii) the turbine and (iii) the generator.

   (c) The electricity is transferred to our homes through a national network of cables. What is this network called?

   (d) Some energy is lost between the power station and our homes. Where is it lost from and in what form is it lost?

   (e) The transformer increases the voltage before the electricity enters the grid. How does that help reduce energy losses?

13. Calculate the current used by the following appliances.

   (a) 500 W, 230 V television

   (b) 2 kW, 230 V kettle

   (c) 60 W, 230 V bedside lamp

14. John and Chris are looking at two systems (A and B) of electrical heating and trying to decide which best suits their needs. Their flat has a standard and an off-peak electricity supply.

A Fixed night storage heaters working on Economy 7 only Cost £250 per radiator Rating 230 V, 3 kW	**B** Oil-filled portable radiators working with the standard mains supply and Economy 7 Cost £50 per radiator Rating 230 V, 2500 W
Standard cost per unit = 7p Economy 7 cost per unit = 3p Economy 7 operates for 7 hours per day	

   (a) How many units of electricity does each heater use in one hour? (1 unit = 1 kWh)

   (b) How much would it cost to use a night storage heater for 4 hours?

   (c) How much would it cost to use an oil-filled radiator for 4 hours with the standard supply?

   (d) Chris and John are often away from home for three days at a time during the winter and they leave some heating on.

       (i) Calculate the cost of using one 'A' type heater for three days.

       (ii) Calculate the cost of using one 'B' type heater for three days.

       (iii) Why do you think they leave some heating on?

15. The diagram below shows the inside of an electric fan heater.

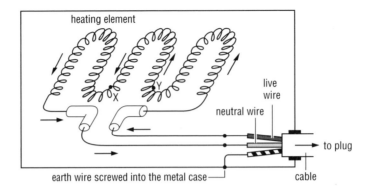

(a) What are the colours of (i) the live, (ii) the neutral and (iii) the earth wires?

(b) A fault causes the heating element to 'short circuit' between X and Y.
   (i)   What does this do to the heating element's resistance and the current flow?
   (ii) What would you expect to happen in the 3 pin plug to the heater?

(c) The earth wire comes loose and the heating element rests against the metal case.
   (i)   What will happen to the case when the fan heater is switched on?
   (ii) If the earth wire had remained fixed how would it and the fuse (in the plug) have worked together to make the heater safe?

(d) Some appliances have no need for an earth wire because they are double insulated. What does this mean?

16. (a) Calculate the total resistance in each of the circuits shown below.

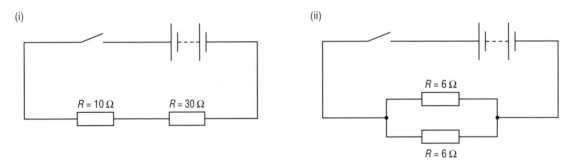

(b) Calculate the voltage supply to the circuit for each of the combinations of cells below.

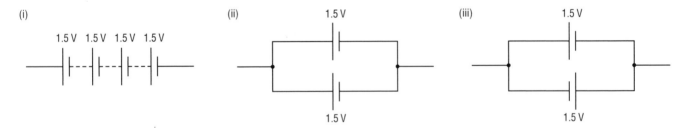

(c) Calculate the current flowing through the circuit shown below.

(d) What would happen to the current in the circuit below if another bulb was added? Explain your answer.

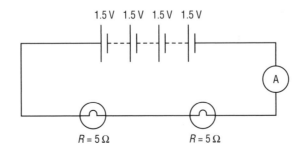

(e) Write the value of the current which would be shown on each of the ammeters X, Y in this circuit.

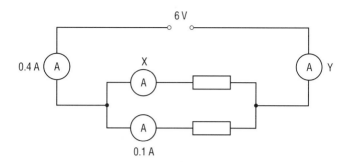

17. In the circuit shown below, the lamps are **identical**.

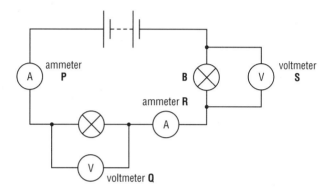

(a) If ammeter **P** gives a reading of 0.2 A, what does ammeter **R** read? [1]

(b) If voltmeter **Q** gives a reading of 3 V, what does voltmeter **S** read? [1]

(c) If lamp **B** were removed from its holder, what would be the reading of ammeter **R**? Explain your answer. [2]

(SEG, Foundation, 1998 Specimen)

18. The 13 amp plug shown below is connected to a hairdryer.

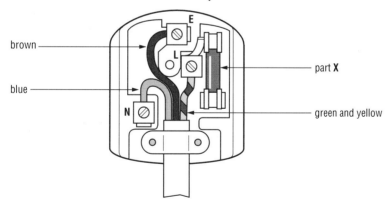

(a) What is part **X**? [1]

(b) What **two** mistakes were made when this plug was wired up? [2]

(c) The plug which connects a hairdryer to the mains electricity supply sometimes has only two wires. Which **two** wires are used and why is it still safe? [2]

(d) Use these equations to answer the following question:

$$\text{units of electricity} = \text{power} \times \text{time}$$

$$\text{cost of electricity supplied} = \text{energy transferred} \times \text{price per unit}$$

The hairdryer has a power rating of 0.5 kilowatts. During one month it is used for **5 hours**. The price of electricity is 8p per kilowatt-hour. Calculate the cost of the electricity used for the hairdryer during that month. [2]

(SEG, Foundation, 1998 Specimen)

19. (a) Graham has a solar powered calculator. Its solar cell supplies **direct current (d.c.)**.
Sabrina has a battery powered calculator. It will work with an adapter that plugs into mains electricity.

      (i) What type of current do **batteries** supply?   [1]

      (ii) What type of current does **mains electricity** supply?   [1]

(b) **(i)** Graham did an experiment with electricity. Look at the diagram of his circuit.
Look at his results.

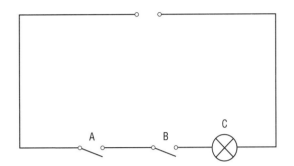

Graham's results

Switch A	Switch B	Bulb C
open	open	off
open	closed	off
closed	open	x
closed	closed	y

    Some of Graham's results are missing. Complete Graham's results table. What are x and y?   [1]

    (ii) Sabrina did an experiment with a different circuit. Look at the diagram of her circuit.
Look at her results.

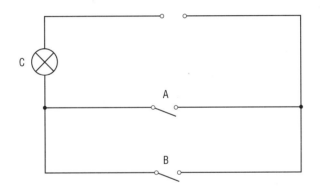

Sabrina's results

Switch A	Switch B	Bulb C
open	open	off
open	closed	x
closed	open	y
closed	closed	z

    Some of Sabrina's results are missing. Complete Sabrina's results table. What are x, y and z?   [1]

(c) Look at these circuits.

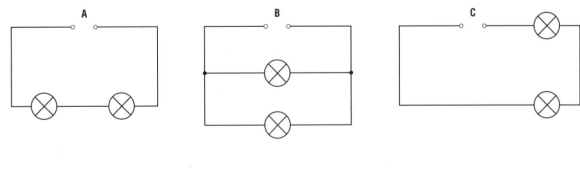

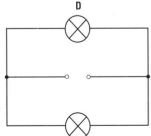

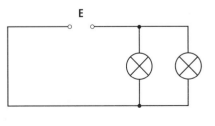

      (i) Which circuits are **series** circuits? Choose from **A**, **B**, **C**, **D** and **E**.   [1]

      (ii) Which circuits are **parallel** circuits? Choose from **A**, **B**, **C**, **D** and **E**.   [1]

(d) Graham wants to measure the potential difference (p.d.) and current for bulb 1. Look at the diagram below.

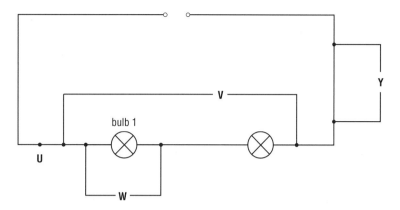

(i) Which letter shows the correct place for the **voltmeter**? Choose from **U**, **V**, **W** and **Y**. [1]

(ii) Which letter shows the correct place for the **ammeter**? Choose from **U**, **V**, **W** and **Y**. [1]

(iii) Current is measured in amps. What is **potential difference** (p.d.) measured in? [1]

(e) Sabrina does an experiment to brighten and dim a bulb. She uses a length of resistance wire. She slides the contact along the resistance wire. Look at the diagram of her circuit.
Sabrina's results are shown in the table.

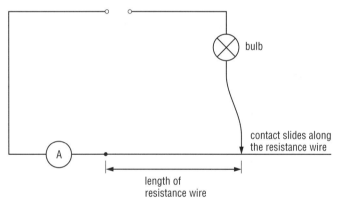

Length of resistance wire/cm	Current /amps	Brightness
0	1.5	very bright
20	1.3	bright
40	1.1	less bright
60	0.9	dim
80	0.7	very dim
100	0.5	none

Explain why the bulb brightens and dims. Use the ideas of current and resistance in your answer. [2]

(MEG, Foundation, 1998 Specimen)

Higher Level

1. The circuit below was used to measure the current through a resistor for a range of values of the potential difference across the resistor. The results are shown in the table.

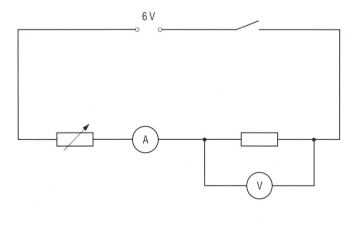

Potential difference/V	Current/A
0	0
1.0	0.5
2.0	1.0
3.0	1.5
4.0	2.0
5.0	2.5
6.0	3.0

(a) Plot a graph of potential difference against current and use it to find the resistance of the fixed resistor.

The resistor was then replaced by a filament lamp and the experiment repeated, producing the following results.

Potential difference/V	Current/A
0	0
0.25	0.25
0.75	0.5
1.5	0.75
2.5	1.0
3.75	1.25
5.25	1.5

(b) On the same axes as you used for part (a), plot a graph of potential difference against current for the filament lamp.

(c) Comment on the similarities and differences between the two graphs.

(d) Why does the relationship between V and I for the filament lamp change in the way it does?

2. (a) A car battery is rated at 40 Ah (amp-hours). This means that it can, for example, supply a current of 2 A for 20 hours before it becomes 'flat'. Calculate how much charge passes through the battery in that time.

(b) A 60 watt lamp is connected to a 230 V supply. Calculate the current flowing through the lamp and the charge which would flow through it per minute.

(c) In a circuit in which the current is 5 A, how long would it take for a charge of 1000 C to flow past a point in the circuit?

3. Calculate the current which will flow in each of the following circuits.

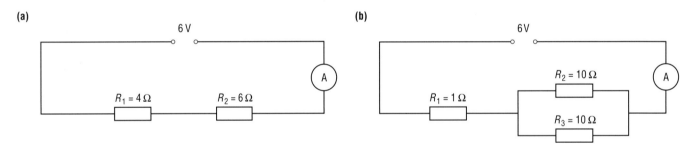

(a) 6 V — $R_1 = 4\,\Omega$ — $R_2 = 6\,\Omega$ — A

(b) 6 V — $R_1 = 1\,\Omega$ — $R_2 = 10\,\Omega$ — $R_3 = 10\,\Omega$ — A

4. The circuit below is a simple moisture-sensing circuit. The moisture sensor consists of two metal plates, placed close together. When dampness is present, current can be conducted across the gap.

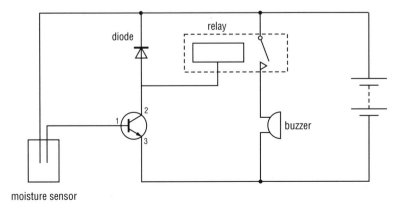

moisture sensor

(a) Describe how the circuit is able to operate the buzzer when the sensor gets wet.

(b) What is the purpose of the diode in this circuit?

(c) A transistor can be used as a current amplifier. Which of the transistor terminals in the diagram is (i) the collector, (ii) the base, (iii) the emitter?

The current gain of a transistor is calculated using the equation:

$$\text{current gain} = \frac{\text{collector current}}{\text{base current}}$$

(d) If the relay operates with a current of 20 mA and the current gain of the transistor is 40, what base current is needed for the buzzer to sound?

5. (a) A piece of polythene is cut from a food bag and hung over a plastic ruler as shown in diagram A below.

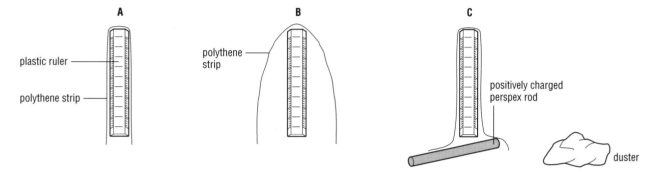

When the ends of the polythene are rubbed between the fingers they move apart as shown in diagram B. Diagram C shows a perspex rod that has been rubbed with a duster and is then placed between the ends of the piece of polythene.

(i) Why do the ends of the polythene move apart in B?

(ii) Why does the perspex 'stick' to the polythene in C?

(iii) If it is known the perspex has a positive charge, what can you say about the charge on the polythene and the duster?

(iv) Explain your answers to part (iii) in terms of electron transfer.

(b) Explain in terms of electrons the difference between electrical conductors and electrical insulators.

6. The diagram shows two metal conducting spheres X and Y. The spheres are touching each other and each is on top of an insulating base. A negatively charged rod is placed near to X.

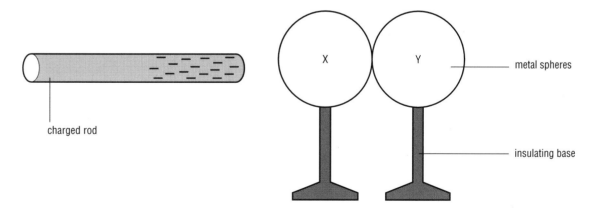

(a) Why are the spheres on insulating bases?

(b) Describe and explain the effect the rod will have on the electrons on the spheres.

(c) With the rod still close to X, X and Y are moved apart. The rod is then removed. Describe the charge on X and Y.

(d) Keith then touches X with his hand. What will happen to the charge on X and how will it differ from that on Y?

7. The diagrams below show the primary and secondary coils on three transformers.

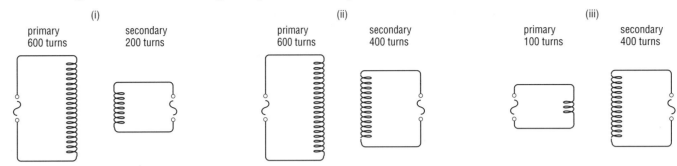

(i) primary 600 turns — secondary 200 turns

(ii) primary 600 turns — secondary 400 turns

(iii) primary 100 turns — secondary 400 turns

(a) In which transformer(s) will the secondary voltage be bigger than the primary voltage?

(b) In which transformer(s) will the secondary voltage be smaller than the primary voltage?

(c) One of the transformers in the National Grid must reduce the voltage of the supply from 33 000 V to 11 000 V. The primary and secondary coils of the transformer are shown on the right.
Calculate the number of turns which would be needed on the secondary coil to bring about the voltage reduction that is needed.

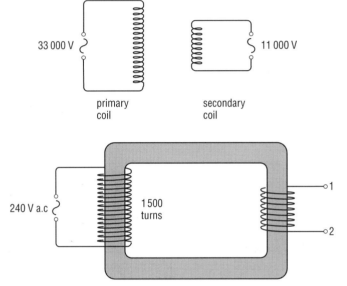

12 000 turns

33 000 V

11 000 V

primary coil

secondary coil

(d) The adapter unit on an electric shaver contains a transformer as shown below right. When a shaver of resistance 300 ohms is connected between terminals 1 and 2 a current of 0.4 A flows through it. Assume the transformer is 100% efficient.
(i) Calculate the potential difference across terminals 1 and 2.
(ii) Calculate the number of turns on the secondary coil.

240 V a.c

1 500 turns

1

2

(e) There is no electrical connection between the primary and secondary coils of a transformer. Explain, in as much detail as you can, why a voltage is induced across the secondary coil when an a.c. voltage is applied across the primary coil.

8. The diagram below shows a circuit used in an experiment to find the resistance of a resistor.

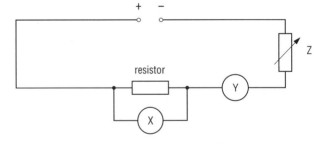

+ −

resistor

Z

Y

X

(a) (i) Name the meters shown in the diagram as 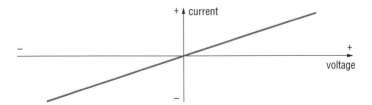 X and Y. [1]

(ii) Name the component shown as **Z**. [1]

(iii) A student plotted the results of the experiment. The following sketch graph shows this.

+ current

−

+

voltage

−

How can the resistance of the resistor be obtained from this sketch graph? [1]

(b) The student then carried out the experiment in (a) using a **diode** in place of the resistor.
  (i) Draw the symbol for a diode. [1]
  (ii) Draw a sketch graph of current against voltage to show the results you would expect the student to have obtained. [3]
(c) The following diagram shows a filament bulb.

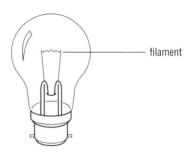

The filament is a coil of very thin wire. When the bulb is switched on, the temperature of the filament quickly increases to about 2500 °C and it glows white hot. The filament is made of tungsten.
  (i) Tungsten conducts electricity and can be made into very thin wires with a high resistance. Give **one** other reason why tungsten is used. [1]
  (ii) The student then carried out the experiment in (a) using a **filament bulb** in place of the resistor. Draw a sketch graph of current against voltage to show the results you would expect the student to have obtained. [2]
  (iii) Explain clearly why a filament bulb is more likely to fail immediately after it is switched on than at any other time. [4]

(SEG, Higher, 1998 Specimen)

9. **(a)** A transformer has 1000 turns on the primary coil and 30 000 turns on the secondary coil. If the input voltage is 10 volts what would be the output voltage? Include in your answer the equation you are going to use. Show clearly how you get to your final answer and give the unit. [2]
  (b) A second transformer has an input voltage of 25 000 V and an input current of 16 A.
    (i) Calculate the power input to this transformer. Include in your answer the equation you are going to use. Show clearly how you get to your answer and give the unit. [3]
    (ii) What is the maximum useful power output of this transformer, assuming it to be 100% efficient? [1]
  (c) Electricity is transmitted through the National Grid at a very high voltage and at a relatively low current. This is because it is cheaper than sending it at a lower voltage and higher current.
    (i) Explain why it is cheaper. [2]
    (ii) Apart from the risk of electric shocks and the cost and appearance of the transformers, cables and pylons, explain **one** other **disadvantage** of transmitting the electricity at very high voltages through cable supported by steel pylons. [2]
  (d) The sketch graph shows how the costs of the cables used in the National Grid are related to the thickness of the cable.

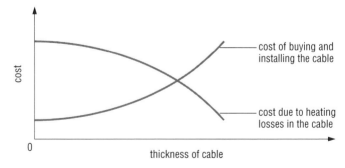

    (i) Why does the cost of buying the cable increase as it is made thicker? [1]
    (ii) Why does the cost of installing the cable increase as it is made thicker? [1]
    (iii) Why does the cost due to the heating loss **decrease** as the cable is made thicker? [1]

(SEG, Higher, 1998 Specimen)

2.1 Forces and their effects

A force can be thought of as a push or a pull. The units of force are **newtons (N)**. Larger forces may be measured in kilonewtons (kN). 1 kilonewton = 1000 newtons.

Forces can have several effects. They may:

- Keep a body stationary ('at rest').
- Cause a body which is at rest to begin to move.
- Change the speed of a moving body (make it accelerate or decelerate).
- Change the shape of a body (squash, stretch or bend it).
- Change the direction of a moving body.

In most situations you will need to consider several forces at work on the same body. To judge the effects of the forces you must consider the size of the forces *and* the direction in which they act.

Consider a stationary bag of sand suspended above the floor.

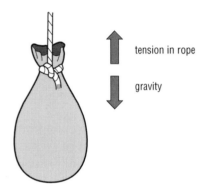

Figure 2.1.1 Balanced forces

There are two forces at work on the bag. Gravity pulls down on the bag. The rope exerts an upward force on the bag. The forces on the bag must be equal in size and opposite in direction if the bag is at rest (not moving). We say the forces are 'balanced'.

What happens if a horizontal force is applied to the bag?

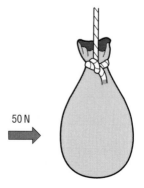

Figure 2.1.2 Now a 50 N force acts towards the right. Because this is the only force acting (horizontally), the bag will begin to move (accelerate) towards the right

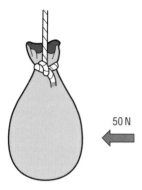

Figure 2.1.3 Now the force on the bag is still 50 N but it acts towards the left. Because it is the only force acting (horizontally), the bag will begin to move (accelerate) towards the left

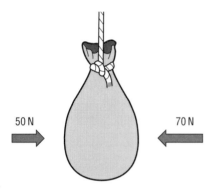

Figure 2.1.4 Here there are two (opposing) forces acting on the bag. The effect of the 50 N force to the right is 'balanced out' by 50 N of the force acting to the left. There is, however, an extra 20 N of force still acting towards the left. The horizontal forces on the bag are therefore unbalanced. The 'extra' force (20 N to the left), called the **resultant force**, causes the bag to begin to move (accelerate) towards the left – in the same direction as the resultant force

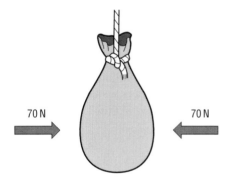

Figure 2.1.5 Here the two horizontal forces are balanced. They are equal in size and opposite in direction, so the resultant force is zero (0 N) and the bag remains at rest

We can generalise the effect of the forces on a stationary object by saying:

- It will remain at rest when balanced forces act on it.
- It will begin to move (accelerate) when unbalanced forces act on it. It will accelerate in the direction of the **resultant** (extra) force.

The effects of gravity

Every object exerts a **gravity** force on every other object. The effects are not usually noticeable unless one of the objects has a huge mass compared with the other. Because the earth is so massive it exerts a gravity force large enough to have a noticeable effect on other things – it pulls everything towards its centre. Because of gravity, things 'fall' to earth.

Imagine the gravity force between the earth and a parachutist. While the earth's gravity pulls on the parachutist, the parachutist also exerts a gravity force which pulls on the earth.

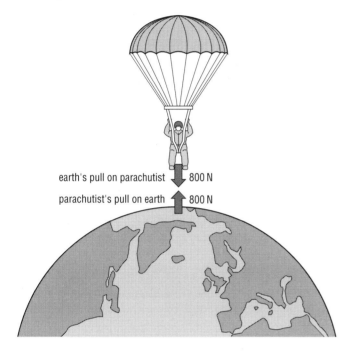

earth's pull on parachutist — 800 N
parachutist's pull on earth — 800 N

Figure 2.1.6 The gravity force acts on both objects equally

They pull on one another with the same force – about 800 N. That force is big enough to make the parachutist move but is *not* big enough to make something as massive as the earth move. As a result the parachutist falls to earth.

What affects the size of a gravity force?

The size of the gravity force between two objects depends on:

- The mass of each object – the bigger the masses, the bigger the force.
- How far they are apart – the further they are apart, the smaller the force.

Mass and weight

The **mass** of an object is a measure of its inertia – the resistance against any attempt to change its motion. The mass depends on the amount of matter in the object and is measured in kilograms. At the earth's

surface, gravity pulls on each kilogram of matter with a force of 10 newtons (10 N). The value (10 newtons per kilogram) is the **gravitational field strength** of the earth. A 1 kg mass will therefore exert a downward force of 10 N on anything on which it rests. This force is what we call its **weight**.

We can think of the weight of an object as being the force due to gravity. Weight, like other forces, is measured in newtons (N). To change mass into weight:

weight (N) = mass (kg) × gravitational field strength (N/kg)

On earth, the gravitational field strength = 10 N/kg. So:

weight (N) = mass (kg) × 10

Quick Questions

1 What effect will the following forces have on the motion of the object?

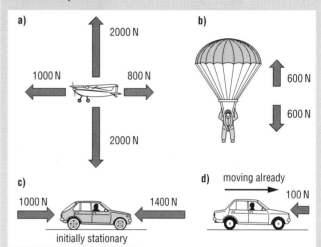

a) 2000 N, 1000 N, 800 N, 2000 N

b) 600 N, 600 N

c) 1000 N, 1400 N, initially stationary

d) moving already, 100 N

Figure 2.1.7

2 The table below shows the gravitational field strength at the surface of some of the planets and the moon. Complete the gaps in the table.

Planet	Gravitational field strength (N/kg)	Mass of object on planet's surface (kg)	Weight of object (N)
Earth	10	20	
Moon	1.66		1.66
Venus		2	18
Mars	4		16
Jupiter	26		104
Neptune	14	10	

2.2 Deformation

Forces can change the shape of a material, causing it to become:

- stretched,
- compressed (squashed),
- bent, or
- twisted.

A particle view of deformation

The particles are evenly distributed throughout a solid material. Balanced forces act between the particles, holding them in position. Any extra force (applied externally) may rearrange the positions of the particles, thus changing the shape of the material.

Inward-acting forces squash or compress the material – the particles are pushed closer together. The particles resist this **compression** by exerting repulsive forces on one another. Externally this is manifested as a restoring force, acting in the opposite direction to the applied force. It is the restoring force that you feel 'pushing back' when you try to squash something such as foam rubber.

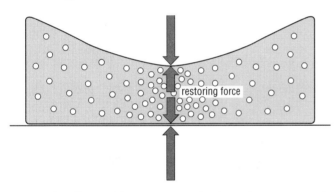

Figure 2.2.1 The material exerts a restoring force when compressed

If the external applied force is removed, the forces between the particles return the particles to their original positions and the material regains its original shape.

Outward-acting external forces pull the particles further apart, stretching the material and placing it in **tension**. Once again, the particles resist this by exerting attractive forces on one another, creating a restoring force that can be felt, for example when you stretch a rubber band.

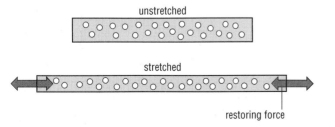

Figure 2.2.2 The material exerts a restoring force when stretched

If the external applied force is removed, the forces between the particles return the particles to their original positions and the material regains its original shape (provided the elastic limit of the material has not been exceeded – see page 52).

In both cases, the larger the force, the more the material is deformed. Excessive stretching forces may tear the particles apart, snapping, breaking or tearing the material.

Bending

When a material bends, the particles on the 'outside' of the bend are pulled further apart (they are in tension). Those on the 'inside' of the bend are pushed together (compressed). When the deforming force is removed, the forces between the particles return them to their original positions and the material regains its original shape.

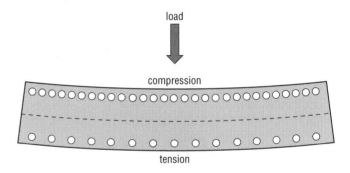

Figure 2.2.3 Particles in a bent beam

Concrete beams bend in this way, although the effect is generally so small to be unnoticeable. Concrete is strong in compression but weak in tension. Concrete beams are therefore weaker (and more likely to break) on the underside where the particles are in tension.

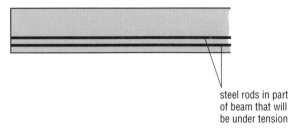

Figure 2.2.4 Reinforced concrete beam

To overcome this weakness, steel rods are placed in the concrete. Steel is strong in compression and in tension. The rods reinforce, or strengthen, the concrete beam.

Preventing deformation

Often steps need to be taken to prevent **structures** being deformed. In many structures, **ties** and **struts** are used to distribute the forces throughout the structure. They help to prevent the shape of any part of the structure changing. Ties tend to be in tension. Struts tend to be in compression, supporting one part of the structure against another.

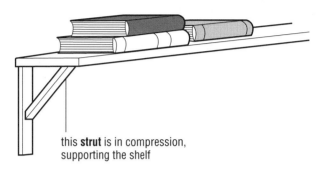

this **strut** is in compression, supporting the shelf

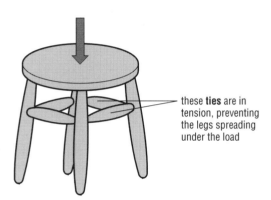

these **ties** are in tension, preventing the legs spreading under the load

Figure 2.2.5 Struts and ties enable structures to withstand forces

In tunnels the weight of the earth above is spread across the individual sections that make up the arch. Each section is therefore in compression.

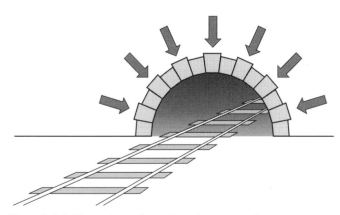

Figure 2.2.6 The sections of an arch are in compression

The important thing to note is that, at any point in a structure, all downward forces are balanced by upward forces and all horizontal forces are balanced by equal and opposite forces.

Elastic and plastic behaviour

Some materials (such as rubber) regain their shape after being deformed. They are described as **elastic** materials. The word 'elastic', used in this sense, describes how the material behaves. Other materials, such as Plasticine, remain deformed. Their behaviour is described as **plastic**.

Most materials show both elastic and plastic behaviour, depending on the size of the deforming forces involved. The steel panel on a car, for example, may bend under the action of small external forces. When released it springs back into shape, showing it has elastic properties. Larger forces cause the steel to bend permanently – under these circumstances it shows plastic behaviour.

Quick Questions
● ●

1 **a)** Describe four ways in which the shape of a material can be changed by forces.
  b) What differences would you notice between a material that showed elastic behaviour and one that showed plastic behaviour?

2

Figure 2.2.7

  a) Copy the diagram above. Mark with a 'C' regions that are in compression. Mark with a 'T' any regions that are in tension. Mark the weakest point in the structure with an 'X'.
  b) How would changing the distance between the pillars affect the strength of the horizontal slab (i.e. its ability to support a load)?

3 **a)** Concrete is an important building material. Write down three advantages of concrete as a building material.
  b) Under what circumstances is concrete weak?
  c) How is the weakness in part (b) overcome?

2.3 Springs

When a weight is attached to a supported spring, the spring stretches. The amount by which the spring stretches is called the extension.

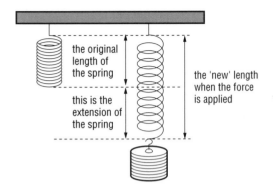

Figure 2.3.1 The extension of a stretched spring

Hooke's Law

The relationship between the extension of a spring and the force acting on it can be seen on this graph.

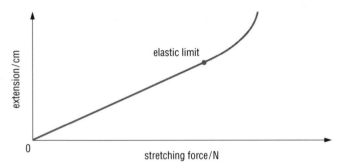

Figure 2.3.2 Extension against stretching force for a spring

The graph is a straight line up to a point called the elastic limit. The straight line shows us that *the extension is directly proportional to the applied force (load)* – if the force is doubled the extension will double; if the force trebles the extension will treble, and so on. This relationship is known as **Hooke's Law**.

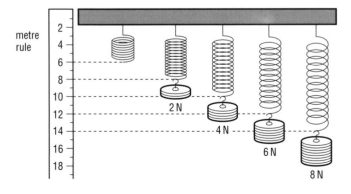

Figure 2.3.3 The extension of a stretched spring is directly proportional to the stretching force, provided the elastic limit is not exceeded

The elastic limit

All springs display elastic behaviour up to a point called the **elastic limit**. Provided the elastic limit is not exceeded the spring will regain its original shape when the load is removed. If subjected to a load beyond the elastic limit, however, the spring will become permanently deformed – its behaviour becomes plastic. The elastic limit is the point at which the behaviour of the spring stops being elastic and becomes plastic. A spring extended beyond the elastic limit will never regain its original shape. When the load is removed it will be left longer than when it started.

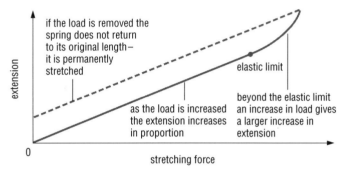

Figure 2.3.4 Behaviour beyond the elastic limit

Note that, beyond the elastic limit, small increases in the load result in larger increases in the extension.

Stretching other materials

When forces act on strips of elastic or polythene we find they display a similar relationship to that obtained for a spring.

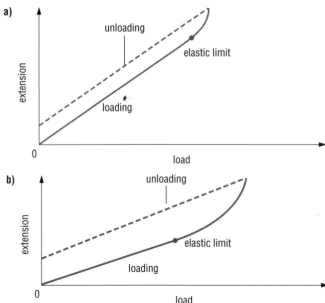

Figure 2.3.5 Extension against load for strips of **a)** elastic, **b)** polythene

For small loads, the extension increases steadily as the stretching force increases. The materials therefore obey Hooke's Law. Eventually both materials reach a point where the extension (for the same increase in load) increases. The materials have reached their elastic limit.

Metal wires also show elastic behaviour, but to varying degrees. The loads will be significantly greater than those needed to stretch a spring.

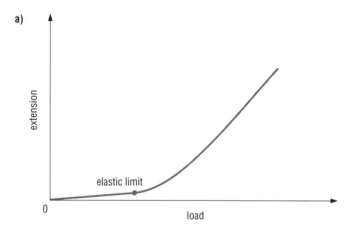

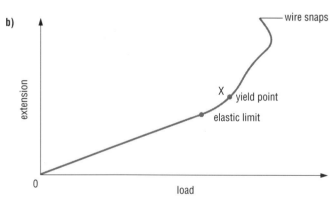

Figure 2.3.6 Extension against load for metal wires: **a)** steel, **b)** copper

You can see from the graphs above that both steel and copper wires show elastic properties when (relatively) small loads are applied, but they rapidly reach their elastic limit. Copper retains its elastic properties over a wider range of loads than steel, shown by the longer straight line section on graph (b).

The point marked X on graph (b) is sometimes called the yield point. Beyond the yield point the wire suddenly stretches much more easily as the load is increased, and eventually snaps.

A particle view

As the wire is stretched, the particles are pulled further apart. Provided the elastic limit has not been exceeded, if the load is removed the attractive forces between the particles will draw them back together and the wire regains its original length.

Quick Questions

1 Use the following words or phrases to complete the section below.

plastic   elastic   directly proportional
elastic limit   original length

Provided the ……… ……… is not exceeded, the extension (stretch) of a spiral spring is ……… ……… to the load suspended from it. When the load is removed the spring regains its ……… ……… so we can say that it is showing ……… behaviour. If the elastic limit is exceeded, the spring remains permanently stretched – its behaviour has become ……… .

2 Explain the following terms:
  a) elastic behaviour;
  b) plastic behaviour;
  c) directly proportional.

3 An unstretched spring is 10 cm long. When a load of 6 N is placed on it, the spring stretches by 7.5 cm. Assuming that the elastic limit has not been exceeded, what will be the length of the spring when a load of 2 N is placed on it?

4 These graphs are for two different springs. They show what happened as weights were added to the springs (the full lines) and what happened as the weights were slowly removed (the dotted lines). The axes are the same in both cases.

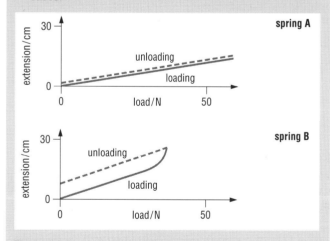

Figure 2.3.7

  a) Which spring is strongest (i.e. stretches least under a given force)?
  b) Which spring retains elastic properties for the largest loads?
  c) Which spring was permanently stretched by the applied load?
  d) Draw another sketch graph for a spring which was easier to stretch than either of those shown above. Assume your axes will have similar values to those shown above.

2.4 Pressure

When you are standing, your weight is spread over the area of your feet. We say you exert a pressure on the ground. **Pressure** is defined as the force (N) acting on unit area (1 m²) and is calculated using the equation:

$$\text{pressure} = \frac{\text{force (N)}}{\text{area (m}^2)}$$

In symbols:

$$P = \frac{F}{A}$$

The standard unit of pressure is N/m². Another unit, the **pascal (Pa)** is also used. 1 pascal is the equivalent of 1 N/m².

The pressure exerted by a force depends on:

- The size of the force – the greater the force, the greater the pressure (assuming the area is constant).
- The area on which the force acts – the greater the area over which the force acts, the smaller the pressure.

The 'caterpillar' tracks on some heavy vehicles are designed to reduce the pressure which the vehicle exerts on the ground, by increasing the area over which the weight acts.

weight = 200 000 N

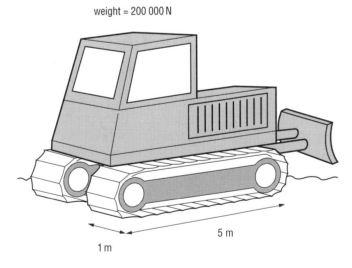

1 m   5 m

Figure 2.4.1 Wide tracks reduce the pressure

The pressure exerted on the ground by the vehicle above would be:

$$\text{pressure} = \frac{\text{force}}{\text{area}}$$

$$= \frac{200\,000}{10} \quad \text{(note that the total area = 10 m}^2 \text{ because the weight is distributed over } both \text{ tracks)}$$

$$= 20\,000 \text{ Pa (or } 20\,000 \text{ N/m}^2)$$

Reducing the pressure reduces the depth to which the vehicle sinks into soft ground. Other things, such as drawing pins, knives and forks, are designed to increase the pressure by concentrating the applied force onto a small area.

Pressure in liquids

When an object is immersed in a fluid (liquid or gas), the fluid exerts a pressure on all sides of the object. The pressure depends on the depth of the object in the fluid, as can be shown using the equipment below.

Figure 2.4.2 Water pressure is greater at greater depths

The lower the tube is below the surface of the water, the further the water 'spurts' from the tube. The pressure must therefore increase as the depth increases.

The pressure at any point in a fluid depends on:

- The depth of the fluid – the greater the depth, the greater the pressure.
- The density of the fluid – the greater the density, the greater the pressure at any depth.

The pressure at any point in a fluid can be calculated using:

$$P = hdg \quad \text{where } h = \text{depth below surface (m)}$$
$$d = \text{density of fluid (kg/m}^3)$$
$$g = \text{gravitational field strength (N/kg)}$$

In a fluid the pressure acts equally in all directions.

Hydraulic systems

Fluids can be used to transfer forces from one place to another. The fluid in a **hydraulic** braking system, Figure 2.4.3, transfers the force on the brake pedal to the brake cylinder. The basic principle is that the fluid transfers pressure equally throughout the system.

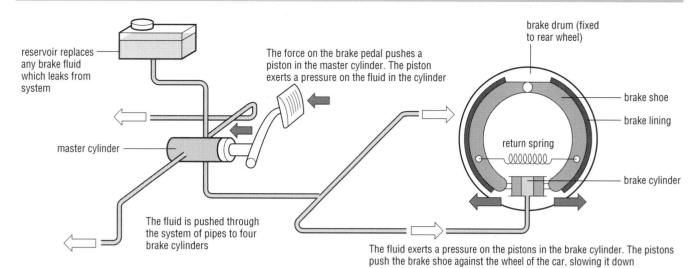

reservoir replaces any brake fluid which leaks from system

The force on the brake pedal pushes a piston in the master cylinder. The piston exerts a pressure on the fluid in the cylinder

master cylinder

The fluid is pushed through the system of pipes to four brake cylinders

brake drum (fixed to rear wheel)

brake shoe

brake lining

return spring

brake cylinder

The fluid exerts a pressure on the pistons in the brake cylinder. The pistons push the brake shoe against the wheel of the car, slowing it down

Figure 2.4.3 Hydraulic car brakes

Imagine, for example, that a force of 400 N is exerted on a master cylinder of cross-sectional area 2 cm²; and that the cross-sectional area of the brake cylinder is 4 cm².

In the master cylinder:

$$\text{pressure on the fluid} = \frac{\text{force}}{\text{area}} = \frac{400}{2} = 200 \text{ N/cm}^2$$

In the brake cylinder:

The pressure that the fluid exerts on the piston in the brake cylinder is exactly the same as the pressure exerted on the fluid by the master cylinder: 200 N/cm². So the force exerted on the brakes is (rearranging pressure = force/area):

$$\begin{aligned} \text{force (N)} &= \text{pressure} \times \text{area} \\ &= 200 \times 4 \\ &= 800 \text{ N} \end{aligned}$$

You can see that the force on the brakes is greater than the force exerted by the person on the pedal. This system is a **force multiplier** – the output force is greater than the input force.

A key feature of hydraulic systems is that they transfer force throughout the system almost immediately – there is no delay between the foot pushing on the brake pedal and the brakes acting.

Note. In the calculation above the area of the cylinders is given in cm². We have therefore calculated the pressure in N/cm². Sometimes you might be required to convert cm² to m² (1 m² = 10 000 cm²) to give the pressure in N/m² or Pa.

Quick Questions

1 **a)** Which quantities affect the pressure exerted by a solid on a surface?
   b) Which quantities affect the pressure exerted by a liquid?

2 Calculate the pressure exerted by:
   a) a car weighing 8000 N, if the tyres rest on a total area of 0.4 m²;
   b) a table lamp weighing 50 N resting on a base area of 0.1 m².

3 **a)** Calculate the pressure on a submarine at a depth of 300 m in sea water of density 1025 kg/m³; the gravitational field strength is 10 N/kg.
   b) Explain why the walls of a dam are designed to be thicker as they get further below water level.

4 Which of the following is designed to:
   a) reduce pressure by spreading the applied force over a large area?
   b) increase pressure by concentrating the applied force over a small area?

   snow shoes   knife   ice skates   tractor tyres   nail
   cheese cutter   tigers' teeth   wide bag strap

5 Garages use hydraulic lifts to raise cars.

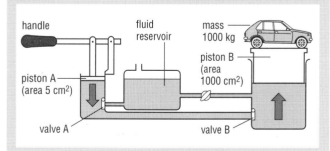

handle

fluid reservoir

mass 1000 kg

piston B (area 1000 cm²)

piston A (area 5 cm²)

valve A

valve B

Figure 2.4.4

Calculate:
   a) the pressure on piston B;
   b) the force exerted on the fluid by piston A.

2.5 Pressure exerted by gases

The weight of the air exerts a pressure (called **atmospheric pressure**). The experiment in Figure 2.5.1 is often used to demonstrate the existence of atmospheric pressure. Note that the can is crushed inwards from the top, sides and bottom – suggesting that atmospheric pressure acts in all directions.

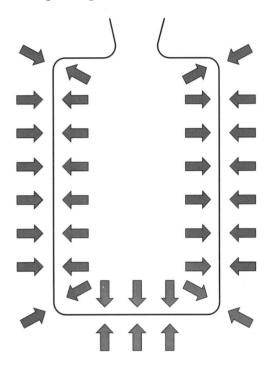

Figure 2.5.1a An empty can is under pressure from the air outside and inside. The pressure on the inside (acting outwards) is equal to the pressure on the outside of the can (acting inwards)

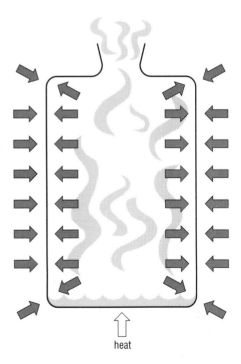

heat

Figure 2.5.1b A small amount of water is placed in the can and boiled. The can fills with steam, driving out the air

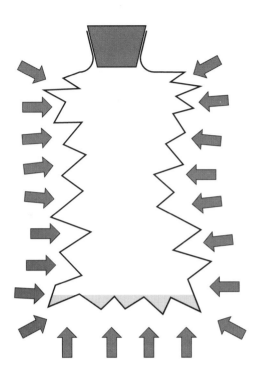

Figure 2.5.1c The can is sealed and cooled. The steam condenses, leaving a partial vacuum inside the can. The pressure inside is now much lower than the (inward-acting) pressure from outside the can and the can collapses

What causes a gas to exert a pressure?

Consider a gas trapped inside a container. The gas consists of millions of tiny molecules which move quickly, changing direction as they collide with the sides of the container.

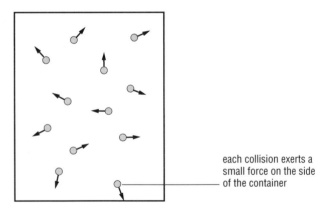

each collision exerts a small force on the side of the container

Figure 2.5.2 The pressure of a gas is due to the collisions of its rapidly moving molecules with the container

Although the force exerted by one molecule on the container is tiny, there may be millions of collisions each second. These produce a significant force which is spread over all sides of the container. The force that acts on unit area of the container is the pressure exerted by the gas.

The relationship between pressure and volume

Under normal circumstances, gases can be readily compressed (because the molecules are relatively far apart). You may have experienced this yourself if you have ever tried to squash the air inside a bicycle pump.

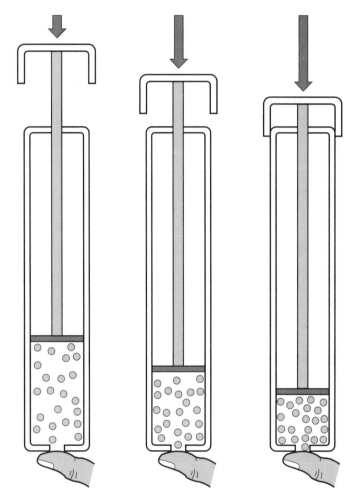

Figure 2.5.3 As you push the plunger further in, the pressure of the air inside increases

Assuming the air cannot escape, as the pump is pushed in the molecules are pushed closer together. Because the molecules are travelling at the same speed, but are now confined to a smaller volume, they collide with the walls more often, exerting a greater pressure. The pressure of the gas increases due to the decrease in the volume in which it is contained.

If, on the other hand, you draw the piston out, increasing the volume of the gas, the pressure decreases.

There is a simple mathematical relationship (called Boyle's Law) between pressure and volume: *for a fixed mass of gas at constant temperature, the pressure is inversely proportional to the volume.*

The relationship can also be expressed in the form of an equation. For a fixed mass of gas at constant temperature:

$$\text{pressure} \times \text{volume} = \text{a constant value}$$

or:

$P \times V = \text{a constant}$ where P = pressure (Pa)
V = volume (m^3)

Worked example

Consider a fixed mass of gas, at a pressure of 100 000 Pa and with a volume of $2\ m^3$. If the gas is compressed to a volume of $0.4\ m^3$, what will be the new pressure of the gas?

Because pressure $\times$ volume = a constant for a fixed mass of gas, we can write:

$$P_1 \times V_1 = P_2 \times V_2$$
$$\underset{\text{conditions}}{\underset{\text{initial}}{}} \qquad \underset{\text{conditions}}{\underset{\text{new}}{}}$$

so:

$$100\,000 \times 2 = P_2 \times 0.4$$

$$P_2 = \frac{100\,000 \times 2}{0.4}$$

$$= 500\,000\ \text{Pa}$$

At the reduced volume of $0.4\ m^3$, the pressure of the gas will be 500 000 Pa, *assuming the temperature remains constant.*

The relationship between pressure and volume can be shown by plotting a graph of P against $1/V$.

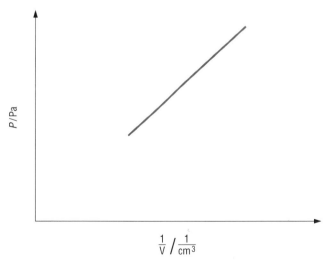

Figure 2.5.4 Pressure against 1/volume for a gas at constant temperature

The straight line confirms that the pressure is inversely proportional to the volume.

Absolute temperature

The relationships between the pressure, volume and temperature of a gas require an understanding of the 'absolute' scale of temperature. On this scale, also called the Kelvin scale, temperature is measured in kelvin (K); it is an alternative to the Celsius (°C) scale.

Absolute zero (0 K) represents the lowest temperature that can be reached by anything, and is equivalent to a temperature of -273 °C. Above this each 1 K increase is equivalent to a rise of 1 °C.

Table 2.5.1

Kelvin scale	0 K	273 K	373 K
Celsius scale	-273 °C	0 °C	100 °C

To convert from degrees Celsius to kelvin:

$$K = °C + 273$$

To convert from kelvin to degrees Celsius:

$$°C = K - 273$$

The relationship between pressure and temperature

Any change in the temperature of a gas affects its pressure. Consider what happens to a gas inside a sealed container.

If the gas is heated, the molecules gain energy and move faster. The rate at which they strike the sides of the container increases, so the gas exerts a greater pressure. Conversely, if the temperature decreases, the molecules lose energy, slow down, and the pressure decreases.

If a graph of the pressure *of a fixed mass of gas at constant volume* is plotted against the absolute temperature, a straight line is obtained.

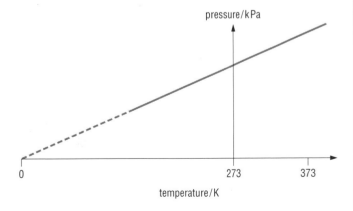

Figure 2.5.5 Pressure against temperature for a constant volume of gas

This relationship is expressed as: *for a fixed mass of gas at constant volume, the pressure is directly proportional to the absolute temperature.* In other words, if the absolute temperature is doubled, the pressure will double, or, if the absolute temperature is halved, the pressure will halve.

In mathematical terms we can write the relationship as:

$$\frac{\text{pressure}}{\text{absolute temperature}} = \text{a constant}$$

(for a fixed mass of gas at constant volume), or:

$$\frac{P}{T} = \text{a constant value} \qquad \text{where } P = \text{pressure (Pa)}$$
$$T = \text{absolute temperature (K)}$$

Worked example

The gas in an aerosol can is at a pressure of 300 000 Pa at a temperature of 20 °C. What will be the pressure of the gas at a temperature of 40 °C?

Because $\dfrac{\text{pressure}}{\text{absolute temperature}} = \text{a constant}$, we

can write:

$$\frac{P_1}{T_1} = \frac{P_2}{T_2}$$

where P_1 and T_1 are the conditions at 20 °C and P_2 and T_2 are the conditions at 40 °C.

So (remembering to change the °C temperatures to K temperatures):

$$\frac{300\ 000}{293} = \frac{P_2}{313}$$

$$P_2 = \frac{300\ 000 \times 313}{293}$$

$$P_2 = 320\ 500 \text{ Pa (approximately)}$$

The pressure of the gas at 40 °C will be about 320 500 Pa (320.5 kPa).

The ideal gas equation

The pressure, volume and temperature of a fixed mass of gas are interrelated. If the value of any quantity changes, then the others may also undergo some change. All three quantities are related by the **ideal gas equation**, which states that, for a fixed mass of gas:

$$\frac{\text{pressure} \times \text{volume}}{\text{absolute temperature}} = \text{a constant}$$

Another way of stating this is that, for a fixed mass of gas undergoing some change in pressure, volume or temperature:

$$\frac{P_1 V_1}{T_1} = \frac{P_2 V_2}{T_2}$$

initial conditions   new conditions

Worked example

A bubble of gas is released on the ocean floor. Its volume is 0.001 m³. The pressure of the gas is 7 200 000 Pa and its temperature is −15 °C (258 K). Calculate the volume of the bubble as it reaches the surface, if the temperature is 10 °C (283 K) and the pressure of the gas has become 102 000 Pa.

In this example the pressure, volume and temperature all change. We must use the ideal gas equation:

$$\frac{P_1 V_1}{T_1} = \frac{P_2 V_2}{T_2}$$

where P_1, V_1 and T_1 are the conditions on the ocean floor and P_2, V_2 and T_2 are the conditions just below the surface.

Using the values given:

$$\frac{7\,200\,000 \times 0.001}{258} = \frac{102\,000 \times V_2}{283}$$

$$V_2 = 0.077\,\text{m}^3$$

The volume of the bubble just below the surface will be 0.077 m³.

Quick Questions

1 **a)** Before leaving on a long journey, a car driver notices the tyre pressures are low. He adds extra air to the tyres at a garage. Explain how this will increase the tyre pressure.
  b) At the end of the journey the pressure is found to be higher than when he started. Explain why. Why should he not let air out of the tyre to reduce the pressure?
2 **a)** Convert the following to temperatures on the Kelvin scale:

  270 °C   2000 °C   −230 °C

  b) Convert the following to temperatures in degrees Celsius:

  127 K   600 K   373 K

3 Using your knowledge of gases explain why:
  a) a damaged table tennis ball can sometimes be repaired by placing it in hot water;
  b) old aerosol cans should not be thrown on fires;
  c) when heating canned food by placing the can in a pan of boiling water you are advised to puncture the can first.

4 A large steel gas cylinder contains gas at a pressure of 100 000 Pa and at a temperature of 300 K. The cylinder can withstand pressures of up to 400 000 Pa. At what temperature will this pressure be reached, assuming the cylinder does not expand?

5 The air inside a weather balloon on the earth's surface is at a pressure of 100 000 Pa at a temperature of 300 K and has a volume of 10 m³. As the balloon rises the temperature falls to 200 K and the pressure to 50 000 Pa. What will be the volume of the balloon under these conditions?

2.6 Levers and moments

Machines allow us to do jobs using less effort. A car jack, for example, is a machine that allows us to lift a car - a job we could not do without assistance.

Levers are machines that pivot around some point. The pivot point is sometimes called the fulcrum. When a force acts on any lever it creates a turning effect around the fulcrum.

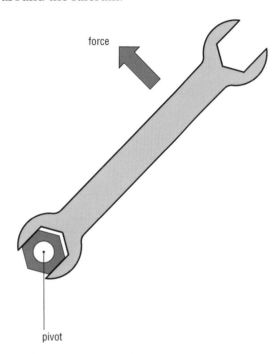

Figure 2.6.1 The spanner acts as a lever

The force applied to the spanner above creates a turning effect (or **moment**) in an anti-clockwise direction – the spanner moves in the direction of the applied force.

The moment of a force depends on:

- The size of the force.
- The distance at which the force acts from the pivot.

It is calculated using the equation:

moment (N m) = force (N) × distance from pivot (m)

Note the units of a moment - newton metres (N m).

Worked example

A force of 50 N is exerted at the end of a spanner at a distance of 0.2 m from the pivot. Calculate the moment of the force.

The moment is calculated using:

moment = force × distance

        = 50 × 0.2

        = 10 N m

The principle of moments

The forces on a see-saw exert moments in opposite directions.

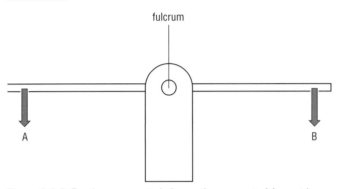

Figure 2.6.2 For the see-saw to balance, the moment of A must be equal to the moment of B

Force A, for example, creates an anti-clockwise moment about the fulcrum. Force B, on the other hand, creates a clockwise moment. If the anti-clockwise moment is equal to the clockwise moment the see-saw will be in **equilibrium** (balanced). This is known as the principle of moments.

The same principle can be applied to any number of forces acting on a see-saw, each of which is creating a turning effect, as shown in the example below.

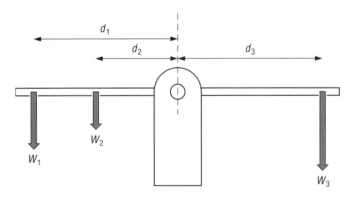

Figure 2.6.3 The total anti-clockwise moment must equal the total clockwise moment

Here there are two forces tending to create an anti-clockwise turning effect. The total anti-clockwise moment is the sum of the moments created by the two loads on the left hand side.

$$\text{anti-clockwise moment} = (W_1 \times d_1) + (W_2 \times d_2)$$
$$\text{clockwise moment} = (W_3 \times d_3)$$

So, applying the principle of moments to the see-saw, for the see-saw to be in equilibrium:

$$\text{anti-clockwise moment} = \text{clockwise moment}$$
$$(W_1 \times d_1) + (W_2 \times d_2) = (W_3 \times d_3)$$

Centre of gravity

If you place the mid-point of a ruler on your finger the ruler will balance. The ruler is made of millions of particles, each of which has weight. Each particle therefore exerts a turning effect about the pivot. The ruler balances because the sum of the clockwise moments of the particles on the right is equal to the sum of the anti-clockwise moments created by the particles on the left.

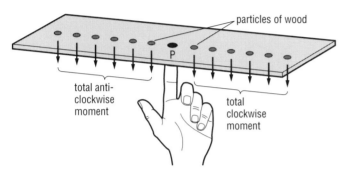

Figure 2.6.4 The ruler will balance at its mid-point

The effect is as if the weight of all of the particles in the ruler is acting at point P. The weight of the ruler can be thought of as a single force acting at P. The point P on the ruler is called the **centre of gravity**.

For any regular shape of uniform density, the centre of gravity is at the geometrical centre of the object. The centre of gravity of a rectangular or square shape, for example, will be at the point where the diagonals intersect.

To find the centre of gravity of an irregular shape, the following steps 1 to 5 may be taken.

1 The object is suspended so that it can move freely (Figure 2.6.5a).
2 A piece of thread supporting a small weight is hung from the same pivot as that which supports the object.
3 The line of the thread is drawn across the object.
4 The object is pivoted at some other point (Figure 2.6.5b) and steps 2 and 3 are repeated.
5 The centre of gravity is the point at which the lines intersect. If the object is supported at this point, it will be in equilibrium.

Balance and moments

Some objects topple over when they are slightly displaced. They are unstable. Other objects must be displaced to a much greater degree before they will topple. They are more stable. How well an object is able to retain its position when displaced is its 'stability'.

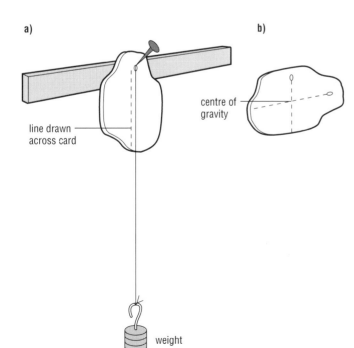

Figure 2.6.5 Finding an object's centre of gravity

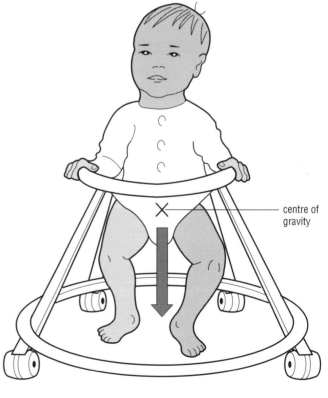

Figure 2.6.6 The broad base area, accompanied by the low centre of gravity (X) when the baby is in it, ensures that this babywalker is stable – it will be almost impossible to topple

The stability of an object depends on the position of its centre of gravity, as shown in Figure 2.6.7.

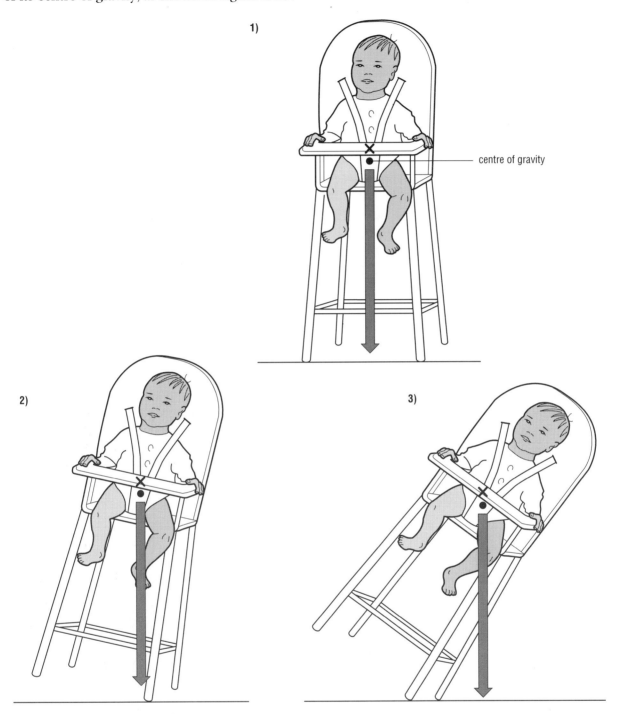

Figure 2.6.7 The high chair will topple when its weight acts outside the base area

- Under normal circumstances (diagram 1) the centre of gravity of the chair and baby lies within the base area formed by the legs. The chair is stable.
- If the chair is tilted slightly (diagram 2), you can see that the mentre of gravity still lies vertically above a point within the base area (between the legs) of the chair. The turning effect (of the weight acting at the centre of gravity) will tend to pull the chair anti-clockwise, back onto its base.

- When the chair is tilted further (diagram 3), the centre of gravity then lies vertically above some point outside the base area. The clockwise moment will then cause the chair to topple over.

A high chair can be made more stable by designing it so that (a) the legs are further apart, and (b) the centre of gravity is lower.

Types of equilibrium

An object such as a pear can be in stable, unstable, or neutral equilibrium, as shown in Figure 2.6.8.

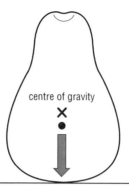

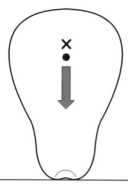

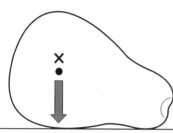

Figure 2.6.8a Here the pear is in stable equilibrium. Most of the mass is concentrated into the lower region of the pear. The centre of gravity will therefore be low. If the pear is pushed slightly to the side, it will return to this position. The moment of the weight (acting at the centre of gravity) will cause it to fall back to its original position

Figure 2.6.8b Here the pear is in unstable equilibrium. Most of the mass is concentrated in the upper portion of the pear. Its centre of gravity will be high. A slight push to the side will cause the centre of gravity to move beyond the narrow base area and the pear will topple due to the moment of the weight

Figure 2.6.8c In this position the pear is in neutral equilibrium. If pushed slightly to one side it will come to rest in a similar position, but slightly displaced

Quick Questions

1 Write down the names of **five** machines that you have used. In what way did each one make it easier for you to do the job for which it was intended?

2 Someone pushes with a force of 400 N on the centre of a 1 m wide door.
   a) What is the moment of this force about the hinges?
   b) Someone on the other side of the door is trying to stop it being opened. Where is the easiest place for them to push and what force would this require?

3 Figure 2.6.9 shows a Bunsen burner in three different positions.

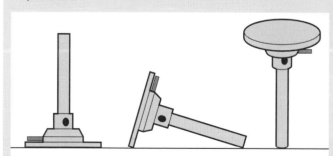

Figure 2.6.9

   a) Which diagram shows the Bunsen burner in stable equilibrium?
   b) Which diagram shows the Bunsen burner in unstable equilibrium?
   c) Which diagram shows the Bunsen burner in neutral equilibrium?

4 A window cleaner carries his ladder over his shoulder. The ladder is 4 metres long and weighs 200 N. The weight of the ladder seems to act at the mid-point – 2 metres from each end. The ladder pivots on his shoulder.

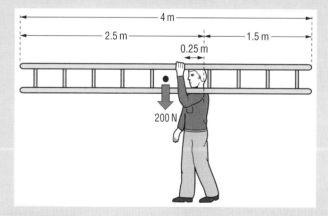

Figure 2.6.10

   a) Which force causes a clockwise moment on the ladder?
   b) Which force creates the anti-clockwise moment that keeps the ladder in equilibrium?
   c) What force will his arm need to exert to balance the ladder?
   d) His bucket weighs 200 N with the water and cloths in it. Where could he hang the bucket so that he would not need to counteract the effect of the weight of the ladder with his arm?

2.7 Forces and motion

The way in which something is moving (whether it is moving at a steady speed, or whether its speed is changing) depends on the forces acting on it at the time. The effect of the forces on the motion of the body depends on:

- The size of the forces.
- The direction in which they act.

Consider the moving car in the diagrams below.

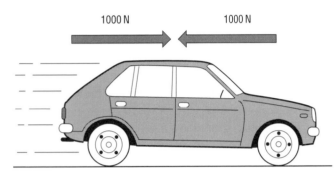

Figure 2.7.1a Here the engine exerts a force on the wheels which drives the car forwards. Air exerts a 'drag' on the moving car – a force that opposes the motion. Because the forces are balanced (equal in size but opposite in direction) the car will move at a steady speed

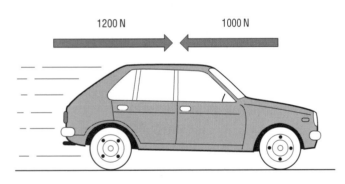

Figure 2.7.1b Here the force from the engine is greater than the drag exerted on the car by the air. There is a resultant force (acting to the right) of 200 N. Because the 'extra' force acts in the same direction as that in which the car is already moving, it causes the speed of the car to increase

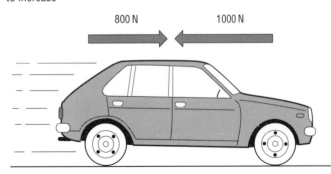

Figure 2.7.1c Here the force from the engine is smaller than the drag exerted by the air on the car. A resultant force of 200 N acts to the left. Because the 'extra' force is in the opposite direction to that in which the car is already moving, it causes the car to slow down

We can summarise the effects of forces on a moving object by saying:

- If there are balanced forces acting on a moving object it will continue to move at the same speed and in the same direction.
- If there are unbalanced forces acting on a moving object it will accelerate (its speed will change). If the resultant force acts in the same direction as the motion of the body then the speed will increase. If the resultant force is in the opposite direction to the motion, the speed will decrease.
- If the resultant force on a body is in a direction other than that in which it is currently moving, then it will change direction.

Friction between surfaces

If you give something a push, it begins to move but soon slows down and eventually stops. There must be a force acting against the motion (otherwise it would continue moving). The force is **friction**. Friction is caused by the roughness of the surfaces which are in contact.

Figure 2.7.2 As the book moves across the table, the tiny humps and hollows in the surfaces in contact cause a 'drag'. This is the force of friction, which slows down the book

Friction always acts in the opposite direction to the motion of an object.

The frictional force between car tyres and the ground creates 'grip'. If there was no grip the wheels would just spin around and the car would not move. On an icy road, the surface is smoother so there is less friction. When the brakes are applied, the tyres cannot 'grip' the surface so the car may slide forward, unable to stop.

Frictional drag in fluids

Things that are moving through air (like the car in Figure 2.7.1) experience a 'drag' – a frictional force which acts in the opposite direction to the motion. The drag can significantly affect motion. Downhill skiers reduce the frictional drag by crouching down, enabling them to travel faster. The suits they wear are extremely smooth and close-fitting.

Some animals, such as the shark, have a naturally streamlined shape, which minimises the frictional drag and allows them to move through water more freely.

Vehicles that experience a high frictional drag must use extra fuel to create the extra driving force needed to overcome friction. Designers go to great lengths to streamline cars, giving them higher speed capability and better fuel consumption.

Terminal velocity

Skydivers experience the effects of air resistance (frictional drag) as they fall towards the ground.

a)
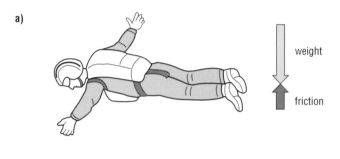

b)

c)

d)
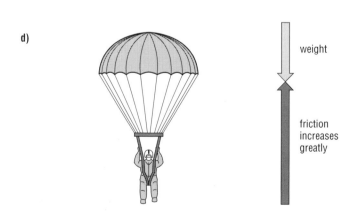

Figure 2.7.3 A skydiver's fall is affected by air resistance (friction)

- When the diver leaves the aircraft, the only force on his body is gravity. This causes him to accelerate towards the ground. As he falls, the frictional drag of the air opposes his motion (a).
- As his speed increases, the frictional force of the air on his body increases (b). The upward force of friction reduces the rate at which he accelerates (because the resultant downward force decreases).
- At some point the upward frictional force is just equal to the weight of the skydiver (c). There is now no resultant force on his body – the two forces acting on it are equal and opposite. The skydiver now falls at a constant velocity, called the **terminal velocity**.
- When the parachute opens there is a sudden increase in the frictional force (d). The upward force is (momentarily) greater than the downward force. The resultant (upward) force causes the skydiver to decelerate. The frictional force then decreases as his velocity decreases, until it is again equal and opposite to the skydiver's weight. He then falls to the ground at a constant, lower velocity.

Quick Questions

1 Explain each of the following statements.
   a) Cars with worn tyres are dangerous.
   b) To gain maximum speed, skiers wear close-fitting suits and crouch low down.
   c) The hull of a ship must be kept free of shellfish.
   d) Small particles of rock from space burn up as they enter the earth's atmosphere.

2 The pictures show the forces acting on stationary and moving objects. Describe clearly how the motion of the objects will change under these circumstances.

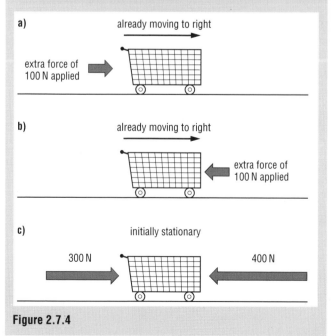

Figure 2.7.4

2.8 Speed and velocity

Speed is the rate at which a moving object covers distance. A car travelling at a steady speed of 50 kilometres per hour (50 km/h) will cover a distance of 50 kilometres in one hour. Note the link between speed, distance and time. As the speed increases:

- The distance travelled in a given time interval increases, or:
- A given distance can be covered in a shorter time.

Speed, distance and time are related by the equation:

$$\text{speed} = \frac{\text{distance}}{\text{time}}$$

The units of speed depend on those in which distance and time are measured. Some examples are given in Table 2.8.1 below.

Table 2.8.1 Some possible units of speed

Distance	Time	Speed
centimetres (cm)	seconds (s)	centimetres/second (cm/s)
metres (m)	seconds (s)	metres/second (m/s)
kilometres (km)	hours (h)	kilometres/hour (km/h)

Average speed

Few things travel at the same steady speed for any length of time – their speed changes throughout any journey. Whilst we could describe their speed at any instant during the journey, it is far more convenient to think in terms of the average speed over the whole journey:

$$\text{average speed} = \frac{\text{total distance covered during a journey}}{\text{total time taken for the journey}}$$

It follows that the actual speed at some times will be higher than the average; at other times it will be lower than the average.

Velocity

Any moving object must move in a particular direction. The word speed describes how quickly it moves (the rate at which the distance covered changes). The **velocity** is the speed at which it is moving in a particular direction.

Velocity–time graphs

A velocity-time graph shows how the magnitude of the velocity, i.e. the speed, of something changes over a period of time (Figure 2.8.1).

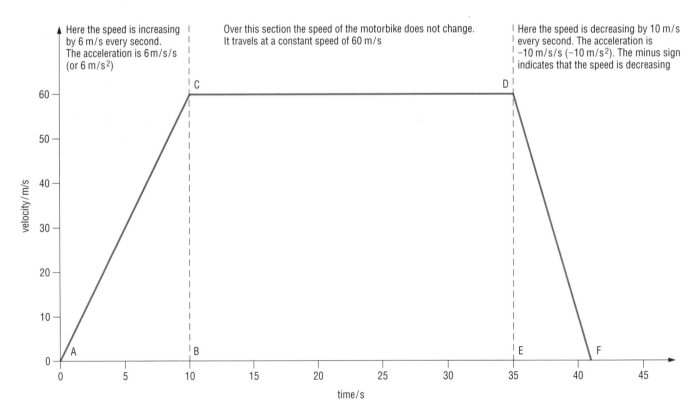

Figure 2.8.1 Velocity–time graph for a motorcycle starting from rest

The distance travelled during the journey can be found by calculating the area under the graph. You often have to break down the space under the graph into triangles and rectangles. For the graph in Figure 2.8.1:

$$\frac{\text{area under}}{\text{graph}} = \frac{\text{area of}}{\text{triangle ABC}} + \frac{\text{area of}}{\text{rectangle BCDE}} + \frac{\text{area of}}{\text{triangle DEF}}$$

The area of a triangle = base length × height/2; the area of a rectangle = length × width. So:

$$
\begin{aligned}
\text{area under graph} &= (AB \times BC/2) + (BC \times CD) + (EF \times DE/2) \\
&= (10 \times 30) + (60 \times 25) + (6 \times 30) \\
&= 1980 \text{ m}
\end{aligned}
$$

Quick Questions

1 Calculate the values of *x, y* and *z* in the table on the right (including units).
2 **a)** Explain the difference between speed and velocity.
  b) A motorist travels 145 km between two towns in 3 hours 45 minutes. Calculate the average speed in
    (i) km/h and
    (ii) m/s.

Distance	Time taken	Average speed
200 m	40 s	*x*
y	2 hours	50 km/h
50 cm	*z*	5 cm/s

3 Traffic speed cameras take photographs of cars as they pass over marked sections of road (see Figure 2.8.2). White lines are marked on the road 2 m apart.
  a) Calculate the speed of a car which takes 0.06 s to pass between two marks.
  b) If the speed limit is 22 m/s (50 mph), what is the fastest time in which a car could *legally* pass between the marks?
4 A cyclist accelerates uniformly from rest to a velocity of 10 m/s in 3 s. He then moves with a constant velocity of 10 m/s for 6 s, before decelerating uniformly to rest in a further 5 s.
  a) Draw a velocity–time graph representing the cyclist's motion.
  b) Calculate the distance travelled by the cyclist during the journey.
5 Look at the velocity–time graph of a car journey, shown on the right. Describe what is happening during sections OA, AB, BC and CD. What is the difference between sections OA and BC?

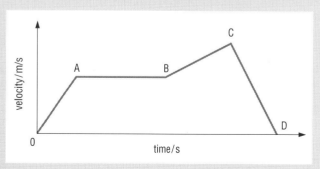

Figure 2.8.2

Figure 2.8.3

2.9 Acceleration

An object whose velocity is changing is said to be accelerating. The rate at which its velocity is changing is its **acceleration**. Acceleration may mean something is getting faster (its speed is increasing) or getting slower (its speed is decreasing, i.e. it is decelerating). It may also mean that the object is changing direction (even though the object may be travelling at a constant speed).

Consider a bus accelerating from a bus stop along a straight road.

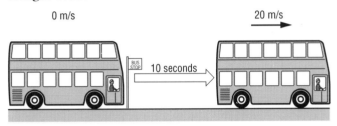

Figure 2.9.1 The bus accelerates from rest

Its velocity has increased from 0 m/s to 20 m/s in 10 seconds. The change in velocity is therefore 20 m/s in the 10 seconds we are considering here. Assuming its velocity changed by the same amount each second (called uniform acceleration), then it must have increased by 2 m/s every second. We say its acceleration is 2 m/s/s or 2 m/s^2.

We can also calculate acceleration using the equation:

$$\text{acceleration (m/s/s)} = \frac{\text{change in velocity (m/s)}}{\text{time taken for the change (s)}}$$

Velocity–time graphs and acceleration

The velocity–time graph shown below is for a body moving with uniform acceleration. This means that the velocity of the body changes by equal amounts in equal intervals of time.

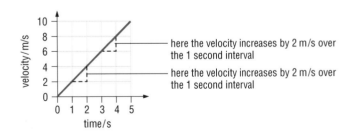

here the velocity increases by 2 m/s over the 1 second interval

here the velocity increases by 2 m/s over the 1 second interval

Figure 2.9.2 Uniform acceleration

The slope or gradient of the graph represents the acceleration of the body. The gradient is calculated by noting the change in velocity over some (significant) period of time on the graph and then using the equation:

$$\text{acceleration} = \frac{\text{change in velocity}}{\text{time taken}}$$

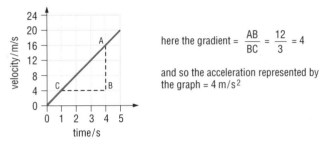

here the gradient = $\dfrac{AB}{BC} = \dfrac{12}{3} = 4$

and so the acceleration represented by the graph = 4 m/s^2

Figure 2.9.3 Calculating the gradient

Force and acceleration

There is a relationship (connection) between the acceleration of a body and the force that is causing the acceleration. In general, the acceleration depends on:

- The size of the force – the bigger the force, the greater the acceleration.
- The mass of the object – the greater the mass, the smaller the acceleration.

Force and acceleration are related by the equation:

$$\text{force (N)} = \text{mass (kg)} \times \text{acceleration (m/s}^2)$$

Worked example

In an emergency, a 1000 kg car travelling at 50 m/s stops in 4 seconds. What is the value of the force which causes it to stop?

Using the equation above:

$$\text{force (N)} = \text{mass (kg)} \times \text{acceleration (m/s}^2)$$

We must first calculate the value of the acceleration, using the equation:

$$\text{acceleration} = \frac{\text{change in velocity}}{\text{time taken for the speed to change}}$$

$$= \frac{(50 - 0)}{4}$$

$$= 12.5 \text{ m/s}^2$$

We can now calculate the force needed:

$$\text{force} = \text{mass} \times \text{acceleration}$$
$$= 1000 \times 12.5$$
$$= 12\,500 \text{ N}$$

The force needed to slow down the car from 50 m/s to a stop in 4 seconds is 12 500 N.

The acceleration due to gravity

Imagine throwing a ball upwards into the air. As soon as it leaves your hand there is no upward force acting on it. The only force on the ball (ignoring air resistance) is the force of gravity which acts against its motion. The ball therefore slows down. Eventually it will stop. The force of gravity then causes it to accelerate towards the ground.

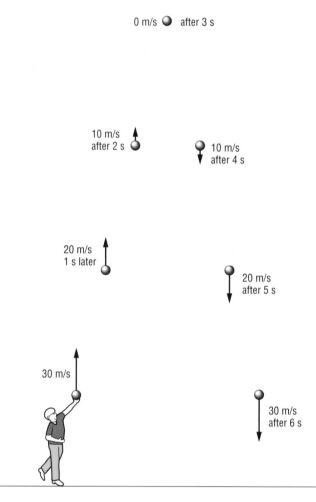

Figure 2.9.4 The force of gravity changes the ball's motion

Close to the earth's surface:

- All objects moving vertically upwards experience an acceleration of −10 m/s² (the minus sign indicating that they are slowing down).
- All objects moving vertically downwards experience an acceleration of +10 m/s².

The value 10 m/s² is the value of the **acceleration due to gravity** and is the same for all objects regardless of their mass (assuming air resistance is ignored).

Worked example

A stone is dropped from a bridge. If the stone falls for 3 seconds before reaching the water, what will be its velocity when it hits the water?

We can rearrange the equation:

$$\text{acceleration} = \frac{\text{change in velocity}}{\text{time}}$$

to give:

$$\text{change in velocity} = \text{acceleration} \times \text{time}$$

The value of the acceleration here will be 10 m/s² – the acceleration due to gravity. So:

$$\text{change in velocity} = 10 \times 3$$
$$= 30 \text{ m/s}$$

Because the ball was at rest (velocity = 0 m/s) before being released, its velocity when it reaches the water will be 30 m/s.

Quick Questions

1 A 100 m runner increases her velocity from 0 m/s to 12 m/s in the first 4 s of a race.
   a) Find her acceleration during these 4 s.
   b) What is the average velocity during these 4 s?
   c) How far does she run in these 4 s?
   d) If the runner is able to maintain a velocity of 12 m/s until the 100 m line, how long will her run have taken?

2 A car of mass 1500 kg stops from a velocity of 40 m/s in 5 s. Calculate:
   a) the value of the acceleration;
   b) the force needed to stop the car.

3 In the following examples, state if the objects are accelerating, decelerating, or moving with constant velocity.
   a) A stone is thrown vertically upwards.
   b) A skydiver falls with the parachute open.
   c) A person falls from a ladder.
   d) A coin is dropped down a wishing well.
   e) A pendulum bob on the downward part of its swing.

4 **a)** A ball is thrown vertically upwards with a velocity of 40 m/s. Find the time it takes the ball to return to the thrower. ($g = 10 \text{ m/s}^2$)
   b) A coin is dropped down a ravine. It takes 3 s to reach the bottom. Find the depth of the ravine. ($g = 10 \text{ m/s}^2$)

2.10 Moving in a circle

The velocity of any object moving in a circle is continually changing – the velocity change is due to the change in direction, even though its speed may be constant.

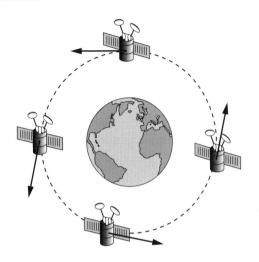

Figure 2.10.1 The satellite's velocity is constantly changing because its direction is constantly changing

If the velocity changes, there must be an acceleration. Objects moving in a circle must therefore be accelerating. There must be a force acting on the object which causes this acceleration – and the force must act towards the centre of the circle. In the example above it is the force of gravity (acting on the satellite) which causes the acceleration. In other situations the force may be caused by other factors.

In a loop-the-loop ride (Figure 2.10.2), the force that causes the change in direction is exerted by the rails on the car.

The loop-the-loop ride illustrates one of Newton's Laws of Motion – that *a moving object will continue to move in a straight line unless some (unbalanced) force acts on it*.

The force acting on any object moving in a circle is a **centripetal force** – a force that always acts towards the centre of the circle in which motion takes place. The value of the centripetal force (in newtons) can be calculated using the equation:

$$F = \frac{mv^2}{r}$$

where m = the mass of the object (kg)
r = the radius of the circle (m)
v = the velocity of the object (m/s)

From this you can see that the faster the object moves, the bigger is the force needed to keep it moving in a circle.

Satellites

Satellites must travel at just the right velocity to keep them in orbit – if they travel too slowly they will fall back towards the earth. Gravity and velocity both play a part in making sure they are kept in orbit.

The gravity force between two objects gets smaller as they get further apart (Figure 2.10.3).

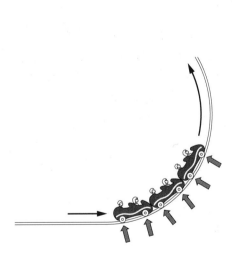

Figure 2.10.2a The force of the curved rails on the cars causes them to move in a circle

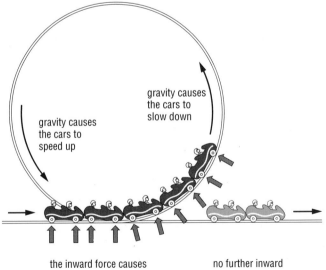

gravity causes the cars to speed up

gravity causes the cars to slow down

the inward force causes a change in direction and the cars begin to follow a circular path

no further inward force is at work so the cars continue in a straight line

Figure 2.10.2b The cars 'loop-the-loop' and then continue in a straight line

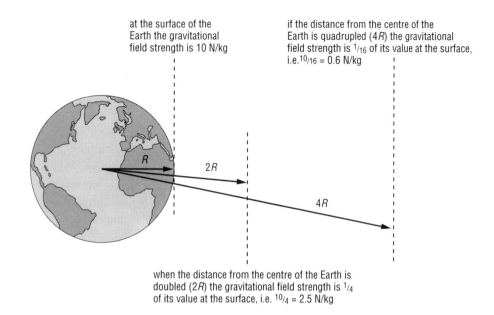

at the surface of the Earth the gravitational field strength is 10 N/kg

if the distance from the centre of the Earth is quadrupled ($4R$) the gravitational field strength is $^1/_{16}$ of its value at the surface, i.e. $^{10}/_{16} = 0.6$ N/kg

R $2R$ $4R$

when the distance from the centre of the Earth is doubled ($2R$) the gravitational field strength is $^1/_4$ of its value at the surface, i.e. $^{10}/_4 = 2.5$ N/kg

Figure 2.10.3 Each time the distance is doubled, the gravitational field strength (the gravity force on unit mass) becomes a quarter of its original value

The gravity force also depends on the masses of the objects – it is bigger between objects with large masses. The speed at which satellites are placed in orbit is carefully calculated to make sure they will continue to orbit at that height. The bigger the gravity force, the higher the speed needed (Figure 2.10.4).

Communications satellites must remain above the same place on the earth – even though the earth is spinning below them. To achieve this, they are placed in an orbit above the equator, with an orbital speed that matches the rotational speed of the earth. As the satellite orbits, the earth rotates under it at exactly the same speed. From the point of view of someone on earth, the satellite remains in the same position all of the time. This is called a geostationary orbit.

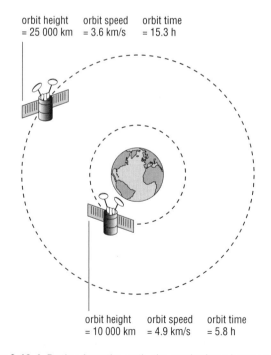

orbit height = 25 000 km   orbit speed = 3.6 km/s   orbit time = 15.3 h

orbit height = 10 000 km   orbit speed = 4.9 km/s   orbit time = 5.8 h

Figure 2.10.4 Further from the earth, the gravity force between a satellite and the earth is smaller, so the satellite will stay in orbit at a lower speed. In an orbit closer to the earth, the gravity force is bigger and a higher speed is needed

Quick Questions

1 A bucket of water of total mass 3 kg is spun around, in a vertical plane, on the end of a 2 m piece of string and with a velocity of 10 m/s. Calculate the force needed to keep it moving in a circle. Why does the water not fall out?

2 Describe how the action of forces helps explain why clothes are dried in a spin drier.

3 Where is the centripetal force acting when a car turns a corner? What would happen if there was no such force?

4 The gravity force between the earth and the moon (or any satellite) depends upon several factors.
   a) What are they?
   b) If the earth had a second moon, but of half the mass, how would its orbit differ from that of our current moon?

5 a) Weightlessness can be very inconvenient in space. An idea for future space stations is to build them as large spinning wheels, with the living accommodation on the outer rim. Can you explain how this would create artificial weight?
   b) Find the rotational speed necessary to create the same gravitational effect as on the earth (where $g = 10$ N/kg) for a spinning space station of radius 40 m.

2.11 Momentum

A cricket ball thrown gently towards you is fairly easy to stop. If the ball is moving faster it is much more difficult to stop. The faster ball has more **momentum** than the slower ball.

Similarly, when a small person runs into you in the corridor they are fairly easily stopped. A larger person moving at the same speed is much more difficult to stop. The reason is that the larger person has more momentum than the smaller person.

Momentum is often used when we talk about moving objects. The momentum depends on velocity and mass, and is calculated using the equation:

$$\text{momentum} = \text{mass} \times \text{velocity}$$

If the units of mass are kilograms (kg) and those of velocity are metres per second (m/s), the units of momentum are kilogram metres per second (kg m/s).

The relationship between force and momentum

When unbalanced forces act on a body it accelerates:

$$\text{force} = \text{mass} \times \text{acceleration}$$

And because acceleration = change in velocity/time, we can write:

$$\text{force} = \frac{\text{mass} \times \text{change in velocity}}{\text{time}}$$

Assume the initial velocity before acceleration is u, and that the final velocity is v. The change in velocity will be $v - u$. Then the equation becomes:

$$F = \frac{m(v - u)}{t} = \frac{mv - mu}{t}$$

But mv is the final momentum of the object, and mu is the initial momentum, so:

$$F = \frac{\text{change in momentum}}{t}$$

In other words, the force which causes a body to accelerate is equal to the rate of change of momentum of the body.

The idea of momentum, and the relationship described above, helps you to understand what happens when bodies collide or when explosions occur.

Collisions

When two bodies collide, the forces they exert on one another are equal and opposite whilst they are in contact – the force on body A is equal and opposite to the force on body B throughout the collision. They also act for the same time – the time for which the bodies are in contact.

It follows that the change in momentum of body A must be equal to the change in momentum of body B. Momentum is quite simply transferred from one body to the other. That means that *the total momentum in the system before collision is equal to the total momentum in the system after collision* – momentum is conserved.

Consider a railway truck moving towards a second, stationary truck.

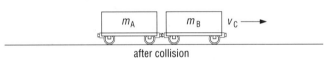
after collision

Figure 2.11.1 The momentum before collision equals the momentum after collision

The momentum in the system before collision

= momentum of truck A + momentum of truck B
= $(m_A \times v_A) + (m_B \times v_B)$

After collision, the two trucks move off with a common velocity, v_c, so the momentum in the system after collision

= momentum of truck A + momentum of truck B
= $(m_A \times v_c) + (m_B \times v_c)$

Because momentum is conserved, we can say:

momentum before collision = momentum after collision
$$(m_A \times v_A) + (m_B \times v_B) = (m_A \times v_c) + (m_B \times v_c)$$

In some circumstances one of the colliding bodies may move in the opposite direction after collision. Then the numerical value of its momentum is given a minus sign in any calculations involving momentum conservation.

Collisions such as that between the railway trucks, where the two bodies move off together after colliding, are called 'inelastic' collisions. In other types of collision, the two bodies may move off independently of one another (with different velocities or in different directions). These are called 'elastic' collisions.

Kinetic energy

In any collision the velocity of one, or both bodies, may change. There will therefore be some transfer of **kinetic energy** (the energy of a body due to its velocity) during the collision.

In an inelastic collision, kinetic energy may be lost from the system. The more kinetic energy is lost, the more inelastic the collision is. In a perfectly elastic collision, kinetic energy is conserved. There will be the same kinetic energy in the system after collision as exists before the collision.

Jet engines and rocket engines

In jet and rocket engines, fuel burns and releases exhaust gases at high speed. The exhaust gases have momentum in a backward direction. As the gases leave the engine they exert an equal and opposite force on the aeroplane or rocket. The plane or rocket is therefore given momentum in a forward direction. As momentum is conserved in an explosion such as this, we can say that:

| momentum of exhaust gases (backwards) | = | momentum of the plane or rocket (forwards) |

Worked example

Two boys are standing on light, frictionless skateboards and a tight string connects them, as shown in Figure 2.11.2.

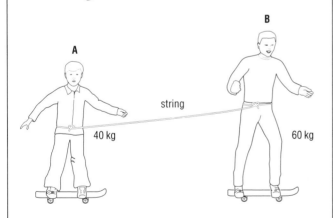

Figure 2.11.2

The heavier boy (B) pulls the string. This gives him a velocity of 2.5 m/s. Find the velocity of boy A.

The momentum of the system before the string is pulled is zero. So after pulling the string.

| momentum of boy A to the right | = | momentum of boy B to the left |

$$40 \times v_A = 60 \times 2.5$$
$$v_A = 60 \times 2.5/40 = 3.75 \,\text{m/s}$$

---

1 Calculate the momentum of:
   a) a 2000 kg car moving with a velocity of 12 m/s;
   b) the same car travelling at a velocity of 24 m/s;
   c) a 40 g ball moving with a velocity of 15 m/s;
   d) a 200 000 kg railway truck moving with a velocity of 5 m/s.

2 Calculate the missing values *x*, *y* and *z* in the table below.

Mass (kg)	**Velocity** (m/s)	**Momentum** (kg m/s)
x	20	400
2000	*y*	30 000
60	30	*z*

3 How much momentum will an object gain if
   a) a force of 10 N acts for 5 s?
   b) a force of 4000 N acts for 10 s?
   c) a force of 10 N acts for 2 minutes?

4 Skier A has a mass of 50 kg and is travelling with a velocity of 10 m/s. She collides with a stationary skier, B, who has a mass of 40 kg. Assuming they both move off together, calculate their speed after colliding.

5 A pellet of mass 0.5 g is fired from an air rifle. It hits a stationary object of mass 89.5 g. After being hit the object moves at 1 m/s. Find the velocity of the pellet just before it hit the object.

6 Find the force necessary to slow a 200 kg go-kart from 20 m/s to 5 m/s in 0.5 s.

7 Figure 2.11.3 shows a car towing a caravan. Unfortunately the connection between them breaks and causes the car's speed to increase as shown. Find the new speed of the caravan.

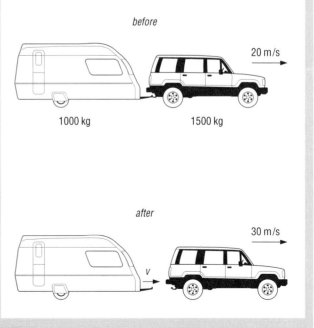

Figure 2.11.3

Section Two: Examination Practice Questions

Foundation Level

1. This list shows things to do with vehicles, roads and safety.

A wet leaves on the road   **B** worn tyres   **C** alcohol and other drugs   **D** crash helmets
E car crumple zones   **F** seat belts in cars   **G** motor cyclists' leather gloves and suits

(a) Which affects how quickly a driver reacts to danger?
(b) Which two could make a car skid?
(c) Which four help to protect people in a crash?
(d) What effect does fog have on a driver's reaction time?

The diagrams below show a racing car tyre and an ordinary car tyre.

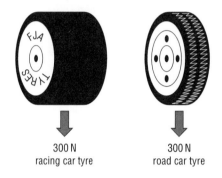

300 N
racing car tyre

300 N
road car tyre

The arrows show that both tyres exert a force of 300 N on the road.
(e) Why does the racing tyre exert a smaller pressure on the road?
(f) The two cars are being tested for fuel economy on a 5 km test circuit. They are both tested for exactly 2 hours. The racing car has a fixed speed of 200 km/h and the ordinary car has a fixed speed of 100 km/h. How many laps of the circuit will each car complete?
(g) If it started to rain during a race, the racing car tyre shown would be unsuitable. The driver would change to tyres with a tread. Explain why the racing tyre is unsuitable in the rain and why tyres with a tread are more suitable.

2. A car is travelling along a level road at a constant speed of 25 m/s, when it comes to a hill as shown in the diagram below.

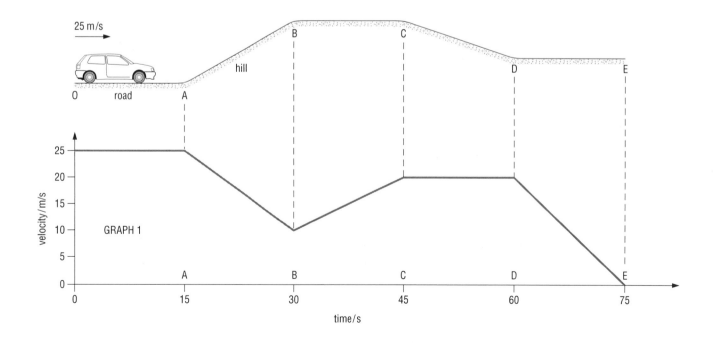

The velocity-time graph (1) shows the motion of the car.
(a) In which of the sections, OA, AB, BC, CD, DE, is the car:
   (i) accelerating? (ii) decelerating? (iii) moving with uniform velocity?
(b) (i) For how many seconds is the car accelerating?
   (ii) For how long is the speed constant during the whole journey?
   (iii) What is the value of the deceleration that brings the car to rest?
(c) The car is then parked on a very steep hill, but its handbrake fails and it rolls down. Graph 2 shows the speed of the car as it rolls down the hill and along the road.

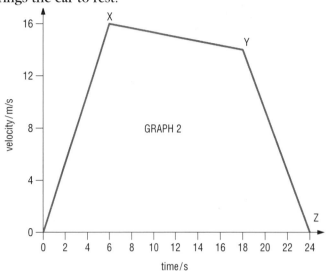

   (i) What is the maximum speed of the car as it rolls down the hill?
   (ii) Why does the car gradually slow down between X and Y?
   (iii) When do you think something was done to start slowing the car?
   (iv) What happens to the kinetic energy of the car as it rolls down the hill?
   (v) How does the total amount of kinetic and potential energy of the car change as it rolls down the hill?

3. Someone steps onto the road in front of a moving car. A short time will elapse between the driver seeing the person and applying the brake. During this time the car continues to travel forwards. The distance travelled is called the thinking distance.
The table below shows thinking distances (for a certain driver) for different speeds.

Speed (m/s)	10	20	50	60	70
Thinking distance (m)	5	10	25	30	35

(a) Draw a graph of thinking distance against speed.
(b) How does thinking distance depend on the speed of the car?
(c) Use your graph to find the thinking distance for a speed of 25 m/s.
(d) The driver had an alcoholic drink with his lunch. His thinking **time** was measured to be 1.0 second some time later. How far would the car travel while the driver was thinking of braking, if his speed was 25 m/s?
(e) How does this compare with your answer for part (c) when the driver had not drunk any alcohol?

4. Caroline runs 400 m in 80 s.
(a) Calculate her average speed.
(b) Her maximum speed during the race is higher than her average speed. Can you explain why?
(c) Caroline then has a 100 m race with a cyclist, Chris. A distance-time graph of the race is shown here.

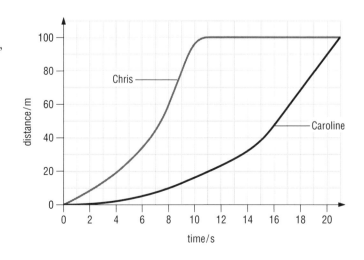

   (i) Who wins the race?
   (ii) What was the distance between them when the winner crossed the finishing line?
   (iii) After how many seconds did Chris's speed start to decrease?
   (iv) When did Caroline's speed stop increasing?

5. Eric, Heather and Trevor run a race. Each has a different mass but, as you will see from the diagram below, they all push off with the same force.

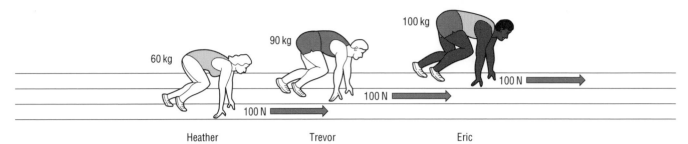

Heather   Trevor   Eric

(a) Who will have the greatest acceleration? Explain why.
(b) Heather wins the race in 15 s. Look at the graph of her race. How far does she run in the first 5 s?
(c) What is the total distance of the race?

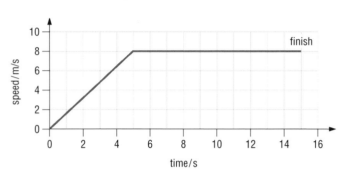

6. Will builds a tower from scaffolding as shown in the diagram on the right.
(a) Why are the wooden pads placed between the scaffolding and the ground?
(b) Calculate the pressure on the ground (beneath the pads) in N/cm².
(c) What would be the pressure if a 1000 cm² pad was used?

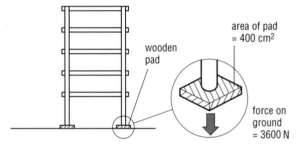

The diagram below shows a hydraulic car braking system.

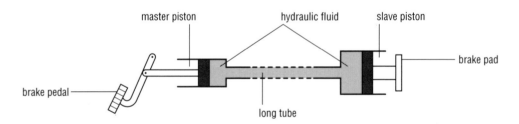

(d) Why does the slave piston move when the driver pushes on the brake pedal?
(e) The brake pads push against the brake disc which is part of the wheel. What kind of force does the brake pad exert on the disc?
(f) At times, air gets into the hydraulic system. Why would that affect the effectiveness of the braking system?
(g) Why is the slave piston larger than the master piston?

7. The diagram below shows three players pushing an ice hockey puck.

John   Susan   Alan

(a) Which player gives the puck the greatest acceleration? Explain your answer.

(b) John hits two different pucks with the same force, as shown below.

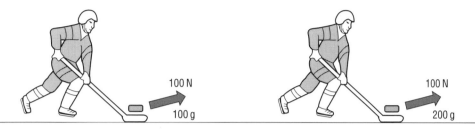

(i) Which puck moves faster? Explain your answer.

(ii) What must John do to make the pucks move with the same speed?

(c) Alan and Susan both push a puck at the same time, as shown below. What will happen to the puck?

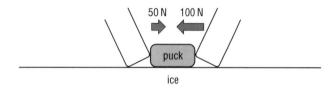

(d) Susan practises ice hockey in a disused car park. What are the main differences she will notice about the speed of the puck on the different surfaces and how hard she needs to hit it? Explain your answers.

8. (a) A racing car is moving along a level road. The arrows show the forces acting on the car.

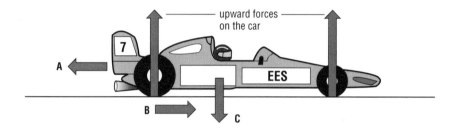

(i) Which arrow shows the weight of the car?

(ii) Which arrow shows the force of friction on the car?

(iii) Which arrow shows the force which pushes the car forwards?

(b) What will happen to the car if:

(i) forces A and B are equal in size?

(ii) force A is smaller than force B?

(iii) force A is greater than force B?

9. A spring stretches 1 cm for every 10 N of force acting on it. The elastic limit of the spring is 110 N.

(a) What is meant by the elastic limit?

(b) What will happen if a load in excess of 110 N is placed on the spring?

(c) Complete the table below using values from this list (each value can be used more than once).

1 cm, 5 cm, 10 cm, 15 cm, 20 cm, 50 cm, less than 15 cm, more than 15 cm, less than 20 cm, more than 20 cm

Length of spring with no load (cm)	Force applied (N)	Extension caused (cm)	Length of spring when force removed (cm)
20	10		
20	50		
20	150		

(d) A spring is 15 cm long with no load on it. The graph shows the extension of the spring against load (force) applied. Use the graph to find:

    (i)   the load that produces an extension of 2 cm;

    (ii) the increase in length produced by a load of 2.7 N;

    (iii) the length of the spring with a load of 2.7 N.

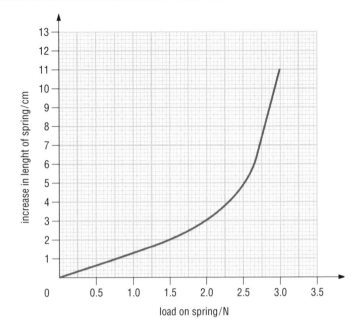

10. A car with an oil leak is travelling along a road. It loses oil at exactly one drop per second. The oil drops on the road are shown below.

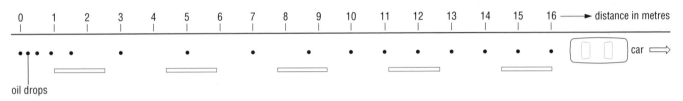

  (a) Where was the car:

    (i)   travelling fastest?

    (ii) accelerating?

    (iii) decelerating?

    (iv) travelling at constant speed?

  (b) Sabina jumps from an aeroplane and falls for a while before opening her parachute. A graph of her motion is shown below.

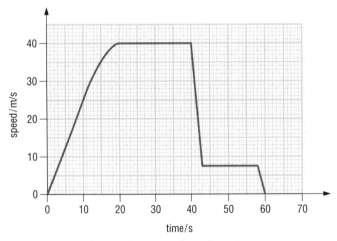

    (i)   What is the name of the force that is pulling her down?

    (ii) What other force acts on Sabina?

    (iii) What happens to the size of the force in (ii) as Sabina accelerates?

    (iv) How can you tell from the graph that her speed is constant between 20 s and 40 s?

    (v) Why is the speed constant between 20 s and 40 s?

    (vi) What causes her speed to change between 40 s and 43 s?

    (vii) What is Sabina's speed when she hits the ground?

11. Study this graph of three athletes running a 800 m race and then answer the questions which follow.

   (a) Who won the race and what was the winning time?

   (b) At what time were A and B together?

   (c) Who was in the lead at half-way?

   (d) How far was C behind the leader when the leader had covered half the distance?

   (e) Which athlete ran the fastest last 300 m?

   (f) How far was A behind C when C finished the race?

   (g) Calculate the average speed of the fastest and the slowest athlete for the whole race.

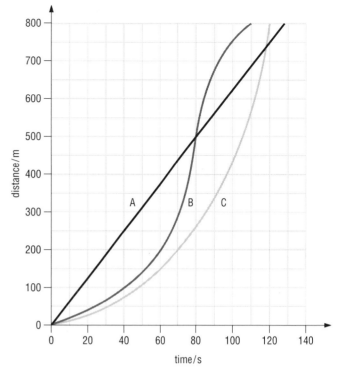

12. Three bank robbers leave the scene of their crime in a getaway car. A police motorcyclist gives chase from the bank and a police car is contacted by radio and gives chase later. Here are the details of the journeys:

Time (mins)	Distance from the bank (km)		
	Getaway car	Police car	Police motorcyclist
0	0	15	0
20	10	28	8
40	30	40	25
60	60	55	54
80	90	68	
100	105	84	
120	105	105	

   (a) Plot distance–time graphs (on one set of axes) to show the journeys of all the vehicles.

   (b) Which police vehicle caught the robbers?

   (c) At what time did the police almost catch the robbers?

   (d) When did the motorcyclist give up the chase?

   (e) How long were the robbers at their hiding place before the police arrived?

   (f) What was the average speed of each of the two cars *over the whole two hours*?

13. This graph is for a moving object.

   (a) For how long did the object accelerate?

   (b) Calculate the value of the acceleration.

   (c) For how long did the object move with constant velocity?

   (d) Calculate the acceleration of the object as it was slowing down.

   (e) Calculate the distance travelled by the object in the 12 seconds of its journey.

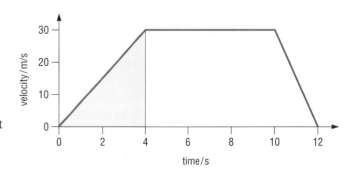

14. A car is dropping oil at a constant rate of exactly 1 drop per second. The diagram shows the pattern of oil drops on the road.

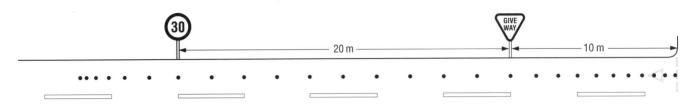

(a) Describe the motion of the car (i) before the first road sign and (ii) between the two road signs.
(b) How long does it take for the car to travel between the two road signs?
(c) What is the car's speed between the two signs?
(d) Find a value for the car's deceleration after the 'Give way' sign.

15. When a space rocket is launched, the empty fuel tanks are released and fall back to earth. As a tank falls to earth two forces will be acting on the tank. The diagram shows the tank and the forces.

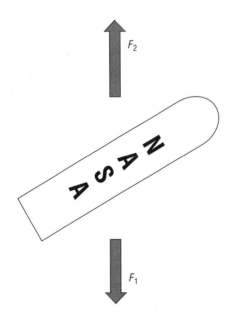

(a) What is force F_1?
(b) What is force F_2?
(c) Initially the tank accelerates (speeds up). What does that tell you about the two forces?
(d) As the tank gets faster, what will happen to the size of force F_2?
(e) Eventually the two forces will be equal in size. How will that affect the speed of the falling tank?

16. An astronaut lands on the moon. On the earth her mass was 60 kg and her weight 600 N. The force of gravity on the moon is one-sixth of that on the earth.
(a) What will be the astronaut's mass on the moon?
(b) What will be the astronaut's weight on the moon?
(c) A second astronaut forgot to measure his weight on earth and was unable to measure it on the journey to the moon. When he arrived on the moon he found his weight to be 120 N.
    (i)   What would be his weight on earth?
    (ii) What would be his mass on earth?
    (iii) What is his mass on the moon?
    (iv) Why was he unable to measure his weight on the journey?

17. This diagram shows a rocket on its launch pad. The total mass of the rocket and its contents is 500 000 kg and each of the three engines exerts a force of 2 000 000 N.

(a) What is the total force exerted on the rocket by the engines?

(b) Why can we predict that the rocket will accelerate upwards?

(c) Calculate the acceleration of the rocket at take-off.

The rocket has a velocity of 5 m/s after 2 s of flight and 13 m/s after 4 s.

(d) Calculate:
(i) its acceleration during the first 2 s;
(ii) its acceleration between 2 s and 4 s.

(e) Why does the value of the rocket's acceleration increase as it gets higher?

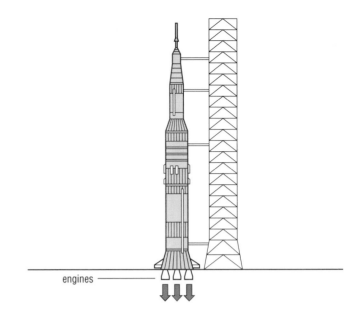

engines ——

18. Alex runs a race as quickly as he can. Here is a simple graph of the race.

(a) Explain the shape of the graph:
(i) between **A** and **B** [2]
(ii) between **B** and **C**. [1]

(b) Estimate the distance travelled in the race. Show your working. [3]

(MEG, Foundation, 1998 Specimen)

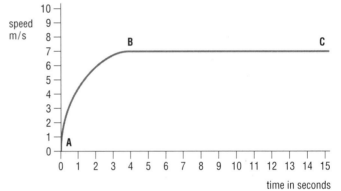

19. Four athletes run. Look at the simple graphs of the motion of the athletes.

(a) Which athlete has a steady speed? Choose from:

Judy   Kate   Rivka   Sally [1]

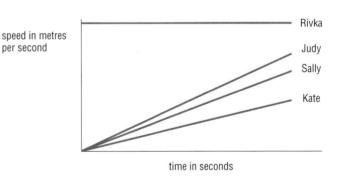

(b) Dave drives his car down a hill. Look at this simple graph of its motion.

(i) Look at the graph. The car is accelerating.
How do you know this? [1]

(ii) Look at the graph. The car reaches the bottom of the hill in 10 seconds. Calculate the **change** in speed of the car. [2]

(iii) The **kinetic** and **potential** energy of the car change as it goes down the hill. Describe how. [2]

(MEG, Foundation, 1998 Specimen)

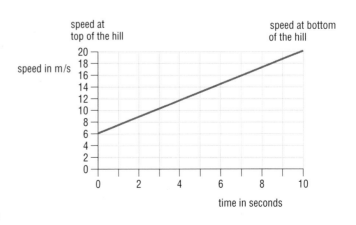

Higher Level

1. A moored hot air balloon is shown in the diagram below.
   The total mass of the balloon and all its contents is 300 kg.
   The tension *T* in each of the two mooring ropes is 250 N and the gravitational field strength is 10 N/kg.
   The mooring ropes have an elastic limit of 450 N and they stretch 1 cm for each 100 N of applied force.

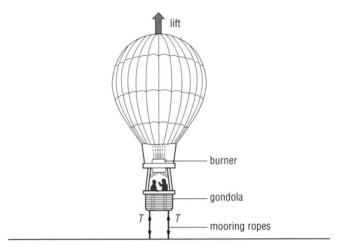

   (a) How much will the mooring ropes have stretched?
   (b) Just before take-off one mooring rope is released. What will happen?
   (c) Calculate the weight of the balloon and its contents.
   (d) Both ropes are released. What is the resultant force on the balloon and in what direction does it act?
   (e) Calculate the initial acceleration of the balloon when it takes off.

   To gain extra height, the burners are used to heat the air in the balloon.
   (f) What effect will this have on the air inside the balloon?
   (g) Describe how heating the air causes the balloon to rise.

   At the end of the journey the balloon begins to fall.
   (h) Explain the changes that take place inside the balloon which cause it to fall.

2. A motorist pumps air into a car tyre until the pressure is 272 700 Pa.
   (a) Explain why the air exerts a pressure on the walls of the tyre.
   (b) The motorist then travels at speed for some considerable distance. The air in the tyre heats up and the pressure rises. Explain why a rise in temperature causes an increase in the pressure.
   (c) If the original pressure was measured at 14 °C, and the air rises to a temperature of 44 °C, calculate the new pressure inside the tyre.

3. The diagram below shows the essential features of a vehicle's hydraulic braking system but in a simplified form.

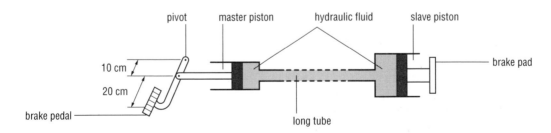

   (a) Calculate the force exerted on the master piston when the driver exerts a force of 500 N on the brake pedal.
   (b) If the area of the master piston is 1.5 cm², calculate the pressure exerted on the fluid.
   (c) What is the pressure exerted on the slave piston?
   (d) If the area of the slave piston is 4.5 cm², calculate the force on the brake pad.

The diagram below shows the thinking distance and the braking distance for a van travelling at 30 m/s.

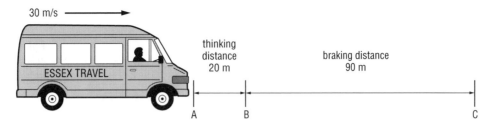

30 m/s ⟶

thinking distance 20 m

braking distance 90 m

A   B   C

(e) What is the stopping distance for the van?

(f) What is the van's speed at point B?

(g) How long does it take the van to cover the thinking distance?

(h) Later on the van crashes into the back of a car. After the crash the vehicles stick together. All the information you require on the crash is shown on the diagram and the graph below.

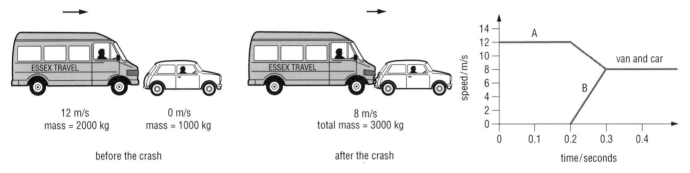

12 m/s
mass = 2000 kg   0 m/s
mass = 1000 kg

before the crash

8 m/s
total mass = 3000 kg

after the crash

(i)   Which of the lines on the graph represents the van and which represents the car?

(ii)   Which vehicle has the greatest change of speed? Why?

(iii) How long does the crash last from the point of impact until the vehicles stick together?

(iv)   What is the acceleration of the car during the impact?

(v)   How far does the van travel from the impact point until the two vehicles stick together?

4. Lindsay, a free-fall parachutist, jumps from an aeroplane and waits 30 s before opening her parachute.

(a) Describe two forces that act on Lindsay during the first few seconds of her fall.

(b) What will happen to her velocity during this period?

(c) How does the size of the forces change as Lindsay falls?

(d) Lindsay has some control over one of the forces. Which force can she control and how?

(e) Eventually the two forces will be equal in size. How will this affect Lindsay's motion?

(f) What is meant by the term 'terminal velocity'?

(g) Explain why Lindsay's velocity decreases when she opens her parachute.

5. During testing, a moving car (A) was made to collide with a stationary car (B). After collision the two cars moved off together.

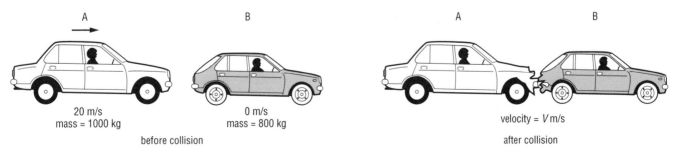

A   B

20 m/s
mass = 1000 kg   0 m/s
mass = 800 kg

before collision

A   B

velocity = *V* m/s

after collision

Using the information on the diagram:

(a) Calculate the momentum of car A before collision.

(b) What will be the total momentum of the cars after collision?

(c) Calculate the velocity with which the cars move immediately after collision.

(d) A 'crash dummy' wearing a seat belt was in car A. The dummy's mass was 80 kg. Assuming the velocity change of car A took 0.4 seconds, calculate the force exerted by the seat belt on the dummy.

Some cars now feature impact-absorbing bumpers. One particular design makes use of 'crumple zones' in the bodywork, as shown below. In the event of a collision, these crumple slowly.

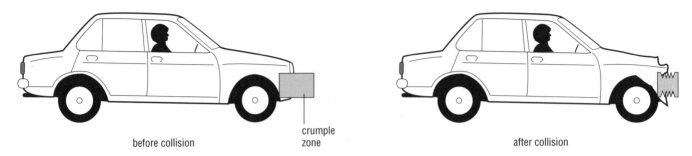

before collision   crumple zone   after collision

(e) Explain how crumple zones such as these improve the safety of the car and its occupants in the event of a collision.

6. Two satellites, R and S, are in orbit around the earth. R is twice as far from the earth's surface.
   (a) On which satellite will the earth's gravitational force be greater?
   (b) Which satellite will be travelling faster?
   (c) R is in a geostationary orbit. What does 'geostationary orbit' mean?
   (d) What benefits are gained by placing satellites into geostationary orbit?
   (e) Explain how satellites stay in orbit despite being acted upon by the force of gravity.

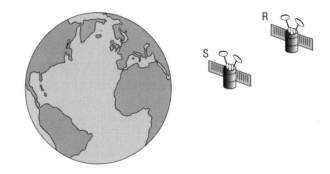

7. This question is about the use of wooden planks on building sites.
   (a) The diagram below shows a plank being used as a simple bridge across a ditch. The wheelbarrow is full and the plank sags in the middle.

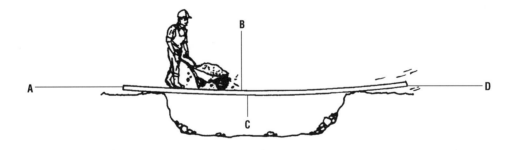

   (i) At which of points **A**, **B**, **C** or **D** is the plank:
       1 under compression;
       2 under tension? [2]
   (ii) Choose phrases from the list below to complete the following sentences. Each phrase may be used once, more than once or not at all.

       less than   the same as   more than

       If the wheelbarrow is empty the sag of the plank is .... that shown in the diagram.
       If the plank is thicker the sag of the plank is .... that shown in the diagram. [2]

(b) The diagram below shows another plank being used as a simple machine. The crate is slid up the plank into the back of the lorry.

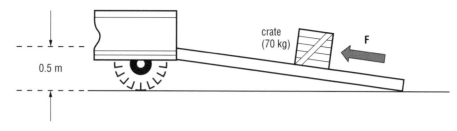

0.5 m

crate (70 kg)   F

    (i)   The mass of the crate is 70 kg. Calculate the weight of the crate.   [2]
    (ii) Calculate the work done when the crate is lifted a vertical distance of 0.5 m.   [4]

(c) The work done in pushing the crate up the plank is 1400 joules.
    (i)   Calculate the efficiency of the process.   [3]
    (ii) Suggest **one** reason to explain why the efficiency is less than 100%.   [1]
    (iii) Write down **one** advantage of using the plank.   [1]

(NEAB, Higher, 1997)

8. (a) The graph shows the motion of a lorry. In the first 10 seconds it travels a distance of 25 m.

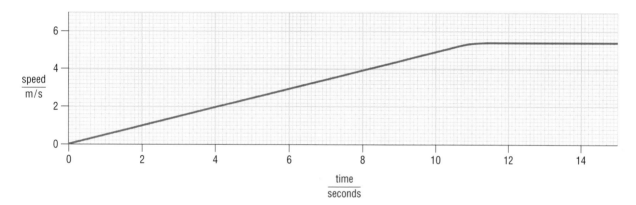

    (i)   Calculate the average speed of the lorry during the first 10 seconds.   [3]
    (ii) Use the graph to calculate the acceleration of the lorry during the first 10 seconds.   [3]
    (iii) The force accelerating the lorry is 3500 N. Calculate the mass of the lorry.   [2]

(b) The lorry goes along the same road every day. Sometimes it takes longer for the lorry to get to its top speed. Suggest why.   [2]

(c) Write down **one** thing that can increase the lorry's stopping distance.   [1]

(d) Patrick wants to pump up his tyres. He uses a foot pump. Look at the diagram.

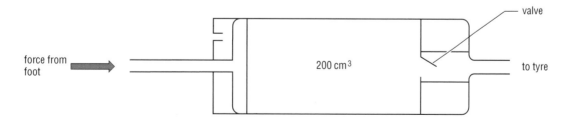

valve

force from foot

200 cm³

to tyre

Before he starts the volume of air in the pump is 200 cm³. Its pressure is 100 000 Pa.
When the pressure inside the pump is 250 000 Pa the valve opens and the air passes into the tyre.
Calculate the volume of air in the pump at 250 000 Pa.   [3]

(MEG, Higher, 1998 Specimen)

3.1 Sound waves

Sound is made by anything which vibrates – which moves 'to-and-fro'. A guitar string, for example, vibrates when it is plucked. A drum skin vibrates in a similar way when it is struck. One complete to-and-fro motion is a single vibration or **oscillation**.

Frequency

The number of vibrations made each second is the **frequency** of the sound produced. The higher the frequency of the vibration, the higher the **pitch** of the sound produced (the higher it sounds).

- When a drum skin is struck it vibrates fairly slowly, producing few vibrations per second. The vibration is described as having a low frequency, and the sound which we hear is low-pitched.
- When a guitar string is plucked it vibrates much faster, producing more vibrations per second. The vibration has a higher frequency than the drum, and the note we hear has a higher pitch.

The unit of frequency is the **hertz (Hz)**. Something that produces 250 vibrations every second is said to have a frequency of 250 hertz (250 Hz). Most people can hear frequencies between 20 Hz and 20 000 Hz although the upper limit reduces a little with age.

A larger unit used for higher frequency sounds is the kilohertz (kHz): 20 000 vibrations per second could be written as 20 000 Hz or 20 kHz. An even bigger unit is the megahertz (MHz). A wave with a frequency of 20 MHz is vibrating 20 million times each second.

How does sound travel?

If we are to hear sound, the vibrations must be transferred to our ears. The vibrations of a loudspeaker, for example, are transferred by air particles as shown in Figure 3.1.1.

As the loudspeaker cone vibrates it causes the air particles directly in front of it to vibrate at the same frequency. They, in turn, cause their neighbours to vibrate. The vibration of the loudspeaker cone is transferred through the air by displacing successive layers of air particles. Eventually the air particles next to your ear drum are made to vibrate. They make your ear drum vibrate and you hear the sound. The frequency at which the air particles vibrate (and the frequency at which your ear drum vibrates) is the same as the frequency of the loudspeaker cone. The pitch of the note you hear is therefore exactly the same as that produced by the loudspeaker.

Because the air particles are vibrating to and fro, at any instant some will be displaced to the left of their original position, while others are displaced to the right. There are regions, such as A (Figure 3.1.1), where the air particles are 'squeezed' closer together. This is a region of high pressure, known as a **compression**. At other places, such as B, neighbouring particles are displaced away from one another, creating a region of low pressure known as a **rarefaction**.

If the sound is produced by a regular vibration, the compressions and rarefactions will be evenly distributed through the air. The regularity of the pattern of compressions and rarefactions is an indication of the frequency of the vibration. In higher frequency sound waves, the compressions and rarefactions are closer together.

The pattern of vibrations through the air is a **sound wave**. The wave is the means by which *energy is transferred* from one place to another – in this case (sound) from the loudspeaker to the ear.

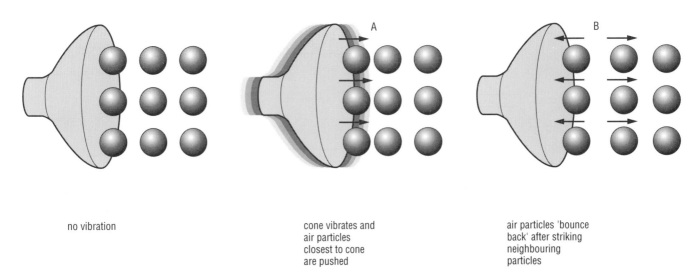

no vibration

cone vibrates and air particles closest to cone are pushed

air particles 'bounce back' after striking neighbouring particles

Figure 3.1.1 The vibration is transferred through the layers of air particles

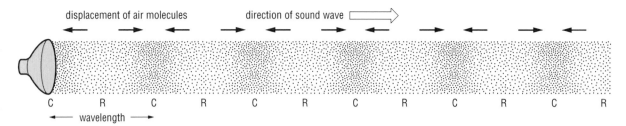

Figure 3.1.2 A sound wave: C = compression, R = rarefaction

This type of wave, in which the particle movement is parallel to the direction in which the energy is transferred, is described as a **longitudinal wave**. All sound waves are longitudinal waves, regardless of what is producing them, or what they are passing through.

Simulating sound waves

Longitudinal waves can be demonstrated using a long spiral spring (called a slinky spring), as shown in Figure 3.1.3. When one end of the spring is flicked in and out, a 'pulse' appears to travel through the spring. Each coil of the spring transfers the vibration to successive coils, eventually reaching the other end of the spring.

If the end of the spring is flicked in and out regularly, a continuous 'train' of pulses appears to travel through it. Evenly distributed regions representing compressions and rarefactions can be seen, as shown in Figure 3.1.4. The distance from the centre of one compression to the next, or from one rarefaction to the next, is the length of one wave – the **wavelength**.

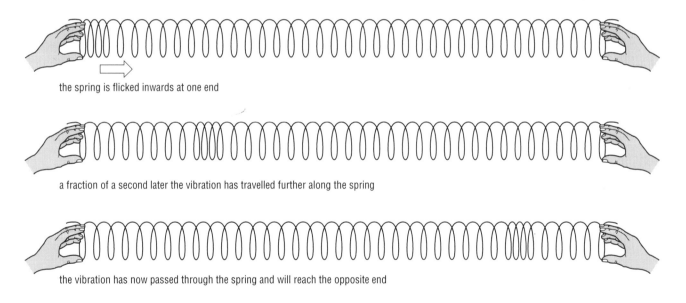

the spring is flicked inwards at one end

a fraction of a second later the vibration has travelled further along the spring

the vibration has now passed through the spring and will reach the opposite end

Figure 3.1.3 A longitudinal vibration can be sent down a slinky spring

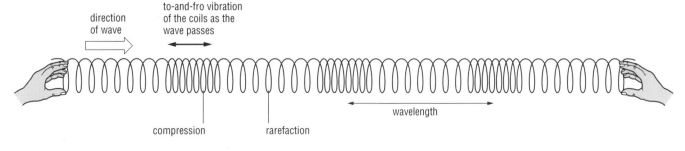

Figure 3.1.4 Simulation of a sound wave

High frequency waves have shorter wavelengths because there is a shorter time interval between one vibration and the next. Lower frequency waves have longer wavelengths because there is a longer time interval between successive vibrations.

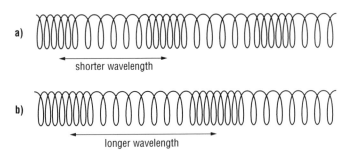

Figure 3.1.5 Wave a) has a higher frequency than wave b)

The important features to note about the vibrations of each coil of the spring (which resemble the movement of air particles as a sound wave passes through) are:

1 The particles vibrate parallel to the direction in which the wave is travelling.
2 Energy is transferred from one point to another as the vibration passes along the spring.
3 The particles vibrate at the same frequency as the source of the vibrations.
4 In practice, the vibrations get smaller as the wave moves along the spring. This is because there is energy loss (due to friction). Similarly, sounds get quieter the further you move from the source because the energy becomes more and more spread out.
5 The vibrations may be reflected from the opposite end of the spring (rather like the echo of a sound wave).
6 Each coil of the spring vibrates to and fro within a fixed region – only the vibration passes through the spring.

The amplitude of the sound

When a drum is struck the drum skin vibrates, causing the air around it to vibrate at the same frequency. If the drum is struck harder, the drum skin vibrates at the same frequency but the to-and-fro movement is much bigger – we say it vibrates with a larger **amplitude**. The amplitude of the vibration is the maximum displacement of the vibrating source from its rest position (i.e. where it would be when at rest). The loudness of the sound we hear depends on the amplitude of the vibrations. The larger the amplitude, the louder the sound.

Oscilloscope 'waves'

We can also study sound waves by changing the vibrations of the air into an electrical signal, using a microphone. If the microphone is connected to an oscilloscope, the pattern of the sound wave appears on the screen as a 'trace'.

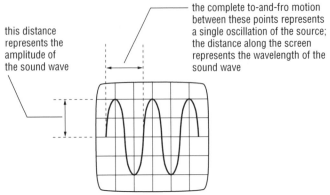

Figure 3.1.6 A sound wave viewed on an oscilloscope screen

The waveform really shows us the changes in pressure as the sound wave strikes the microphone. The crests (top parts) of the wave represent the compressions on the sound wave, whilst the troughs (bottom parts) represent rarefactions. The diagrams below show the oscilloscope traces for different sounds.

this waveform shows a low-pitched note (low frequency)

this waveform shows a higher-pitched note (higher frequency) – note that the wavelength is shorter

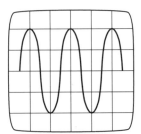

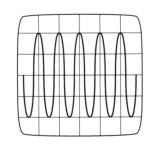

Figure 3.1.7 Comparing sound waves of different frequencies

this note has a small amplitude

this note has a greater amplitude but the same frequency – the sound will be louder but the pitch will be the same

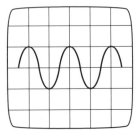

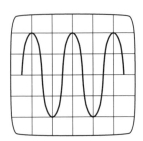

Figure 3.1.8 Comparing sound waves of different amplitudes

The speed of sound

Sound travels at 330 metres per second in still air at 20 °C. Light travels much faster – about 300 000 000 metres per second, or 186 000 miles each second. That is why, when you are watching a fireworks display, you see a rocket burst high in the sky and hear the sound a fraction of a second later – the light reaches you before the sound.

The speed of sound depends on the nature of the material through which it is passing. In general, sound travels faster through solids than through liquids, and faster through liquids than through gases.

An estimate of the speed of sound in air can be obtained simply by standing about 100 metres from a tall wall and making a sharp noise, perhaps by bringing two pieces of wood together sharply. The sound travels to the wall and reflects back to the observer. The time between producing the sound and hearing the echo is measured. The distance travelled in that time - the distance from the point where the sound is produced to the wall, and then back again - is measured. The equation:

$$speed = \frac{\text{total distance travelled}}{\text{time taken}}$$

can then be used to calculate the speed of sound.

The wave equation

The velocity (speed), frequency and wavelength of a sound wave are related by the **wave equation**:

velocity (m/s)= frequency (Hz) × wavelength (m)

Worked example

A fog horn has a frequency of 40 Hz. In still air (at 20 °C) the speed of the wave through the air will be 330 m/s. Calculate the wavelength of the wave.

We can rearrange the wave equation, velocity = frequency × wavelength, to calculate wavelength:

$$wavelength = \frac{\text{velocity}}{\text{frequency}}$$

$$= \frac{330}{40}$$

$$= 8.25 \text{ metres}$$

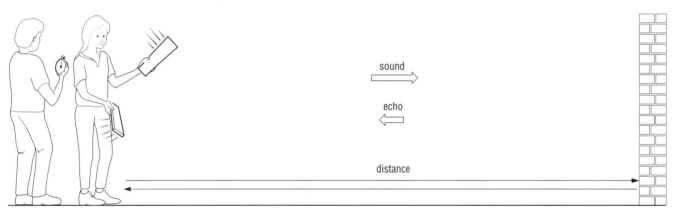

Figure 3.1.9 Estimating the speed of sound

Quick Questions

1 Describe how a sound wave transmits sound from one place to another.
2 a) How is the frequency of a note related to its pitch?
  b) How is the loudness of a note related to its amplitude?
  c) Explain what is meant by the words *compression* and *rarefaction*.
3 A whistle of frequency 10 000 Hz is blown producing a sound wave of wavelength 3 cm. Calculate the velocity of the wave.
4 Two pupils are provided with a starting pistol and a stop clock which reads to 0.01 of a second. They stand 160 m apart and discover it takes 0.50 s for the sound to travel the 160 m.
  a) Calculate the speed of sound.
  b) They realise that a strong wind was blowing. How should they modify the experiment?
  c) Why is it important to do this experiment in an open space?
  d) What does this tell you about the velocities of sound and light?
5 During a thunderstorm it took 10 s to hear the thunder after seeing the lightning. How far away is the storm if the sound travels at 330 m/s?

3.2 Reflection of sound; ultrasound

Reflected sound

Sound waves reflect from hard surfaces in such a way that the angle of reflection is the same as the angle at which they meet the surface. The apparatus shown below is often used to demonstrate this.

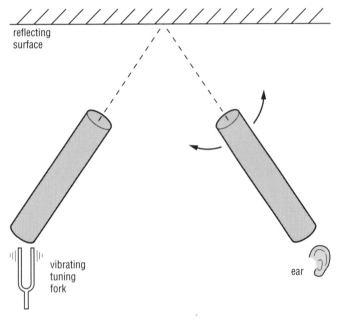

Figure 3.2.1 Finding the angle of reflected sound

The second tube is moved around at different angles until the sound is heard most clearly. The angles of the two tubes are then measured.

Sound waves reflected from hard surfaces are generally described as **echoes**.

Echo-sounding

Sound waves are used in 'echo-sounding' to find the depth of the sea bed below ships. They can also be used by fishing boats to detect shoals of fish.

A pulse of sound is emitted from a source below the ship. The waves travel to the sea bed. They are then reflected and return to a receiver on the ship. The transmission and detection system is called 'sonar'.

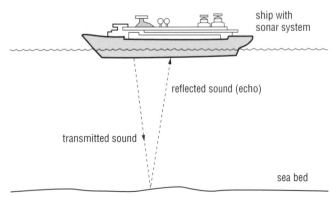

Figure 3.2.2 The principle of echo-sounding

Assuming the speed of sound in water is 1400 m/s, and if the time between the pulse being transmitted and the reflected pulse returning to the ship is 0.5 seconds,

$$\text{distance travelled by sound} = \text{speed} \times \text{time}$$
$$= 1400 \times 0.5$$
$$= 700 \text{ m}$$

But the sound has travelled down to the sea bed and then returned, so the depth of water below the ship is 350 m.

Absorbing sound

Sound waves reflect well from hard surfaces, such as rock and brick. Soft surfaces, however, absorb much of the energy carried by a sound wave. As a result little sound is reflected, and this may be reflected in many different directions by the irregularities in the surface. The energy of the sound becomes spread out and little reflected sound is heard.

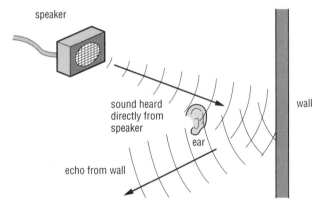

Figure 3.2.3a Most of the energy of a sound wave is reflected from hard, smooth surfaces

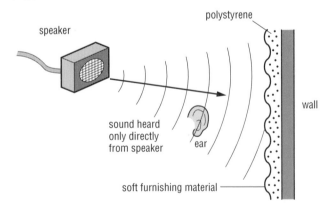

Figure 3.2.3b Soft, irregular surfaces reflect very little sound in any one direction – most of the energy is absorbed

The walls of professional recording studios are often irregular and surrounded by softer materials so that reflected sound does not spoil the quality of the recording.

Ultrasound

Very high frequency 'sound' which humans cannot hear is described as **ultrasound**. Ultrasound waves are longitudinal waves similar to all other sound waves and have a frequency between 20 kHz and 10 MHz.

Checking the baby

An ultrasound source and a detector can be tuned to exactly the same frequency – the detector will then pick up signals that have come only from that particular source. Other sounds will not be detected.

In hospitals ultrasound is used to check the progress of unborn babies. X-rays could be used to provide similar information, but could prove harmful to both the mother and the baby – ultrasound is believed to be painless and safe. An ultrasound scan can provide more information than an X-ray photograph, because soft tissue is detected as well as bone.

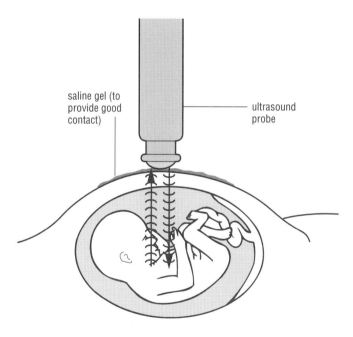

saline gel (to provide good contact)

ultrasound probe

Figure 3.2.4 An ultrasound scan of the womb

The ultrasound probe generates ultrasound waves with a frequency of about 3.5 MHz. The ultrasound waves are reflected from tissues within the body. At the boundary between two different types of tissue (such as where muscle and bone meet) the pulses are reflected strongly and travel back to the probe. At the boundary between similar types of tissue (such as fat and muscle) the reflected signals are much weaker. A sensor (built into the probe) detects the reflected waves which are then processed by a computer to form a 'picture' of the developing baby inside the womb. The operator can move the probe across the mother's abdomen until the required view is obtained.

Other uses of ultrasound

Ultrasound can also be used:

- For cleaning clothes and other materials. The very high frequency of the ultrasound vibrations loosens dirt from the fibres of clothing.
- By dentists who use the ultrasound to 'shake' the hard coating of tartar from your teeth, helping to prevent gum disease.
- In industry, to detect flaws (such as cracks) in the metal of aircraft bodies and wings where continuous flexing may have caused 'stress fractures'.
- In hospitals, to shatter kidney stones, possibly avoiding the need for surgery.

Quick Questions

1 What can you say about the reflection of sound from hard surfaces? Compare this with how sound behaves when it hits a soft surface.
2 A fishing boat uses sonar to detect shoals of fish. The time between the sound being emitted and received on the ship is 0.1 second. Calculate the depth of the fish below the boat, assuming that the speed of sound in water is 1400 m/s.
3 a) Your family is looking around a house and considering buying it. Downstairs is fully furnished but all the upstairs rooms are empty. The upstairs rooms seem very noisy when you are talking but the downstairs rooms do not. Explain why.
　 b) The fully tiled bathroom is the noisiest. Why?
　 c) There is also a lot of traffic noise from a busy road. What could you do i) to the house and ii) in the garden, to reduce the noise levels in the house?
4 What is meant by the term *ultrasound*? State its frequency range.
5 a) Describe how ultrasound can be used to provide an image of an unborn baby.
　 b) An ultrasound image has several advantages over an X-ray image. What are they?
　 c) Describe three other uses of ultrasound.
6 The speed of sound in human tissue is about 100 m/s. If a baby in the womb is 10 cm below an ultrasound probe, how long will it take the pulse of ultrasound to travel from the probe to the baby and back to the probe?

3.3 Light waves

Light from the sun travels through millions of miles of 'empty' space. Light cannot, therefore, travel in the form of a longitudinal wave (which needs particles to transfer the energy). Light energy (and many other forms of radiant energy) is transferred in the form of a **transverse wave**.

A transverse waveform can be demonstrated using a length of rubber tubing. By flicking one end of the tubing, a pulse can be seen passing along the tubing. Energy is transferred from one end to the other by the pulse.

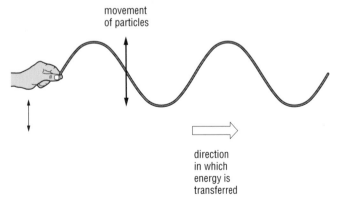

Figure 3.3.1 A transverse pulse can be sent along a length of rubber tubing

If the tubing is flicked hard enough, the pulse is reflected and travels back towards the source.

By flicking the tubing regularly, a wavetrain (a regular series of successive pulses) can be seen travelling continuously along the tubing.

In a transverse wave, the oscillations are at right angles to the direction in which the energy is being transferred (whereas in a longitudinal wave the oscillations are parallel to the direction in which energy is transferred).

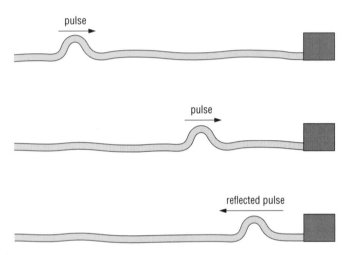

Figure 3.3.2 A transverse wave

Wavelength, frequency and amplitude

The wavelength is the distance occupied by one complete wave (the distance between any two points which are in the same position and moving in the same direction, such as AB, CD, EF in Figure 3.3.3). The wavelength is measured in any of the units of length – mm, cm, m or km.

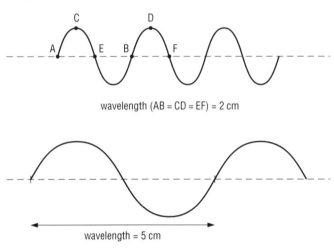

Figure 3.3.3 The wavelength of a transverse wave

The frequency of a wave is the number of complete oscillations made each second. A wave with a frequency of 100 Hz transfers 100 oscillations or vibrations each second. The higher the frequency, the shorter the wavelength – assuming the velocity of the wave does not change.

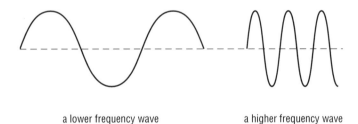

a lower frequency wave   a higher frequency wave

Figure 3.3.4 The higher the frequency, the shorter the wavelength

The amplitude is the maximum displacement of any point from its mean position.

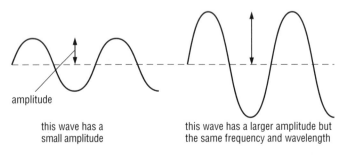

this wave has a
small amplitude

this wave has a larger amplitude but
the same frequency and wavelength

Figure 3.3.5 The amplitude of a transverse wave

Velocity, frequency and wavelength

Light waves consist of oscillating electric and magnetic fields – they are **electromagnetic waves**. All electromagnetic waves (see pages 94–97) have a common velocity (in a vacuum) of 300 000 000 m/s. The frequency and wavelength characterise the kind of waves being considered – whether they are, for example, light waves, microwaves or X-rays. The amplitude of the wave depends on the energy transferred at the source.

Because all electromagnetic waves have the same velocity, any change in frequency will result in a different wavelength as shown by the simplified illustrations below.

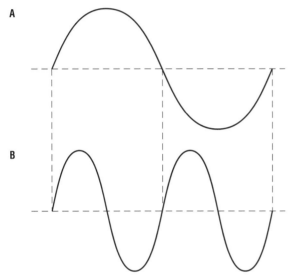

Figure 3.3.6 If the frequency of an electromagnetic wave doubles, its wavelength is halved

- Imagine that wave A has a frequency of 5 Hz (5 complete oscillations or vibrations per second). One complete wave will occupy a distance equivalent to the distance travelled by the wave in one-fifth of a second.
- If the frequency is doubled to 10 Hz (wave B), then one complete wave is produced every one-tenth of a second. The distance occupied by one wave (the wavelength) will be one half of the original value, so the wavelength will be one half of the original value.

If the frequency is doubled, the wavelength is halved.

The wave equation

The velocity, frequency and wavelength of electromagnetic waves are related by the wave equation:

velocity (m/s) = frequency (Hz) × wavelength (m)

Knowing, for example, that the frequency of Radio 1 FM is 99.8 MHz (99 800 000 Hz), we can calculate the wavelength of the waves which carry the signal to us:

$$\text{wavelength} = \frac{\text{velocity}}{\text{frequency}}$$

$$= \frac{300\ 000\ 000}{99\ 800\ 000}$$

$$= 3 \text{ metres}$$

Quick Questions

1 Describe three differences between light waves and sound waves.
2 On the wave below, which letter(s) show **a)** a crest, **b)** a trough, **c)** one wavelength, **d)** the amplitude?

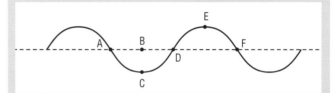

Figure 3.3.7

   e) If 100 complete cycles of this wave pass a point in 1 second, what is the frequency of the wave?
3 The oscilloscope traces for the sounds of three different aircraft at take-off are shown below.

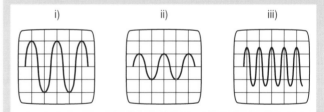

Figure 3.3.8

   a) Which has the highest frequency?
   b) Which is the noisiest (loudest)?
4 Draw the following waves to scale:
   a) wavelength 6 cm, amplitude 2 cm, 1 complete cycle;
   b) wavelength 3 cm, amplitude 4 cm, 2 complete cycles.
   Which wave has the highest frequency?
5 Most radio stations now publish their frequencies in MHz. You only have an old radio which is calibrated in metres for wavelengths. In order to convert frequencies to wavelengths you need to know the velocity of electromagnetic waves and an equation.
   a) What is the velocity of electromagnetic waves?
   b) Write down the equation you would use.
   c) i) Radio 2 has a frequency of 88 MHz. Calculate its wavelength.
   ii) Radio 5 has a wavelength of 693 m. Calculate its frequency.

3.4 Electromagnetic waves

Light is visible only because the cells in the retina of the eye respond to the range of electromagnetic wavelengths occupied by visible light. The same cells cannot respond to other wavelengths, such as X-rays, so those waves cannot be 'seen'. Different colours of light have different characteristics. Red light, for example, has a longer wavelength and a lower frequency than blue light. They therefore affect the retina differently and the brain senses the difference.

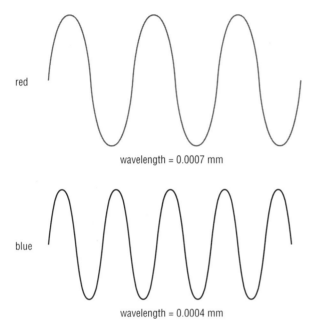

Figure 3.4.1 The red light has a longer wavelength and a lower frequency than blue. Both travel at the same speed in air

Visible light is one form of **electromagnetic wave**. All electromagnetic waves transfer energy (in the form of radiation). They are arranged in order of their wavelength in the **electromagnetic spectrum**, Figure 3.4.2.

All electromagnetic waves have the following properties:

- They transfer energy from place to place.
- They are transverse waves.
- They travel at the same speed (the speed of light) – around 300 000 km/s in a vacuum.
- They travel in a straight line (unless they pass from one substance to another).
- They can all be reflected, refracted and diffracted (see pages 98, 100 and 110).

The different wavelengths and frequencies give each group of waves quite different properties from the others.

Radio waves

Radio waves (including those that carry TV signals) have the longest wavelengths in the electromagnetic spectrum. They are produced by oscillating electric currents in a transmitting aerial. The frequency of the emitted radio wave is the same as the frequency at which the current oscillates in the aerial. In the receiving aerial the waves are converted back into an alternating current with the same frequency as the wave. This is then converted into sound by the radio.

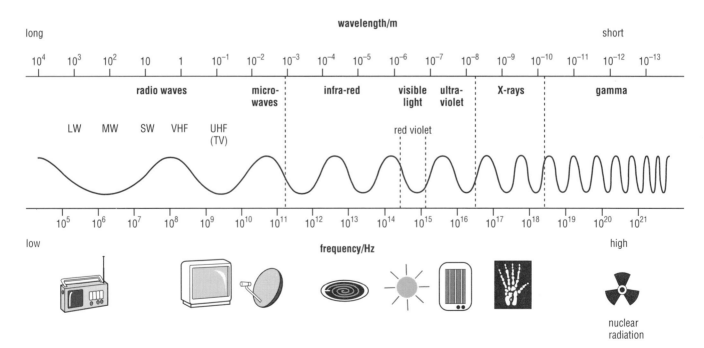

Figure 3.4.2 The electromagnetic spectrum. Notice that:
- As you move from left to right the wavelength progressively decreases but the frequency increases
- As you move from right to left the wavelength progressively increases but the frequency decreases

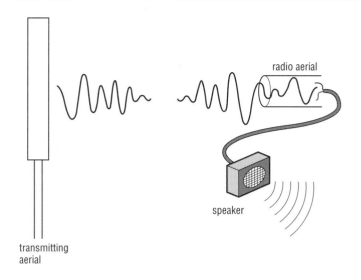

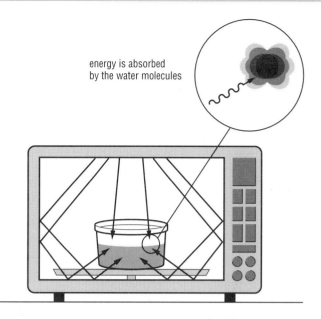

Figure 3.4.3 Radio waves carry energy from the transmitter to the aerial in your home or inside a radio. The radio converts the information carried by the waves back into sound

Figure 3.4.5 Microwave energy is absorbed by the water in food, raising the temperature and cooking the food

Long and medium wavelength radio waves can reflect off a layer of charged particles in the upper atmosphere (the ionosphere). This enables them to travel over long distances despite the curvature of the earth's surface.

Microwaves pass deep into food, cooking it evenly throughout. (A conventional oven cooks food from the outside, so the outer layers can be fully cooked whilst the inner layers remain uncooked.)

Microwaves that have wavelengths similar to shorter wavelength radio waves can pass easily through the atmosphere and can be used for satellite communications.

Like all electromagnetic waves, microwaves travel in straight lines. They can be easily focused on the satellite by the concave dish transmitter. The satellite then re-directs the microwaves to a receiver dish. The broad dish collects the waves over a large area, focusing them onto the transducer to produce a strong signal. Without the dish the transducer would not be able to absorb enough energy to produce either a picture or sound.

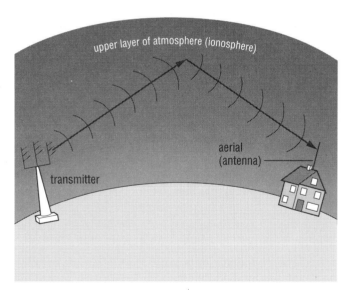

Figure 3.4.4 Long-distance radio transmission via the ionosphere

The waves from different radio stations have different wavelengths and frequencies.

Microwaves

The waves produced by microwave ovens have wavelengths that are readily absorbed by water molecules. As the microwaves pass through food, some of their energy is absorbed by the water molecules and the temperature rises, warming the rest of the food.

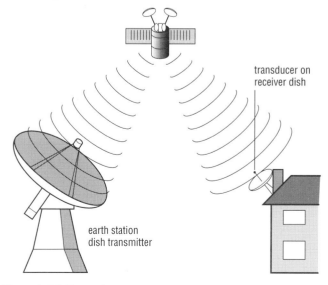

Figure 3.4.6 Transmission and reception of a microwave signal via satellite

The transducer must be positioned at the focal point of the reflector for maximum energy capture. In any other position less energy will be absorbed and reception will be poor.

Short wavelength microwaves (such as those produced in microwave ovens) can damage living cells, sometimes causing severe burning. Excessive exposure may kill the cells altogether. The longer microwaves used for communications (satellite transmissions and mobile phones) are not so dangerous.

Infra-red

Everything emits infra-red radiation, even you. The hotter an object is, the more infra-red radiation it emits.

Infra-red wavelengths lie just beyond 'visible' red in the electromagnetic spectrum. The radiation cannot be detected by the human eye, but can be detected by a thermometer with a blackened bulb positioned just outside the red portion of the visible spectrum (see page 108).

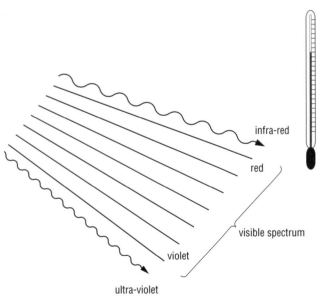

Figure 3.4.7 Detecting infra-red in the spectrum

Black is a good absorber of infra-red radiation. The absorbed energy raises the temperature of the liquid in the bulb and the temperature is seen to rise on the thermometer scale.

Food can be cooked using infra-red grills but, unlike microwaves, infra-red waves penetrate only the first few millimetres beyond the surface of the food. Toasters also emit infra-red radiation.

Visible light

The group of electromagnetic waves that can be detected by the human eye is collectively called 'visible light'. Each colour of the visible spectrum (Figure 3.4.8) is characterised by a wave with a particular frequency and wavelength.

Other colours that we perceive are mixtures – combinations of waves of different wavelengths.

Ultra-violet

Ultra-violet radiation is emitted by any object that has reached a temperature that can be described as 'white hot'. It is also emitted by sun beds. It tans the skin, but some forms of ultra-violet radiation penetrate into the deeper tissues of your skin, damaging the cells.

Like other groups of waves, ultra-violet has a range of wavelengths and frequencies. Some of these are more dangerous than others. The 'ozone layer' in the earth's upper atmosphere absorbs most of the dangerous wavelengths reaching the earth from the sun.

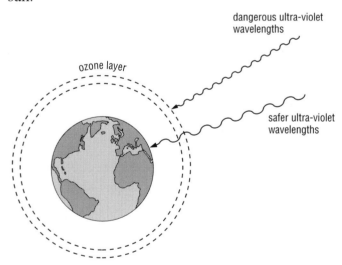

Figure 3.4.9 The ozone layer protects us from dangerous ultra-violet radiation

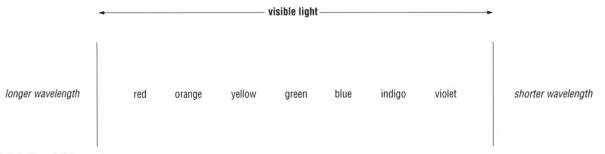

Figure 3.4.8 The visible spectrum

In recent years the ozone layer has been shown to be 'broken', leaving huge gaps in the layer of gases that absorb the ultra-violet radiation. More of the dangerous wavelengths are now reaching the surface of the earth. Excessive exposure to these can cause skin cancer. Attempts are now being made to reduce further damage to the ozone layer.

Glass absorbs most ultra-violet radiation, which is why you cannot get a tan by sunbathing behind the windows in your home.

Because living cells may be killed by too much ultra-violet, ultra-violet (UV) lamps are often used in shops that sell fresh meat, fish or dairy produce. The radiation kills any microbes which may be present.

Some chemicals fluoresce – they absorb ultra-violet radiation and emit visible light. Security paints contain fluorescent chemicals which cannot normally be seen but can be seen clearly when exposed to ultra-violet radiation.

'Ordinary' strip lights produce ultra-violet light. The tubes are coated with a fluorescent chemical which absorbs any ultra-violet radiation and then emits safer white light as it fluoresces. Strip lights are therefore often called fluorescent tubes.

X-radiation (X-rays)

X-rays have very short wavelengths and are able to pass through most solid materials with very little of their energy being absorbed. X-radiation is an **ionising radiation**. Ionising radiation is dangerous. Excess exposure can kill human cells and lower doses can cause cancers. Hospitals use screens containing lead to protect the staff who must work with X-rays regularly.

X-rays affect photographic film. X-ray pictures of inside the body are possible because X-rays do not pass through bone as easily as they pass through flesh. On X-ray film the bones appear lighter (because more X-radiation is absorbed) than the tissues which surround them (which allow more of the X-radiation to pass).

X-rays can also be used to test metal objects for fractures and other weaknesses.

Gamma radiation

Gamma radiation is an ionising radiation with a very short wavelength which enables it to penetrate body tissues easily. Exposure to gamma radiation can cause changes in living cells, causing cancers, and excessive exposure may kill the cells entirely.

Cancers can be treated by killing the cancerous cells with gamma radiation, in limited and carefully directed doses. Medical treatment using radiation is known as **radiotherapy**.

Gamma radiation can also be used to kill bacteria on food, helping to extend its 'shelf life'. It is also used to sterilise surgical instruments in hospitals.

Quick Questions

1 Why are humans only able to see the visible section of the electromagnetic spectrum?
2 List the groups of waves in the electromagnetic spectrum, in order of increasing wavelength.
3 Each group in the electromagnetic spectrum is distinguished by its own wavelength and frequency range. However, the groups have several things in common. Make a list of the features that are common to all electromagnetic waves.
4 Which named group of electromagnetic waves
   a) can be used to detect broken bones?
   b) can be used to treat cancer?
   c) is reflected by a layer in the atmosphere called the ionosphere?
   d) causes fluorescence in strip lights?
   e) transmits satellite TV?
   f) is emitted by human beings?
5 Which colour in the visible spectrum has
   a) the longest wavelength?
   b) the shortest wavelength?
6 a) The sun emits huge amounts of ultra-violet radiation but much of this is absorbed by ozone gas in the atmosphere. Over the past century, more and more ultra-violet has been reaching the earth as the ozone layer 'breaks down'. How might this affect people on earth?
   b) Explain why sitting in a conservatory would not produce a sun tan.
   c) Why do security paints show up when exposed to ultra-violet 'light'?
7 For each group of waves in the electromagnetic spectrum, describe
   a) one way in which they are used (an application);
   b) one danger (if any) that they may pose.

3.5 Light and sight

We 'see' most things because light is reflected off them and enters our eye. The path taken by a narrow beam of light is generally described as a ray of light. On diagrams, rays of light are shown as straight lines.

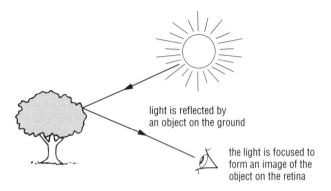

light is reflected by an object on the ground

the light is focused to form an image of the object on the retina

Figure 3.5.1 The eye sees objects by reflected light

Normally light travels in a direct (straight) line from place to place. In situations where we need to change the direction in which light travels, mirrors can be used.

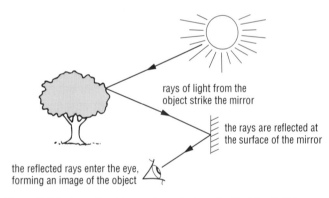

rays of light from the object strike the mirror

the rays are reflected at the surface of the mirror

the reflected rays enter the eye, forming an image of the object

Figure 3.5.2 Smooth, shiny surfaces (mirrors) reflect the light from the object so that an image can be seen

Uneven surfaces reflect light from an object in different directions, producing 'diffused' or scattered reflections which cannot form an image.

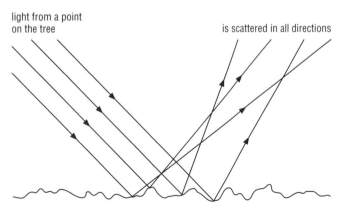

light from a point on the tree

is scattered in all directions

Figure 3.5.3 Uneven surfaces give diffuse reflections which do not produce an image

The angle of incidence and the angle of reflection

The rays of light which reach a mirror from an object are called incident rays. After reflection, they are called the reflected rays. A line drawn at 90° to the mirror where the rays strike it is called the normal. It is not a ray – it is a line that we use to help us draw ray diagrams.

The angle between the incident ray and the normal is called the angle of incidence. The angle between the reflected ray and the normal is called the angle of reflection.

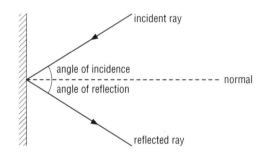

incident ray

angle of incidence

angle of reflection

normal

reflected ray

Figure 3.5.4 Reflection of light by a plane mirror

Whenever reflection occurs, whether from a mirror or any other polished surface, *the angle of incidence is always equal to the angle of reflection*.

The same rule applies when light is incident on curved mirrors, but with quite different results:

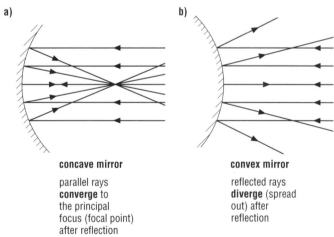

concave mirror

parallel rays **converge** to the principal focus (focal point) after reflection

convex mirror

reflected rays **diverge** (spread out) after reflection

Figure 3.5.5 Reflection of light by curved mirrors

Concave mirrors are used in car headlamps, theatre lights and torches. In each situation the bulb is placed at the focus of the mirror (see Figure 3.5.5a). The mirror then produces a parallel reflected beam.

Convex mirrors (Figure 3.5.5b) are often used in situations where a wider field of view is required. The side (wing) mirrors on cars and security mirrors in shops are examples.

A simple periscope

In some optical instruments several mirrors may be used to change the direction of the incident light. A simple periscope, for example, uses two plane mirrors.

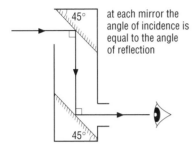

at each mirror the angle of incidence is equal to the angle of reflection

Figure 3.5.6 Mirrors in a simple periscope, as used on a double-decker bus

The eye

When light from an object enters your eye, the eye lens forms an image of the object on the retina.

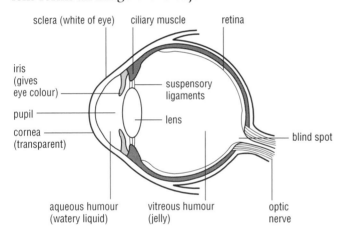

Figure 3.5.7 The human eye

- The retina consists of millions of light-sensitive cells connected to the brain via the optic nerve. The cells transmit information about the image to the brain, which interprets the information.
- The optic nerve carries signals from the retina to the brain.
- The sclera is a thick, tough coating which protects the eye from external dangers.
- The cornea is a thick, convex, transparent layer which refracts light and protects the inner eye from damage.
- The lens is jelly-like. The ciliary muscle acts (via the suspensory ligaments) on the lens to change its shape, ensuring that the image formed by the lens is clearly focused on the retina.
- The suspensory ligaments help retain the position of the eye lens and serve to change its shape.
- The iris is effectively a circular curtain, closing and opening to control the amount of light entering the eye.

- The pupil is the part of the eye through which light passes to the lens. It is effectively a 'hole' in the iris. In dull conditions the pupil will be large so that more light will enter. In bright conditions the iris closes, reducing the size of the pupil and restricting the amount of light entering.
- The blind spot is a region in which there are no light-sensitive cells. Light that falls here is not detected – this part of the image is not 'seen'.

Quick Questions

1 Explain the differences in light reflection from rough and smooth surfaces.

2 a) On the diagram below, state which letters indicate:

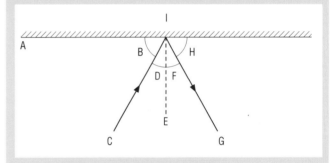

Figure 3.5.8

   i)   the incident ray;
   ii) the reflected ray;
   iii) the normal;
   iv) the angle of incidence;
   v)   the angle of reflection.

   b) What will be the connection between the values of the angle of incidence and the angle of reflection?

3 Describe the function of each of the eye parts listed below:

   retina   cornea   lens   optic nerve   iris   pupil   suspensory ligaments

4 Describe the similarities and differences between the working of the eye and the simple camera shown below.

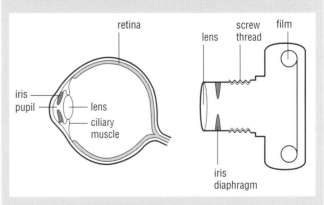

Figure 3.5.9

3.6 Refraction

Light passes easily through substances such as gases. It travels more slowly through other substances, such as glass, water or perspex because these are 'optically denser'. When light passes from one substance into another its speed changes. The change in speed can also cause a change in direction. The changes take place (suddenly) at the boundary of the two substances (where they meet). These changes are called **refraction**.

Figure 3.6.1 shows what happens as light passes through a block of glass. Glass is (optically) denser than air, so light slows down as it enters the glass. As it leaves the glass and re-emerges into the air, it speeds up again.

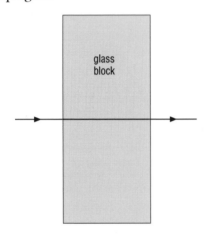

Figure 3.6.1a If the light meets the block at 90° it passes straight through with no change in direction. The light slows down as it passes into the glass and speeds up again as it passes from the glass back into air

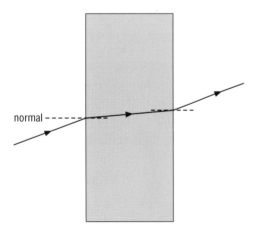

Figure 3.6.1b When the light meets the block at any angle other than 90°, its direction changes at the boundary between the two substances. Because it is passing into a 'denser' material, the ray is refracted towards the normal (a line drawn at 90° to the surface at the point where light strikes it).

As the light passes from the glass back into air (from a dense to a less dense substance) it is refracted away from the normal. Notice that the ray leaving the block is parallel to the incident ray, but slightly displaced to one side.

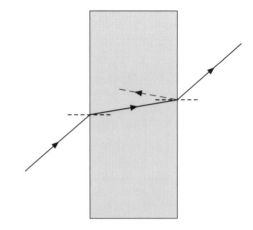

Figure 3.6.1c Larger angles of incidence produce a greater degree of refraction at both surfaces, and the ray which emerges from the block is displaced more to one side

Internal reflection

When light passes from a dense substance into a less dense substance (such as from glass into air), some of the light is reflected, as you can see in Figure 3.6.1c. This is called **internal reflection**. The amount of light reflected depends on the angle at which the incident ray strikes the boundary.

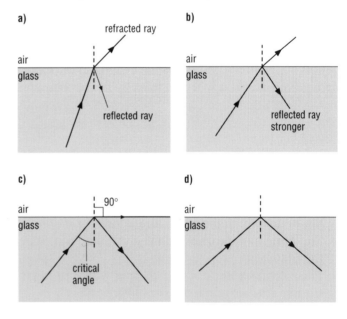

Figure 3.6.2 Internal reflection for different angles of incidence

- At small angles of incidence (Figure 3.6.2a) the refracted ray (leaving the glass) is strong and the reflected ray is weak. The angle at which the ray is reflected at the boundary is equal to the angle of incidence.
- As the angle of incidence increases (b), the reflected ray becomes brighter. Consequently the refracted ray (emerging from the glass) will become dimmer.

- At a particular angle of incidence, called the **critical angle**, the emergent ray is refracted at 90° to the boundary (c). No clear refracted ray emerges into the air.
- If the angle of incidence is bigger than the critical angle, then all of the light is reflected (d). This is described as **total internal reflection**.

Measuring the critical angle

The critical angle for glass or plastic can be measured using the apparatus shown below.

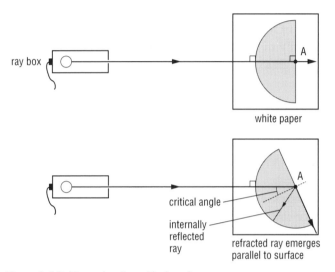

Figure 3.6.3 Measuring the critical angle

The ray is directed towards a point marked on paper below the glass block. Because the light strikes the first surface at 90° it will pass directly to the second surface with no change in direction. If the block is then slowly turned, the emergent ray will 'disappear' just at the point where the angle of incidence is equal to the critical angle. The outline of the block can be drawn on the paper, and the positions of the incident ray and the normal can be marked. The critical angle can be measured from the lines on the paper.

Prism binoculars

Optical telescopes need a long light path, i.e. a long distance between the objective lens and the eyepiece lens, to give a large magnification. Prism binoculars (Figure 3.6.4) are short but can produce large magnification. They contain prisms to reflect the light back on itself, effectively giving a long light path. The prisms are arranged in such a way that the light strikes the boundary between the glass and air at an angle of 45° - greater than the critical angle for glass which is about 42°. The light is then totally internally reflected to the second prism where the same thing happens. After being reflected the light emerges from the eyepiece lens, producing an upright, highly magnified image.

There are two major advantages of using prisms to reflect the light, rather than mirrors:

- The surfaces of prisms do not deteriorate in the same way as the silvered surfaces of mirrors.
- The image is brighter - when total internal reflection occurs, more of the light is reflected than would be the case from the surface of a mirror.

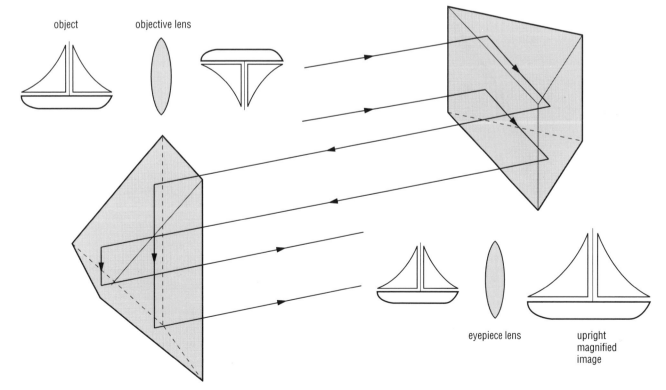

Figure 3.6.4 The arrangement of prisms in binoculars

Optical fibres

Endoscopes are optical instruments that allow doctors to 'see' inside parts of the body, such as the lungs, stomach and intestines, without using surgery. The endoscope consists of a bundle of **optical fibres**.

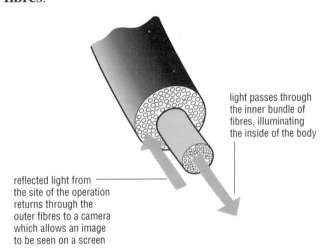

light passes through the inner bundle of fibres, illuminating the inside of the body

reflected light from the site of the operation returns through the outer fibres to a camera which allows an image to be seen on a screen

Figure 3.6.5 An endoscope consists of bundles of optical fibres through which light can pass. There may be two bundles, one inside the other

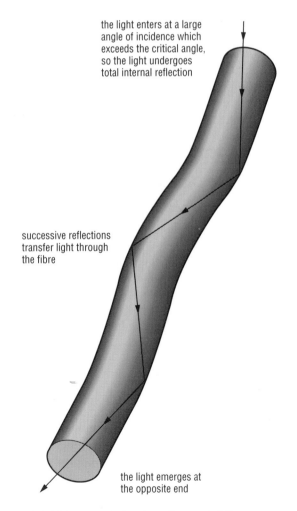

the light enters at a large angle of incidence which exceeds the critical angle, so the light undergoes total internal reflection

successive reflections transfer light through the fibre

the light emerges at the opposite end

Figure 3.6.6 Light transmission through an optical fibre

Light passes through an optical fibre because it enters at a large angle – greater than the critical angle for the material of the fibre. The ray is totally internally reflected from the outer boundary of the fibre, and passes through by successive internal reflections (Figure 3.6.6). Eventually it passes through the opposite end of the fibre, with very little light loss.

Most links between major telephone exchanges are now optical fibre links. Less energy is lost in optical fibres than in conventional cables, so the signal remains strong. The signals are digitised pulses of infra-red light. The signals therefore travel at the speed of light. Optical fibres are also used in the cable TV network which is currently being fitted in some areas of the country.

Apparent depth

The bottom of a swimming pool always looks closer to the surface than it really is. This is due to the refraction of light emerging from the water into the air above.

Imagine another situation: looking at a fish just above the river bed. Reflected light from the fish travels through the water towards you. As it passes from the water into the air, it refracts away from the normal because it has travelled from a denser substance (water) into a less dense substance (air).

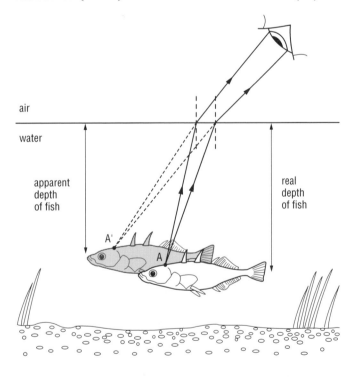

air

water

apparent depth of fish

real depth of fish

A'

A

Figure 3.6.7 Refraction makes the fish appear nearer the surface

The light entering your eye appears to come from point A'. Your eye therefore sees the fish higher up than it really is. The 'apparent' depth is less than the real depth.

Quick Questions

• •

1 a) Explain the following terms:

refraction   internal reflection   critical angle
total internal reflection

b) Copy and complete the following diagrams, by continuing the path of the ray of light. The critical angle of glass is 42°.

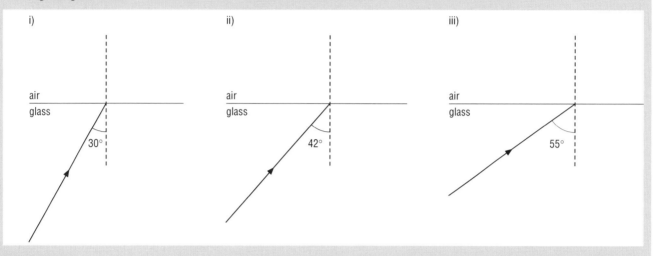

i)

air
glass

30°

ii)

air
glass

42°

iii)

air
glass

55°

Figure 3.6.8

2 a) How is light transmitted through an optical fibre?
  b) Describe two uses of optical fibres.

3 A person is fishing from a river bank. He notices the end of the fishing rod appears to bend when it is dipped into the water. Can you explain, with the aid of a diagram, why?

4 a) Give two advantages prisms have over mirrors when considering the reflection of light.
  b) Look back at the diagram of a periscope on page 99. This is a mirror periscope. Can you draw a similar periscope that makes use of prisms? Also draw the path of two rays of light through the prisms.

5 a) 'Cat's Eyes' are put into roads to help drivers when it is dark or foggy. The diagram below shows one design for a Cat's Eye.
   i) How are Cat's Eyes an aid to the driver?
   ii) Copy the diagram and continue the path of the ray of light.
  b) Cars and bicycles have red plastic reflectors fixed to them at the back. Can you explain why and how they make use of total internal reflection?

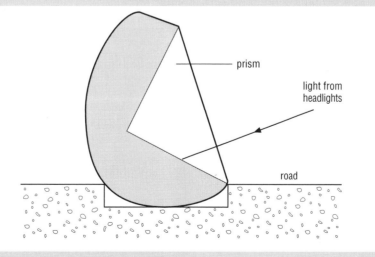

prism

light from
headlights

road

Figure 3.6.9

3.7 Lenses

Any piece of transparent material with at least one curved surface can be considered to be a lens. Most manufactured lenses are made from glass or a plastic and can be classified as convex or concave.

Concave lenses are thinner at the centre than towards the outside. Parallel rays which strike a concave lens diverge (spread out) after being refracted at the surfaces of the lens.

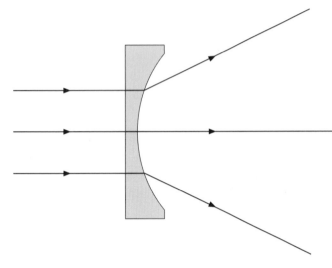

Figure 3.7.1 A concave lens is a diverging lens

Convex lenses are fatter at the centre than towards the outside. Parallel rays of light which strike a convex lens converge (come together) after passing through the lens.

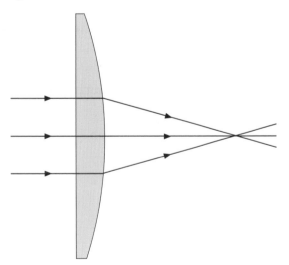

Figure 3.7.2 A convex lens is a converging lens

The emergent rays (those leaving the lens) converge to a single point – the 'principal focus' or focal point of the lens. After passing through the focal point they diverge (spread out). The distance from the centre (pole) of the lens to the focal point is called the 'focal length' of the lens.

The focal length depends on the shape of the lens, as shown below.

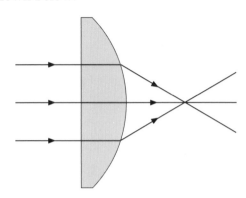

Figure 3.7.3a Convex lenses with greater curvature have shorter focal lengths because the light is deviated through greater angles

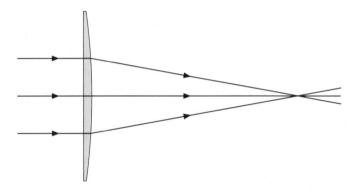

Figure 3.7.3b Convex lenses with less curved surfaces have longer focal lengths because the light is deviated through smaller angles

Real image formation

A convex lens can form an image (picture) of an object on a screen placed in the path of the emerging rays. Images such as this are described as **real images**. The image is always inverted (upside down). Real images are only formed when the object is situated beyond the focal point of the lens.

Figure 3.7.4 Convex lenses can produce real images; the image is inverted

---

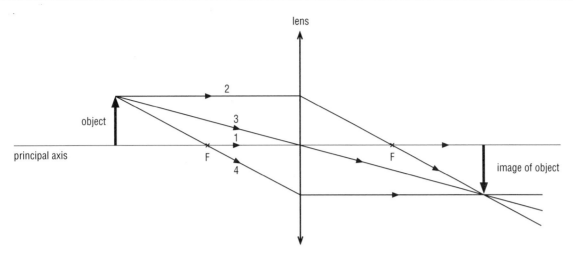

Figure 3.7.5 Locating an image by a ray diagram

Ray diagrams are used to show the path of the rays through the lens to the screen. The paths of four of the rays from any object are always predictable (see Figure 3.7.5):

- One ray (1) will pass from the object along the principal axis (the imaginary line perpendicular to the lens, through the centre (pole) of the lens). It will pass through the centre of the lens, undeviated. The image of that point will, therefore, always be on the same line as the corresponding point on the object.
- One ray (2) will pass from the top of the object, parallel to the principal axis. After passing through the lens it will pass through the focal point (F) *on the opposite side of the lens*.
- One ray (3) will pass from the top of the object through the centre (pole) of the lens. It will continue undeviated.
- One ray (4) will pass through the focal point *on the same side of the lens as the object*. After refraction by the lens, the ray travels parallel to the principal axis.

The point where rays 2, 3 and 4 meet is the point at which the image of the top of the object will be found. Only two of these are needed to locate it.

The position of the image depends on the distance between the lens and the object, and on the focal length of the lens. Figure 3.7.6a shows a convex lens forming a real image of an object on a screen. Figure 3.7.6b shows the same lens forming an image of the same object, but with the object now twice as far from the lens.

The greater the object distance from the lens, the shorter the image distance from the lens. Conversely, the shorter the object distance, the greater the image distance (assuming the lens is not changed).

If the lens is replaced by one with a different focal length, the position of the image will change. If a lens with a longer focal length is used (Figure 3.7.7),

a)

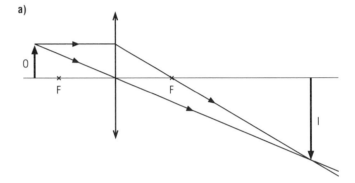

b)

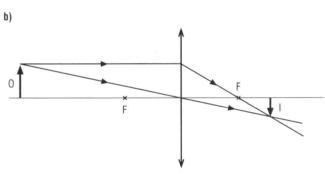

Figure 3.7.6 The greater the object distance, the shorter the image distance

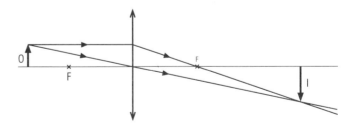

Figure 3.7.7 The longer the focal length of the lens, the greater the image distance

the image distance will be greater. If, conversely, a lens of shorter focal length is used, the image distance will be shorter (assuming the object distance is not changed).

Virtual image formation

If the object is closer to a convex lens than its focal point, a **virtual image** (one that cannot be produced on a screen) is formed. The image under these circumstances is always upright and magnified.

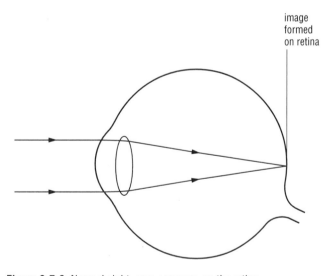

Figure 3.7.8 The eye cannot perceive refraction. To the eye an image appears to exist in the position from which the rays seem to have come. Although the image cannot be formed on a screen, it can be 'seen' by the eye. The convex lens here is acting as a magnifying glass

Eye defects

In a normal eye, the lens and the cornea act together to form an inverted image on the retina (the brain interprets this as an upright image).

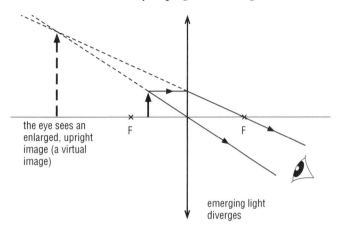

Figure 3.7.9 Normal sight: rays converge on the retina

Some people, however, suffer from eye defects which cause the image to be formed either in front of or behind the retina. The object then appears blurred.

In a short-sighted eye, light from a distant object is brought to a focus in front of the retina. This may be due to the eye itself being too long, or because the lens cannot be made thin enough. People who suffer from short sight can see near objects clearly but distant objects are blurred (Figure 3.7.10a).

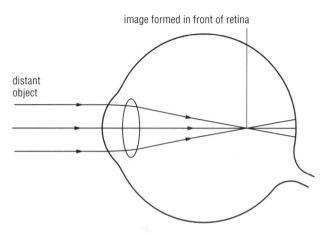

Figure 3.7.10a Short sight

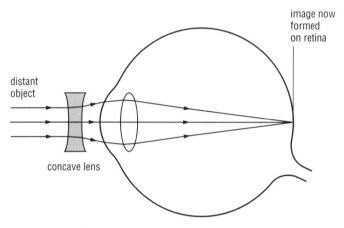

Figure 3.7.10b Correction of short sight

Short sight can be corrected using a concave (diverging) lens. Now the incident light is refracted outwards before reaching the cornea. The cornea and eye lens then refract the light so that it converges to form a clear image on the retina (Figure 3.7.10b).

Other people may be long-sighted. In a long-sighted eye the rays are refracted in such a way that the image would be formed 'behind' the retina. This may be due to the eye being too short, or because the eye lens cannot be made fat enough. Long-sighted people can see distant objects clearly, but near objects appear blurred (Figure 3.7.11a).

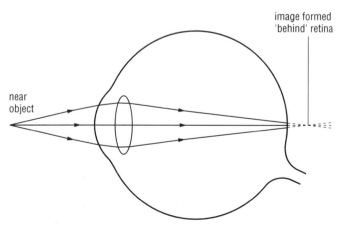

Figure 3.7.11a Long sight

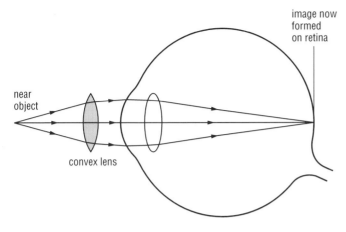

Figure 3.7.11b Correction of long sight

Long sight is corrected using a convex lens. This helps to refract the incident rays (from near objects) inwards before they strike the cornea. The cornea and eye lens then focus the light onto the retina to form a clear image of the near object (Figure 3.7.11b).

The camera

In a simple camera (see Figure 3.5.9, page 99) a converging lens is used to produce an image of an object on film. The image is smaller than the object, inverted, and nearer to the lens than the object.

The object may be a few metres or several kilometres from the lens. The image, however, must always be formed on the film. In many cameras, the position of the lens may be changed by moving it closer to, or further from, the film. The image distance is therefore adjusted to ensure that, for any required object distance, the image is always in focus on the film.

The projector

A projector is used to form a magnified image of a small object (such as a photographic slide) on a screen placed several metres from the lens.

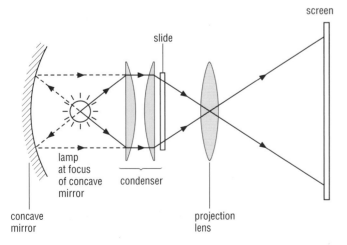

Figure 3.7.12 A slide projector

To ensure that a clear image of the slide is formed, whatever the distance of the screen from the lens, the projection lens can be moved, thus changing the object distance (and therefore the image distance). Because the convex lens produces an inverted image, the slide is placed in the projector upside down (inverted). The final image is then the right way up.

Quick Questions

1 Do the following descriptions apply to a *convex* or a *concave* lens?
   i) is thickest at its centre;
   ii) is a diverging lens;
   iii) is a converging lens;
   iv) can be used as a magnifying glass;
   v) can form a real image;
   vi) is used to correct short sight.

2 Two people discover during a conversation that one is short-sighted and the other is long-sighted. They discuss when they need to wear their spectacles, the type of lenses in their spectacles, and what causes their eye problems. What might they be saying to each other?

3 a) On the diagram below, which letter or letters show:

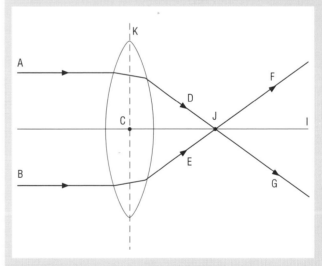

Figure 3.7.13

   i) the focal point, or principal focus;
   ii) the pole;
   iii) the focal length;
   iv) converging rays;
   v) diverging rays;
   vi) parallel rays?

   b) A 4 cm high object is placed 8 cm from a convex lens of focal length 3 cm. Draw a scale diagram to find the position and size of the image. Is the image magnified or diminished, upright or inverted, real or virtual?

3.8 Colour

Light from the sun and from very hot lamps is often referred to as 'white' light because it has no discernible colour to it. The 'white' light is, however, a mixture of colours which cannot be distinguished by the unaided eye. When white light is refracted through a prism, the colours separate so that they can be seen. Seven colours are usually distinguishable. These colours are known as the **spectrum** of white light. The effect of splitting up the white light into these colours is called **dispersion**.

Dispersion through a prism

When a beam of white light enters a glass prism it is refracted. It then passes through the glass, and is refracted again as it leaves the prism. Notice the direction in which the light is refracted at each surface.

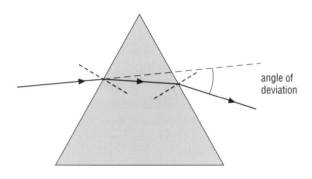

Figure 3.8.1 Deviation of light by a prism

At small angles of incidence, little dispersion is apparent. But above a certain angle of incidence the colours separate to such an extent that they are clearly seen on paper placed below the prism, or on a screen held vertically behind the prism (Figure 3.8.2).

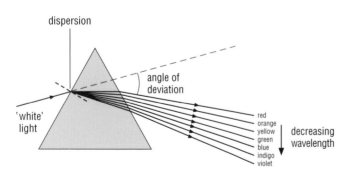

Figure 3.8.2 Dispersion by a prism. Note:
* The red light (with the longest wavelength) is deviated through the smallest angle
* The violet light (with the shortest wavelength) is deviated most
* Your eye has difficulty distinguishing between indigo and violet so they may appear as a purple band

Re-mixing the colours

The colours of the spectrum can be re-mixed by placing a convex lens in the path of the emerging beams. Where they overlap, they form white again.

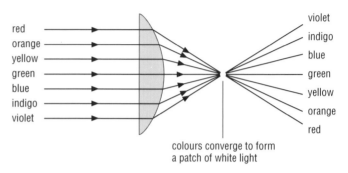

Figure 3.8.3 Re-mixing colours with a lens

Re-mixing can also be shown using a disc on which the seven colours are painted. When the disc is still, the colours are easily seen. When, however, the disc is spun at high speed, the colours merge to form white again. (In this case they merge on the retina because your eye 'holds' an image of each colour for a short time and the colours overlap.)

Note that mixing coloured light in this way is quite different to mixing paints.

Coloured materials

Paints, dyes and coloured materials contain chemicals called pigments. Different pigments reflect different colours. A material that contains only a red pigment reflects red light. It absorbs (soaks up) other colours, so they are not reflected.

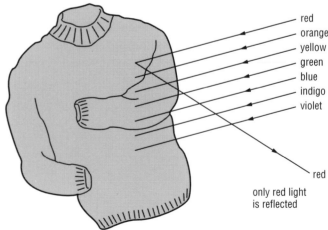

Figure 3.8.4 This jumper will look red

When white light strikes a jumper containing a pure red pigment, only the red part of the light is reflected. All other colours in the white light are absorbed (and converted to heat energy). We see a red jumper because only red light is reflected. If the material contained a pure green pigment, only the green part of the light would be reflected. We would see a green jumper. Most dyes and pigments are not pure. Each reflects a range of colours, producing the wide variety of colours we see.

Some foods also have their colours enhanced using chemical pigments to make them look more appealing.

Black and white

Some materials reflect all the constituent colours of white light. The colours enter your eye and recombine on the retina, forming a white image. The material therefore looks white.

If, on the other hand, the material absorbs all the colours, then no light is reflected and the eye cannot see anything – it perceives the absence of light as black.

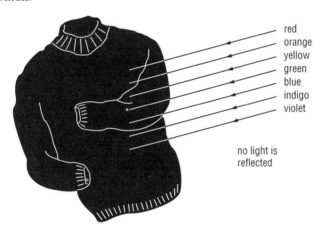

Figure 3.8.5 A black jumper absorbs all the incident colours

Coloured filters

When a coloured filter is placed in front of a white light source, only the light that has the same colour as the filter passes through. The other colours are absorbed by the filter.

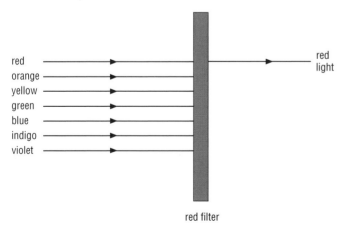

Figure 3.8.6 Red light emerges from a red filter; blue light would emerge from a blue filter

Primary and secondary colours

Red, green and blue are called **primary colours**. By mixing red, green and blue light in different ways you can make any other colour imaginable. If they overlap in equal intensities they produce white light.

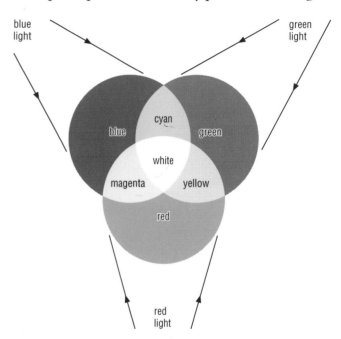

Figure 3.8.7 Combining the primary colours

Yellow, magenta and cyan, each produced by mixing two of the primary colours, are called **secondary colours**. If all three secondary colours overlap they again produce white light.

Each colour also has a 'complementary' colour. When complementary colours are mixed they also produce white light. The illustration above shows that yellow is 'opposite' to blue. They are complementary colours. Similarly red and cyan are complementary colours, as are green and magenta.

Quick Questions

1 a) What are the seven named colours of the spectrum of white light?
   b) What are the primary colours of light?
   c) What are the secondary colours of light?
2 a) Why is violet light refracted more than red light when it passes through a prism?
   b) Explain the meaning of the words *dispersion* and *refraction*.
3 Complete these colour 'equations':
   a) red + blue = ...
   b) green + red = ...
   c) red + cyan = ...
   d) magenta + green = ...
   e) red + blue + ... = white
   f) cyan + magenta + ... = white

3.9 Diffraction

Figure 3.9.1 When water waves pass between two piers they spread out

The photograph above is an example of **diffraction** – the 'spreading out' of waves after passing through or around some narrow gap or obstacle placed in their path. The effect is more evident with waves that have longer wavelengths: the longer the wavelength of the waves, the greater the angle through which the wave is diffracted.

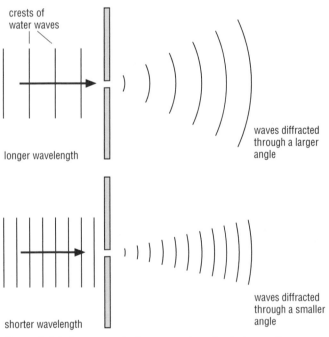

Figure 3.9.2 For any particular gap or obstacle, the longer the wavelength the greater the angle of diffraction

The same effect can be seen when a beam of light strikes a very narrow slit. The emerging beam spreads out, or is diffracted, beyond the edge of the slit. Once again, longer wavelengths are diffracted through a greater angle. The width of the slit needs to be about the same size, or smaller than, the wavelength of the light.

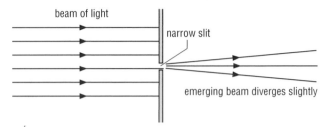

Figure 3.9.3 Diffraction of light at a narrow slit

In general, the narrower the gap relative to the wavelength, the greater the diffraction.

In both of the examples shown, the energy carried by the incoming wave becomes more spread out as the wave is diffracted.

Radio waves

Longer wavelength radio waves passing across high ground undergo diffraction at the edge of mountains. The waves 'spread out' as they pass across the edge of the mountain and some of their energy is transferred into the valley below.

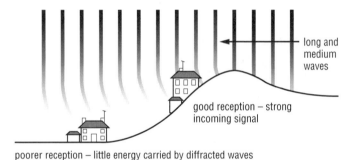

Figure 3.9.4 Longer wavelength radio transmissions are diffracted at 'obstacles'

Because the energy becomes increasingly spread out, the signal is stronger near the top. Lower down, the signal may be so weak that reception is still poor. Aerials are often placed high up (in the areas where signals are stronger) and relay the signal through cables to the homes below.

Longer wavelengths diffract through a greater angle than shorter wavelengths. It may therefore be possible for remote villages to receive one radio station but not another.

Diffraction of sound

All waves, longitudinal as well as transverse, can be diffracted. We can hear around corners because sound is diffracted. Most sounds have fairly long wavelengths, ranging from a few centimetres to a few metres. These long wavelengths diffract around the edges of buildings and doorways.

Waves and light

Water waves can be reflected and refracted as well as diffracted. Electromagnetic waves can also be reflected, refracted and diffracted. These similarities in their behaviour have lent support to the idea that light is transmitted in the form of a transverse wave. (Other situations, however, suggest that the behaviour of light is particulate - like a stream of particles.)

Reflection

When water waves strike a barrier placed in their path they are reflected in much the same way as light reflecting from a mirror, as shown in Figure 3.9.5.

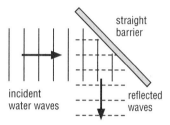

Figure 3.9.5a Water waves are reflected from the barrier at the same angle as they strike it

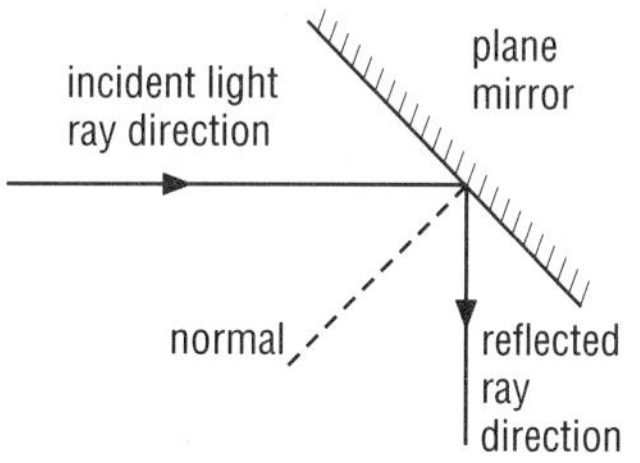

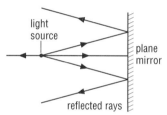

Figure 3.9.5b Light rays behave in the same way – the angle of incidence is equal to the angle of reflection

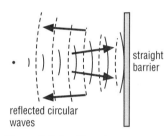

Figure 3.9.5c Diverging (circular) water waves diverge further after being reflected

Figure 3.9.5d Diverging light rays behave in the same way

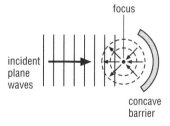

Figure 3.9.5e When parallel water waves strike a concave reflector they converge to a focus in front of the barrier and then diverge from it

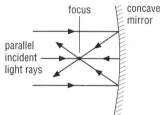

Figure 3.9.5f Similarly, when parallel light rays strike a concave mirror they reflect to a focus in front of the mirror and then diverge

Refraction

Water waves travel more slowly in shallow water than in deeper water. This can be shown by placing a flat perspex or glass plate in the bottom of a ripple tank to reduce the depth of the water in one section.

As the water waves pass into the shallow section, at any angle other than 90°, the direction of the waves changes and their wavelength decreases. The frequency of the wave does not change. These changes happen because the speed changes. As the waves slow down (entering the shallow water) they are 'bent' towards the normal. Their behaviour is exactly the same as that of light passing from one substance into another.

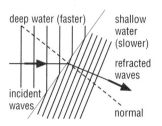

Figure 3.9.6a At a boundary where the speed of the water waves is reduced, the waves are refracted towards the normal

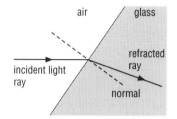

Figure 3.9.6b Light rays are refracted in the same way on entering a denser substance

If the object placed in the tank is convex, then the waves can be seen to behave in the same way as parallel rays of light striking a convex lens.

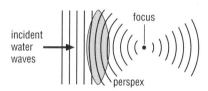

Figure 3.9.7a Parallel water waves converge to a focus after passing through a convex piece of perspex

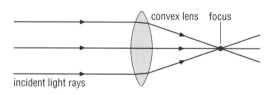

Figure 3.9.7b Parallel light behaves in a similar way on passing through a convex lens

Quick Questions

1 **a)** What is meant by the word *diffraction*?
   b) Give examples of where diffraction occurs for water, sound, light and radio waves.
2 Draw diagrams to show how plane water waves and rays of light behave when they strike
   a) a concave barrier or mirror;
   b) a plane (flat) barrier or mirror placed at 45° to the direction in which the waves/rays are travelling.
3 Why may a remote village obtain one radio station and not another despite them being sent from the same transmitter? How could a very tall aerial help to solve this problem?

3.10 Seismic waves

Earthquakes are caused deep within the earth as two adjacent tectonic plates slip across one another. The damage at the surface is caused by shock waves which travel through the earth. Some of the shock waves are longitudinal; others are transverse.

The structure of the earth

The earth is not a solid structure, but consists of a series of layers.

Much of this information has been obtained by studying the shock waves (seismic waves) following earthquakes. The shock waves are recorded by instruments called seismometers situated around the earth.

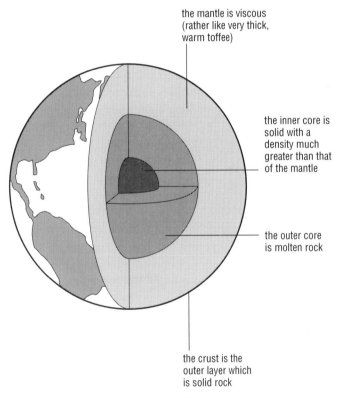

the mantle is viscous (rather like very thick, warm toffee)

the inner core is solid with a density much greater than that of the mantle

the outer core is molten rock

the crust is the outer layer which is solid rock

Figure 3.10.1 Layers within the earth's structure

Types of shock wave

There are two main types of shock wave, called P and S waves.

- P waves (primary waves) are longitudinal and can travel through solids and liquids. They travel faster through denser materials. As this type of wave reaches the surface, the rock is stretched and compressed (like the compressions and rarefactions created as sound waves pass through a material). They make the ground shudder up and down (Figure 3.10.2a).

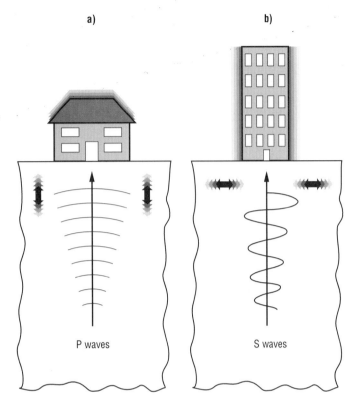

a)   b)

P waves   S waves

Figure 3.10.2 Ground tremors due to **a)** P waves (up and down) and **b)** S waves (side to side)

- S waves (secondary waves) are transverse waves which can only travel through solid materials. They cause the rock in the crust to shudder from side to side as they pass (Figure 3.10.2b). S waves are slower than P waves and so take longer to reach the surface. When they do they cause secondary tremors.

The time delay between receiving the P waves and the first S waves provides some indication of the distance from the focus of the earthquake (where it took place inside the earth) to the seismic stations which detect the shock waves. If, for example, the recording station was 1000 kilometres from the focus, there would be about 1 minute between receiving the P and S waves.

Inside the earth

As both P and S waves travel through the earth they are refracted due to changes in the density (Figure 3.10.3). Both types of wave travel faster through denser rocks. At the boundary between layers with quite different densities the refraction may be quite noticeable. Within any one layer, however, the density changes are more gradual, giving the impression that the waves are 'curving'.

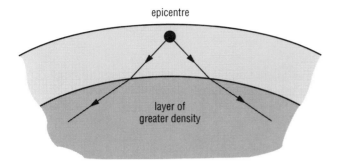

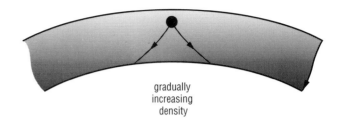

Figure 3.10.3 Refraction of seismic waves as they travel through rocks of different density

If the whole earth simply increased in density towards the centre, then both P and S waves would be refracted in a uniform way. In reality, what happens is that seismic stations on the opposite side of the earth to where the earthquake originated receive P waves but *no* S waves (Figure 3.10.4). This suggests that there must be some molten material in the inner earth which absorbs the S waves.

Surrounding this area is a 'shadow zone' where only some very weak P waves are received. This happens because the P waves from the earthquake are refracted inwards as they enter the outer core. The S waves are absorbed by this liquid layer. The weak P waves are due to 'glancing' reflections from the surface of the inner core.

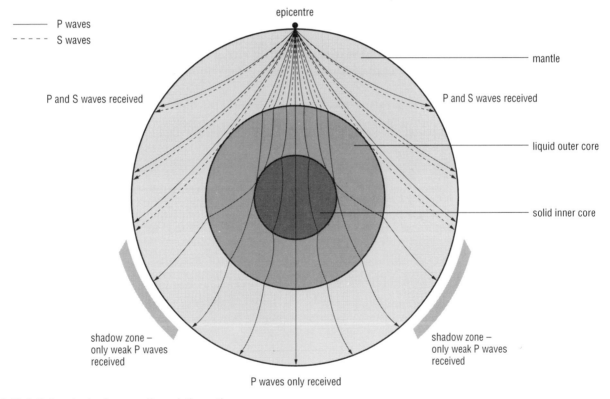

Figure 3.10.4 Paths of seismic waves through the earth

Quick Questions

1 Name the four main layers we would see on a section through the earth. Which of the layers are solid?

2 There are two types of seismic (shock) wave, P and S.
 a) Why are they called P and S?
 b) Which is longitudinal and which is transverse?
 c) Explain the difference between longitudinal and transverse waves.

3 P and S waves travel at different speeds.
 a) Which arrives at the earth's surface first?
 b) What useful information can be calculated from measuring the time delay between the arrival of P and S waves?

4 How can the study of seismic waves lead to the conclusion that part of the core of the earth is liquid?

Section Three: Examination Practice Questions

Foundation Level

1. (a) A guitar string is plucked. The sound travels through the air to the player's ear. Choose the correct word or number in the brackets to complete the following passage:

A sound wave is a (*transverse or longitudinal*) wave and travels at about (*340 or 3400*) m/s. As the wave gets further from the guitar its amplitude will (*decrease or increase*). The frequency of the wave will (*increase or decrease or be constant*) as it travels through the air. The wave consists of a series of compressions and (*expansions or rarefactions*). The sound wave transfers (*energy or force*) but the air (*does or does not*) move from the string to the ear.

(b) You are watching a firework display. As the firework explodes it produces light and sound at the same time.
    (i) Explain why you see the flash from the firework before hearing the 'bang'.
    (ii) The time between seeing the flash and hearing the bang is 0.4 s. If the velocity of sound is 340 m/s, how far are you from the firework?

(c) Many ships are fitted with an 'echo-sounder' which gives them information about the depth of the water. The echo-sounder measures the time it takes for a pulse of sound to travel from the ship to the sea bed and back again.
    If the speed of sound in water is 1500 m/s and it takes 0.2 s for a sound to return to the ship, calculate the depth of water beneath the ship.

(d) Ultrasound scanning is used to monitor the development of unborn babies.
    (i) Why can we not hear ultrasound?
    (ii) What happens to the ultrasound waves when they strike the baby's body?
    (iii) Why is ultrasound used instead of X-rays for monitoring unborn babies?

2. The diagram below shows a narrow beam of white light passing through a prism.

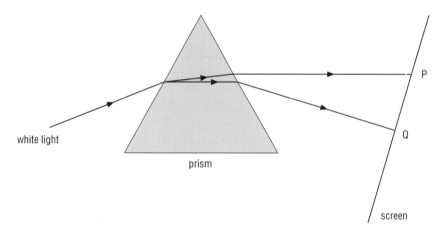

(a) (i) What is the name given to the separation of the colours of white light as it enters the prism?
    (ii) What colour is P likely to be?
    (iii) What colour is Q likely to be?
    (iv) Name the other colours between P and Q.
(b) (i) Where on the screen would a thermometer with a blackened bulb show the greatest reading?
    (ii) What is the thermometer bulb detecting?
    (iii) Why is the thermometer bulb painted black?

3. The following are all forms of electromagnetic radiation:

microwaves   infra-red   ultra-violet   X-rays   gamma waves

(a) Which is emitted by the tubes in sun beds?
(b) Which is used to 'photograph' bones in the body?
(c) Which **two** are used to cook food?

The diagram below shows part of the electromagnetic spectrum.

gamma waves	X-rays	A	light	B	C	radio waves

(d) Which types of wave would be found in the sections A, B and C?

(e) Which group of waves has the longest wavelength?

(f) Which group of waves has the highest frequency?

4. The diagram below shows a transverse wave, travelling from left to right across the paper.

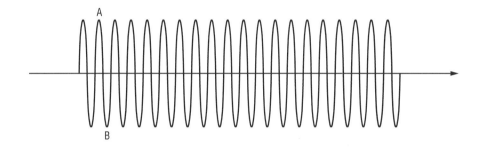

(a) In which direction would the wave be oscillating?

(b) Which letter indicates a peak or crest?

(c) Which letter indicates a trough?

(d) What is the wavelength of the wave (in cm)?

(e) What is the amplitude of the wave (in cm)?

(f) How many complete cycles (waves) are shown on the wave in the diagram?

(g) Draw a second wave with the same amplitude as the one shown above but with a lower frequency.

(h) Draw a third wave with the same wavelength as the one shown above but with a smaller amplitude.

(i) The frequency of the wave shown is 200 Hz. What unit does the abbreviation Hz represent?

(j) How many cycles of the wave will pass any point in 1 second?

(k) If the frequency of the wave was to increase to 300 Hz, what would happen to the wavelength of the wave?

5. The types of radiation listed below are directed (one at a time) towards a hole in a thick piece of lead.

visible light   X-rays   radio waves   gamma waves   infra-red waves   ultra-violet waves

Use the key below to identify each type of wave as it passes through the hole.

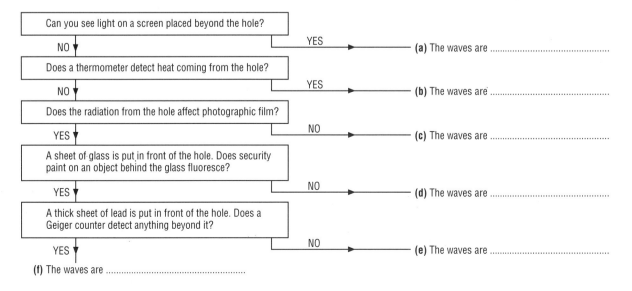

6. Shock waves pass through the earth during earthquakes.
   (a) One type of wave produces vertical vibrations at the surface. What type of wave must this be – transverse or longitudinal?
   (b) A second type causes a rolling (wave) motion across the surface. Will this be a transverse or a longitudinal wave?

7. (a) A dentist uses a plane (flat) mirror to look at a patient's teeth.
      Copy this diagram and draw a single ray of light showing how the dentist is able to see the back of the teeth. Draw an arrow showing the direction in which the ray will travel.

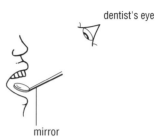

   (b) The dentist changes the mirror for a concave mirror. How will that affect what he sees?
   (c) This diagram shows a periscope being used to look over a wall.
      Copy the diagram and
      (i) draw in the mirrors, showing the angles at which they must be placed;
      (ii) complete the path of the ray of light through to the eye.

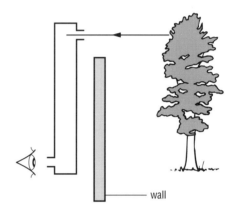

   (d) The diagram below shows two rays of light leaving an object, O, and travelling towards a plane mirror.

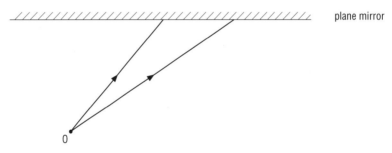

      Copy the diagram and
      (i) draw in the normals where the rays hit the mirror;
      (ii) draw in the reflected rays;
      (iii) use the reflected rays to find the position of the image and label it with the letter I.
   (e) The two diagrams below show light striking curved mirrors.

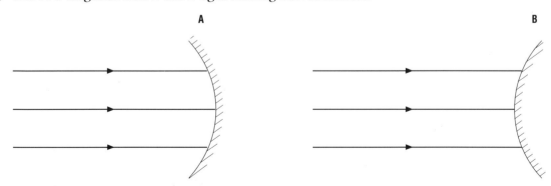

      (i) Which is a concave and which is a convex mirror?
      (ii) Copy each diagram and draw the rays after reflection.
      (iii) Which mirror is a converging mirror? Explain your answer.
      (iv) One of the mirrors might be used as a shop security mirror. Which one would be best? Why?

8. (a) This diagram shows a ray of light passing through a glass block.
Which letters indicate:
   (i)   the incident ray;
   (ii) the refracted ray;
   (iii) the emergent ray;
   (iv) the angle of incidence;
   (v) the angle of refraction;
   (vi) the normal?

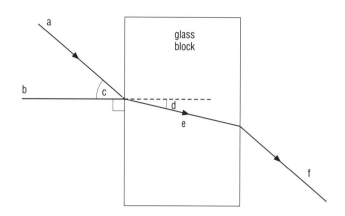

  (b) The diagrams below show light incident on two different lenses.

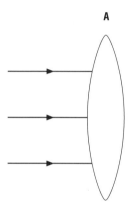
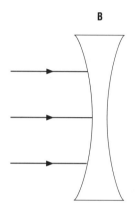

   (i)   Which is a concave and which is a convex lens?
   (ii) Copy each diagram, draw on the refracted rays and label the principal focus.
   (iii) Which lens is a converging lens? Explain your answer.
   (iv) Which type of lens is used as a magnifying glass?

  (c) By just looking at a selection of convex lenses, how could you tell which would refract light through the greatest angle (have the shortest focal length)?

  (d) Consider the three diagrams below.

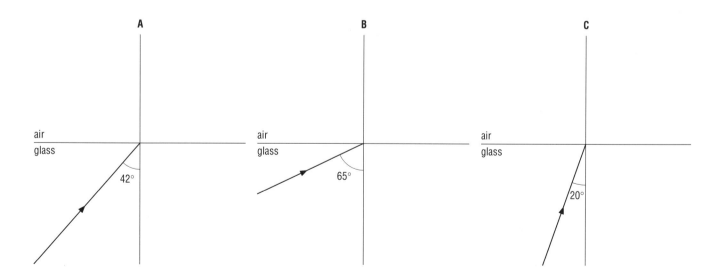

   The critical angle for glass is 42°.
   (i)   In which case, A, B or C, will total internal reflection take place?
   (ii) Copy the diagram that you stated as your answer in (i) and label the normal, the angle of incidence and the angle of reflection.

(e) The diagram below shows a ray of light entering an optical fibre.

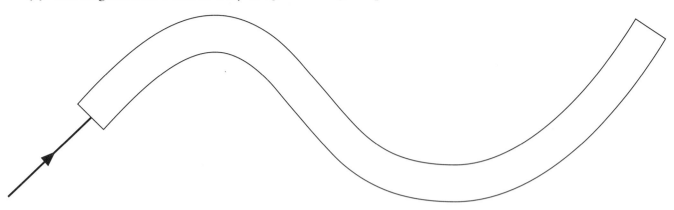

Copy the diagram and continue the path of the light ray through the optical fibre.

9. **(a)** Sounds are made by vibrating objects. The diagram below shows the effect on the molecules in the air as the sound from a vibrating object travels through the air. Each dot represents a molecule.

   (i) Draw a similar diagram to show molecules in the air when there is **no** sound. [1]
   (ii) If a huge meteor crashed into the Moon we would **not** hear the sound of the collision on Earth. Explain why. [2]

   (b) During a thunderstorm you see the flash of lightning before you hear the clap of thunder which was produced at the same time.
   (i) Why is this?
   (ii) Sound travels at a speed of 340 metres per second (m/s) in air. How far away does a clap of thunder occur if you hear it 5 seconds after you see its flash of lightning?
   Include in your answer the equation you are going to use. Show clearly how you get to your final answer and give the unit. [3]

   (SEG, Foundation, 1998 Specimen)

10. Modern ships are able to communicate with each other by radio signals. Unfortunately the radio in the ship **X** has broken down.

ship **X**   ship **Y**

1000 m

   (a) Copy and complete the table below to show **two** ways in which ship **X** could communicate with ship **Y**. For each method of communication state which one of our senses would be involved. [4]

Method of communication	Sense involved

   (b) The two ships moved 40 km apart. Explain why the ships would now **not** be able to communicate. [2]

(c) A dinghy is launched from ship **X** to pick up an object seen floating in the sea. It rows steadily away from the ship, stops for a short while to pick up the object, then rows back again.

(i) Which of these distance–time graphs describes what has happened? [1]

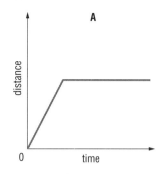

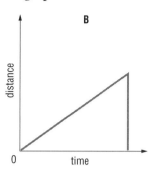

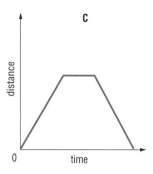

The dinghy rows from the ship to the object at a steady speed.

(ii) State the formula which links speed, journey time and distance travelled. [1]

(iii) The dinghy moves at a speed of 1.5 m/s and it takes 80 seconds to reach the floating object. Calculate the distance of the object from the ship. [2]

(MEG, Foundation, 1998 Specimen)

Higher Level

1. (a) Ultra-violet, visible and infra-red are three types of electromagnetic waves emitted by the sun. Visible light and some shorter wavelength infra-red radiation can pass through glass. Ultra-violet and longer wavelength infra-red radiation are absorbed by the glass. Short wavelength radiation is emitted by *very* hot bodies like the sun. Longer wavelength radiation is emitted by cooler bodies like most objects on earth.

The diagram shows radiation incident on a greenhouse.

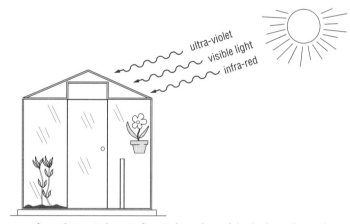

(i) What will happen to the ultra-violet, infra-red and visible light when they meet the glass?

(ii) Why does the soil in the greenhouse become warmer?

(iii) What type of radiation is re-emitted from the soil and how does it differ from the radiation from the sun?

(iv) What happens to the radiation emitted by the soil when it strikes the greenhouse glass?

(v) How do your answers to the above questions explain why a greenhouse stays warm for several hours during the night?

(vi) After several hours the temperature in the greenhouse will fall significantly. How is most heat lost from the greenhouse?

(vii) Why could a gardener not get a sun tan working in his greenhouse?

(b) Long wave radio waves can be received several thousand miles from the transmitter, even though the curvature of the earth prevents 'line of sight' transmission. Explain how this is possible.

(c) A radio station transmits radio waves at a frequency of 80 MHz.

(i) What is meant by the frequency of the radio waves?

(ii) Describe three similarities between radio waves and other parts of the electromagnetic spectrum.

(iii) If the velocity of electromagnetic waves is 300 000 km/s, calculate the wavelength of these radio waves.

2. (a) The diagram below shows plane water waves of frequency 3 Hz passing from a region of deeper water into a shallower region.

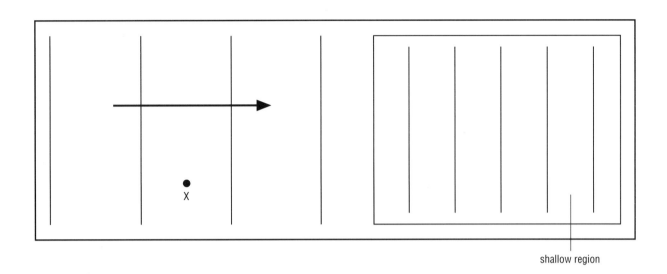

shallow region

    (i)   How many waves are being produced each second?
    (ii) Describe the motion of a tiny float placed at point X.
    (iii) What happens to the frequency of the waves as they pass into the shallow water?
    (iv) What has happened to the wavelength of the waves as they pass into the shallow region?
    (v) Using your answers to parts (iii) and (iv), state and explain what has happened to the speed of the waves as they pass into the shallow region.
    (vi) If the wavelength in the shallow water is 2 cm, calculate the speed of the waves.

(b) This diagram shows a series of plane waves approaching a gap between two barriers.

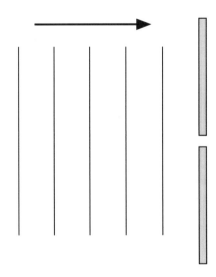

    (i)   Use a ruler to measure the wavelength of the waves.
    (ii) Describe what will happen to the waves as they pass through the gap and draw a diagram to show this.
    (iii) What is the name of the phenomenon shown on your diagram in part (ii)?
    (iv) What would you notice if the gap was made larger?
    (v) Why is this effect more noticeable with sound and less noticeable with light?
    (vi) Find the frequency of a light wave if it has a wavelength of 6×10^{-7} m, knowing the velocity of light to be 3×10^8 m/s.

3. (a) The diagram below represents a transverse wave travelling along a rope.

    (i)   What is the wavelength of the wave? [1]

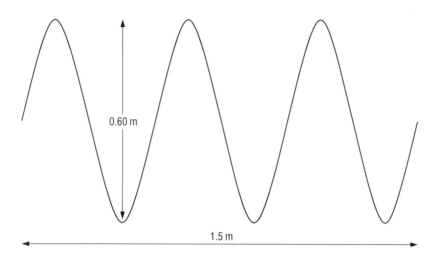

    (ii) What is the amplitude of the wave? [1]

(b) Microwaves and infra-red waves are both used for cooking food. Microwaves can penetrate food to a depth of about 4 cm. Infra-red waves are absorbed at the surface of the food.

    (i)   Name the process by which heat is transferred to the middle of the food when it is grilled using infra-red waves. Explain how this transfer takes place. [2]

    (ii) Frozen bread can be defrosted using microwaves. When infra-red waves are used to defrost bread the surface is burnt and the rest of the bread remains frozen.

          Explain why microwaves can be used to defrost bread but infra-red waves cannot. [3]

    (iii) Explain why a potato wrapped in aluminium foil can be cooked in a gas or electric oven but not in a microwave oven. [2]

(London, Higher, 1998 Specimen)

4. An earthquake is caused by the movement of rocks below the Earth's surface. The rock movement produces an earthquake wave.

The diagram shows a record of the shaking produced by an earthquake wave.

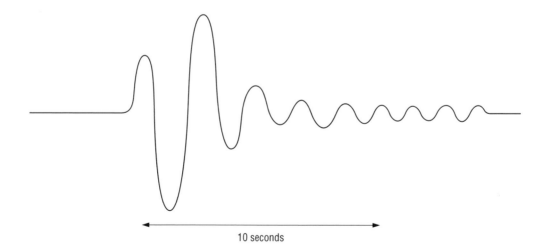

10 seconds

  (a) What is the frequency of the earthquake wave recorded in the diagram? Show how you do your calculation. [2]

  (b) Earthquake waves travel at a speed of 8 km/s. What is the average wavelength of the earthquake wave recorded in the diagram? Show how you do your calculation. [2]

(MEG, Higher, 1994 Specimen, part)

4.1 The universe and the solar system

The universe is a vast space which is continually expanding. Within the universe are regions where billions of stars have grouped together, forming **galaxies**. The galaxies are fairly evenly distributed throughout the universe. Although the galaxies are vast they are billions of miles apart and the space between them is much bigger than the galaxies themselves. The space between them is largely empty.

Each star in a galaxy is a sun. Inside each sun, nuclear reactions release energy which makes the star 'shine'. One of the suns, inside a galaxy called the Milky Way, is our own sun. It looks different to all the other stars we see because it is very much closer.

The force of gravity between the sun and the planets keeps them in orbit around the sun. The size of the gravity force is inversely proportional to the square of the distance of the planet from the sun (i.e. proportional to $1/d^2$). As the distance is doubled, the force becomes one quarter of its original value.

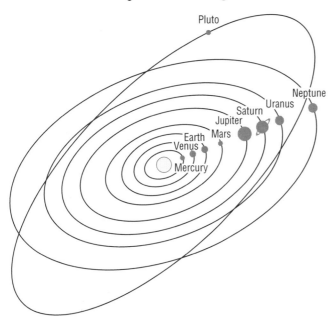

Figure 4.1.1 The planets in our solar system (not to scale)

Note that:

- The orbits of all the planets are elliptical (squashed circles).
- Radiation from the sun warms the earth, maintaining just the right temperatures for life to exist.
- The average surface temperature of a planet decreases with distance from the sun. Venus is an exception to this rule. A thick blanket of gases surrounds the planet, effectively trapping heat close to the surface. As a result its surface temperature is higher than would be expected.

- The time taken for the planets to orbit the sun also depends on the distance from the sun. The further a planet is from the sun, the longer it takes to orbit the sun. The time taken for a planet to orbit the sun is what we call one year.
- Between the orbits of Mars and Jupiter is a region known as the **asteroid belt**. The asteroid belt contains rock debris (varying in size up to several metres across).

Day and night

Each planet also spins on its own axis as it orbits the sun. The earth, for example, spins once every 24 hours. This spinning motion causes each region on earth to experience periods of day and night.

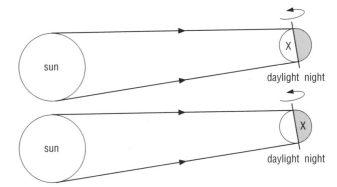

Figure 4.1.2 The earth spins once every 24 hours; at X on the surface of the earth, midday is followed 12 hours later by midnight

This period of time (the 24 hours taken for the earth to spin once on its own axis) is what we call one day.

The seasons

The earth's axis is tilted, that is it is not perpendicular to the plane of its orbit around the sun. Consequently, throughout each year, sometimes the northern hemisphere is tilted towards the sun. At other times, the northern hemisphere is tilted away from the sun. This helps us to understand why we have seasons, and why the equator does not experience similar changes throughout the year.

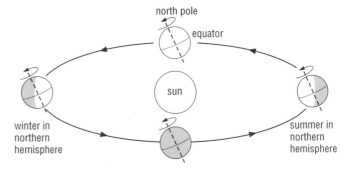

Figure 4.1.3 Explaining the seasons

When the northern hemisphere is tilted towards the sun, the period of daylight is longer and, because more radiation is absorbed at the angles at which it strikes the earth, the earth is warmer. As the northern hemisphere begins to tilt away from the sun, the days become shorter and the surface cools – we are moving from summer, through autumn, into winter.

The apparent movement of the stars

The stars in the night sky appear to move across the sky during each night, but in reality they remain in the same place (in relation to the rest of the galaxy). It is the earth's spinning motion that gives the impression that the stars are moving.

One star, the pole star (Polaris), appears to stay in the same position because it is directly above the pole of the earth.

The moon

The moon is a natural satellite of the earth – it orbits the earth in just under 28 days, held by the gravity force between the two bodies.

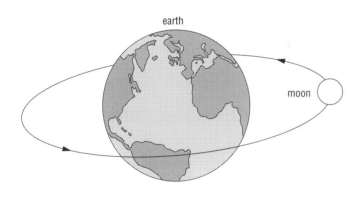

Figure 4.1.4 The moon's orbit

The moon does not emit its own light – it reflects light from the sun. Some of the other planets also have moons. Jupiter, in fact, has 16 moons.

Comets

Comets are bodies that go around the sun in highly elliptical orbits (Figure 4.1.5), and consist largely of frozen gases and dust.

As a comet approaches the sun, the frozen gases begin to release dust, gas and vapour such as water and ammonia. The gases and dust particles form the visible tail of the comet which streams out, possibly for thousands of kilometres, in a direction away from the sun (because of the action of the solar wind). Like the planets, comets do not emit their own light, but reflect light from the sun.

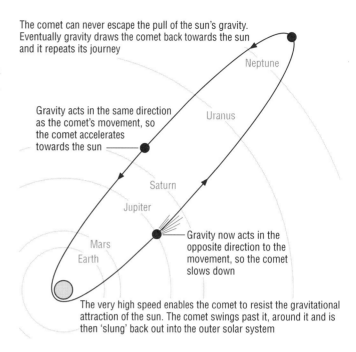

The comet can never escape the pull of the sun's gravity. Eventually gravity draws the comet back towards the sun and it repeats its journey

Gravity acts in the same direction as the comet's movement, so the comet accelerates towards the sun

Gravity now acts in the opposite direction to the movement, so the comet slows down

The very high speed enables the comet to resist the gravitational attraction of the sun. The comet swings past it, around it and is then 'slung' back out into the outer solar system

Figure 4.1.5 The path of a comet

The light year

Because the distances between galaxies, and through the universe, are so vast, they are described in units called 'light years'. One light year is the distance travelled by light in one year. Its equivalent distance can be calculated, knowing that the speed of light is 300 000 000 m/s:

In one year ($365\frac{1}{4}$ days) there are
$(60 \times 60 \times 24 \times 365.25)$ seconds = 31 557 600 seconds

Light travels 300 000 000 metres in one second, so the distance travelled in one year must be 31 557 600 × 300 000 000 = 9 467 280 000 000 000 metres, or roughly 9.47 million million kilometres – a fair journey!

Quick Questions

1 Name the planets, in order of their increasing distance from the sun.
2 Draw a series of pictures showing how the earth experiences periods of day and night.
3 How long does it take for:
   a) the earth to orbit the sun?
   b) the moon to orbit the earth?
   c) the earth to spin once on its own axis?
4 Complete the following paragraph by filling in the spaces.

   The earth and the other planets orbit the sun, following .... orbits. The further a planet is from the sun, the .... its orbit time and the .... its temperature.
   Comets are made up of .... and ....
   Their orbits are not circular but are highly ....

4.2 Origin of the universe

No one really knows exactly how big the universe is, or how it was formed. What we can be sure of is that gravitational forces have had a significant influence on what has happened, and will continue to influence what will happen in future. One theory is that everything started as an extremely hot mixture of basic particles and electromagnetic radiation.

At some time (probably between 15 000 and 20 000 million years ago) this mixture exploded (in what is known as the 'big bang'). For millions of years the debris spread out, cooling all the time. As it expanded and cooled, molecules of hydrogen were formed.

Massive clouds of hydrogen gas formed in some places. Gravitational forces drew the particles closer and closer together, and the clouds contracted and got hotter. Some of the hydrogen began to change into helium, releasing energy in the process. These concentrated regions of matter were the early stars.

Gravitational forces then drew neighbouring stars together, forming huge galaxies (regions where millions of stars are gathered together).

As the original hydrogen in a star begins to run out, some stars expand and explode, becoming **supernovae**. These explosions take place many millions of miles from earth, but are so impressive that they can be seen with the aid of telescopes. As a result of these explosions, atoms, including those of the heaviest elements, are scattered millions of miles through space. Some will form new stars as they are drawn together by gravity. The rest will drift through the galaxies as 'dust' and ice.

The fact that the inner planets of our solar system contain atoms of these heavy elements, and that the sun contains nuclei of the same elements, suggests that the solar system may have formed from one of these explosions millions of years ago.

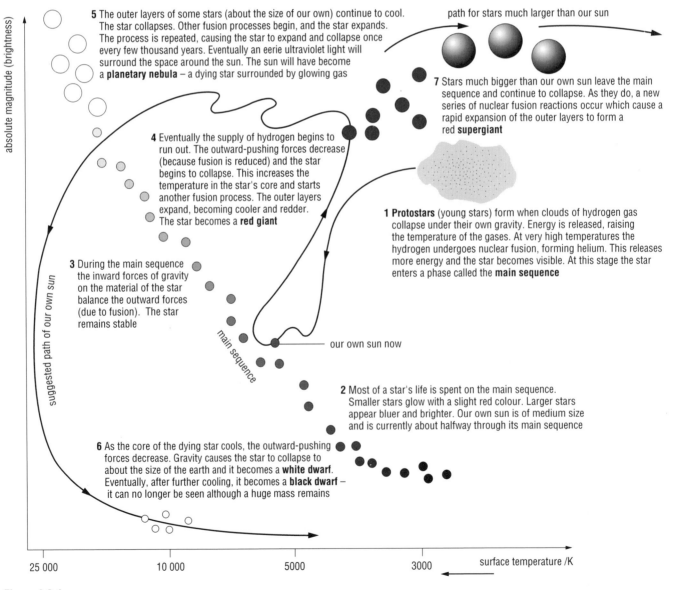

5 The outer layers of some stars (about the size of our own) continue to cool. The star collapses. Other fusion processes begin, and the star expands. The process is repeated, causing the star to expand and collapse once every few thousand years. Eventually an eerie ultraviolet light will surround the space around the sun. The sun will have become a **planetary nebula** – a dying star surrounded by glowing gas

path for stars much larger than our sun

7 Stars much bigger than our own sun leave the main sequence and continue to collapse. As they do, a new series of nuclear fusion reactions occur which cause a rapid expansion of the outer layers to form a red **supergiant**

4 Eventually the supply of hydrogen begins to run out. The outward-pushing forces decrease (because fusion is reduced) and the star begins to collapse. This increases the temperature in the star's core and starts another fusion process. The outer layers expand, becoming cooler and redder. The star becomes a **red giant**

1 Protostars (young stars) form when clouds of hydrogen gas collapse under their own gravity. Energy is released, raising the temperature of the gases. At very high temperatures the hydrogen undergoes nuclear fusion, forming helium. This releases more energy and the star becomes visible. At this stage the star enters a phase called the **main sequence**

3 During the main sequence the inward forces of gravity on the material of the star balance the outward forces (due to fusion). The star remains stable

main sequence

our own sun now

2 Most of a star's life is spent on the main sequence. Smaller stars glow with a slight red colour. Larger stars appear bluer and brighter. Our own sun is of medium size and is currently about halfway through its main sequence

6 As the core of the dying star cools, the outward-pushing forces decrease. Gravity causes the star to collapse to about the size of the earth and it becomes a **white dwarf**. Eventually, after further cooling, it becomes a **black dwarf** – it can no longer be seen although a huge mass remains

absolute magnitude (brightness)

suggested path of our own sun

25 000   10 000   5000   3000   surface temperature /K

Figure 4.2.1

An expanding universe

If the universe began at the time of the big bang, we would expect that:

- Debris from the explosion would be distributed fairly evenly throughout space.
- The furthest particles (from the site of the explosion) would be moving apart faster.
- Therefore all galaxies would be moving apart and those galaxies furthest from the site of the explosion would be moving apart faster.

There is evidence to support each of the expectations described above, notably the evidence first obtained by an American astronomer, Edwin Hubble. Studying the spectra of light from distant galaxies, Hubble noted that some of the lines in the spectra (indicating the presence of particular elements) were not where they should be compared with our own sun's spectrum, but were shifted towards the red end of the spectrum. This phenomenon is now known as 'red shift'. Hubble also noted that galaxies further from the earth showed a greater red shift. The red shift is due to the movement of the galaxies in relation to the earth. The faster a galaxy is moving in relation to the earth, the greater the increase in the wavelength of the radiation received, i.e. the greater the red shift. What Hubble had found out was that the galaxies are moving further apart all of the time, and that those which are most distant are moving further apart faster – tending to support the theory of the big bang.

The life and death of a star

When we look into the sky at night we see millions of stars. During their lifetime they change – sometimes in spectacular fashion – as they follow a sequence which takes them through phases such as 'red giant' or 'white dwarf' (Figure 4.2.1).

8 Eventually the supergiant reaches the stage where fusion cannot take place. The (now unbalanced) gravitational forces cause a rapid contraction. The star heats again and the outer layers explode in a huge flash of light – a **supernova**. The core, in most cases forms a **neutron star**. The most massive stars, however, leave behind an extremely dense core which collapses to form a **black hole**

Quick Questions

1 **a)** What is meant by the 'big bang'?
   b) When did the 'big bang' occur?
2 How do we know the universe is still expanding?
3 List the sequence a star goes through when progressing from:
   a) a small protostar to a black dwarf;
   b) a large protostar to a black hole.
4 Most of the stars in the night sky appear to be in the 'main sequence' stage, but in reality they may have progressed beyond it to a later stage. How can you explain this?

Section Four: Examination Practice Questions

1. (a) Sort the following in order of their size, starting with the smallest:

solar system   earth   universe   Jupiter   galaxy   sun   our moon

(b) (i)   What is the name of the force that holds the planets in orbit around the sun?

(ii)   Explain why we are able to see the planets even though they do not give off their own light.

(iii)   Describe one difference between a star and a planet.

(c) The table gives information about four planets which orbit a star called Sttaw.

(i)   Draw a line graph of *distance from Sttaw* against *time to orbit Sttaw*.

(ii)   A new planet was discovered 400 million km from Sttaw. Use your graph to find out how long it takes to orbit Sttaw.

(iii)   On which of the planets might humans be able to survive? Explain your answer.

(iv)   What else would humans need to survive on this planet?

Planet	Surface temperature (°C)	Diameter compared to earth (earth = 1)	Distance from Sttaw (millions of km)	Time to orbit Sttaw (in earth years)
A	−110	0.5	600	8.5
B	−240	10.0	800	12.0
C	18	1.3	160	1.1
D	70	1.0	250	2.6

2. (a) Earth spins on its axis.

(i)   How long does it take the Earth to spin once on its axis? Choose from:

1 day   1 week   1 month   1 year   [1]

(ii)   Look at the diagram. Each day in Britain part of the day is night time and part is day time. Explain why.   [2]

(b) Earth orbits the Sun.

(i)   What is the Sun? Choose from:

galaxy   nebula   planet   satellite   star [1]

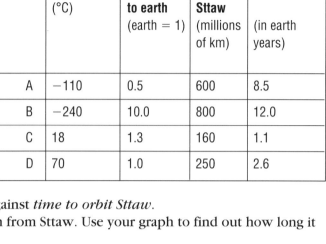

(ii)   The Sun's energy comes from nuclear reactions. What happens to release this energy?   [1]

(c) There are different ways of studying the planet Mars.

(i)   Mike looks at Mars using a telescope. He can see Mars better using the telescope. Explain why.[2]

(ii)   Some scientists use satellites to study Mars. The satellites are in orbit around Earth. A force holds a satellite in orbit. Write down the name of the force.   [1]

(iii)   Many satellites are not used to study space. Write down **one** other use for satellites.   [1]

(MEG, Foundation, 1997, part)

3. (a) Jupiter is the largest planet in the Solar System. It is thought to consist mainly of hydrogen and helium. Explain why the density of Jupiter is less than that of the Earth.   [2]

(b) The table compares some features of Jupiter and Earth.

(i)   Which feature suggests that the core of Jupiter contains iron?   [1]

(ii)   Explain why Jupiter takes much longer than the Earth to orbit the Sun.   [3]

(iii)   Suggest why the temperature at the surface of Jupiter is less than that at the surface of the Earth.   [2]

Feature	Earth	Jupiter
average surface temperature in °C	20	−120
magnetic field	strong	very strong
density in g/cm³	5.5	1.3
time to rotate on axis in hours	24	10
time to orbit the Sun in years	1	11.9
mean orbital speed in millions of km/hour	0.11	0.05
surface gravitational field strength in N/kg	10	23

(c) Jupiter has several moons. One of them, Io, is about the size of the Earth's moon. There is volcanic activity on Io. Conditions on Io differ from those on the Earth's moon. Suggest **two** differences. [2]

(d) A probe entered Jupiter's atmosphere. The probe was fitted with a parachute to reduce its speed as it entered the atmosphere.

The probe sent back information about the atmosphere for over an hour before it was destroyed.
   (i) Suggest why the probe was destroyed as it fell through the atmosphere. [1]
   (ii) Explain how the parachute prolonged the 'life' of the probe as it fell. [2]

(London, Foundation, 1998 Specimen)

Higher Level

1. (a) Young stars form in interstellar space when large clouds of gas collapse under their own gravity. As they do so, the temperature rises, and hydrogen begins to change into helium. This is accompanied by a huge release of energy. What changes does that produce in the developing star?

   (b) What is the name of the reaction in which hydrogen molecules combine to form helium?

   (c) The release of energy inside the sun produces an outward force on the particles of gas. Gravity produces an inward force on the particles. Our own sun is in the main sequence stage of its life cycle. Throughout the main sequence its size will be stable. What does that tell you about the sizes of the forces involved?

   (d) Eventually our sun's supply of hydrogen will begin to run out and the outer layers will begin to cool. The outward pushing forces will decrease. What do you predict will happen to the sun at that stage?

   (e) When analysed, radiation from distant galaxies is found to show that some spectral lines are not where they would be, but are found further towards the red region of the spectrum. What deduction does this 'red shift' enable us to make about the galaxies?

   (f) The amount of matter in the universe will determine what will eventually happen. One theory is that the universe will continue to expand. State **two** other possibilities.

2. This question is about space.
   (a) Look at the list: galaxy   planet   star   universe
      (i) Which one is the smallest? Choose from the list. [1]
      (ii) Which one is the largest? Choose from the list. [1]

   (b) In 1969 people went to our moon. We have not sent people to Pluto. One reason is that Pluto is a very cold planet. Write down another reason. [1]

   (c) Stars evolve over a large time scale. Look at the following statements about stars like our Sun.
      A   the star collapses and becomes a white dwarf
      B   the star spends a short time as a red giant
      C   parts of a large dust and gas cloud move closer together
      D   the star generates energy for a long time
      Write down the correct order for the life of a star. Choose from **A**, **B**, **C**, **D**. [1]

(MEG, Higher, 1998 Specimen)

3. In recent years there has been a rapid growth in the number and use of mobile telephones. Mobile telephones use radio waves for transmitting speech. They have to use frequencies that are not already used by radio stations.

   (a) Radio waves used for mobile telephones have a typical wavelength of 0.30 m. Calculate the frequency of these radio waves, given that their speed is 3.0×10^8 m/s. [3]

   (b) Mobile telephones can be used to communicate throughout Europe using satellite links. A set of three satellites, each in an elliptical orbit, is used to give 24 hour coverage. The diagram shows the orbit of one of these satellites.
      (i)   Copy the diagram and draw an arrow to show the gravitational force acting on the satellite. [1]
      (ii) Describe how the size of this force changes as the satellite makes one orbit of the Earth. [2]
      (iii) Place an **M** on your diagram where the acceleration of the satellite is greatest. [1]

(London, Higher, 1998 Specimen, part)

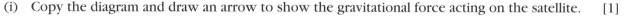

5.1 Work and energy

Work

Work is done:

- when a force causes some change in the motion or position of an object;
- by one object on another.

Consider a crane lifting a girder. Work is done by the crane.

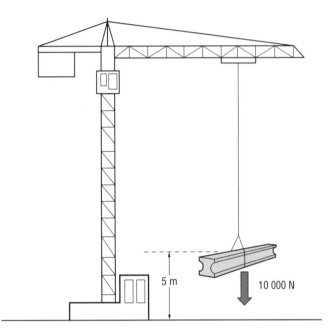

Figure 5.1.1 The crane does work on the girder

The amount of work done in any situation can be calculated using the equation:

> work done = force × distance moved
> (joules)   (newtons)   (metres)

In this example, the force needed to raise the girder is 10 000 N and the girder is raised through a distance of 5 metres.

So, work done by the crane = force (N) × distance (m)
= 10 000 × 5
= 50 000 joules (or 50 kJ)

If the winch is stopped and the girder is held steady then, even though there is still a force acting on the girder (supporting it against gravity), no work is being done by the crane.

Energy

Whenever work is done, energy is transferred. The energy may be changed into a different form, or it may be transferred to other places, as shown by the examples in Figure 5.1.2.

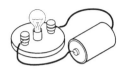

Figure 5.1.2a Here the battery does work driving current through the circuit. Chemicals in the battery release chemical energy which is then transferred to the circuit as electrical energy

Figure 5.1.2b In this example a moving roller boot will exert a force on the second, stationary roller boot, which makes it begin to move. The first boot must therefore do work on the second and some kinetic energy will be transferred

Figure 5.1.2c When released the stretched rubber band does work on the ball. The rubber band can be considered to be a store of potential energy. When the band is released energy will be transferred to the ball as kinetic energy

There are many forms of energy, such as:

- **Kinetic energy** – transferred to or from moving objects when their speed changes.
- **Gravitational potential energy** – stored in a raised object, giving it the potential to do work on some other object.
- **Thermal** (or **heat**) **energy** – transferred when temperature changes occur.
- **Sound energy** – transferred when sound travels from one place to another.
- **Electrical energy** – transferred when an electric current is generated or brings about some change.

Work and energy are measured in units called **joules** (J). One joule is a relatively small amount of energy. A larger unit, the kilojoule (kJ), is often used. 1 kilojoule represents the same amount of energy as 1000 joules. Note that the units of energy are the same as the units of work.

Energy transformation

Most of the things we use transform energy (change it from one form into another). The energy changes are often shown in the form of flow diagrams, such as those below.

In a loudspeaker: electrical energy ⟶ sound energy

In a lamp: electrical energy ⟶ heat energy
                             ⟶ light energy

Energy is conserved

Throughout any process in which energy is transferred, energy is never lost – the total amount of energy in the system remains constant. Consider, for example, the energy changes that take place when an electric kettle is used.

100 joules of electrical energy

100 joules of heat energy

Figure 5.1.3 The electrical energy supplied is equal to the heat energy transferred

Here the amount of energy transferred to the element by the electric current is the same as the amount of energy transferred from the element to the water, the kettle and the air (as heat). Energy has not been lost – it has been transferred elsewhere. In this case it has also been transformed into a different form.
The key ideas about energy are:

- When work is done, energy is transferred from place to place.
- Energy may be transformed, or changed into some other form, during the process of transfer.
- There is the same amount of energy at the end of any process as there is at the beginning, although it may be in different forms or in different places – energy is conserved.
- Throughout any process, energy becomes more and more 'spread out', in different forms and in different places. As it does, it becomes increasingly less useful (more dilute).

Energy 'losses'

Machines are designed to make it easier for us to do work. They bring about energy transfers in a particular way. A crane is designed to raise heavy objects.

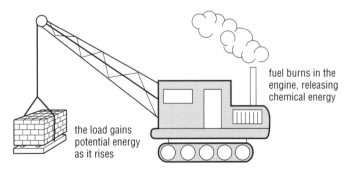

fuel burns in the engine, releasing chemical energy

the load gains potential energy as it rises

Figure 5.1.4 Chemical energy is transformed into potential energy when the crane does work

Chemical energy released in the engine enables the crane to do work. Work is done by the crane on the load, which gains potential energy as it rises. Assuming there are no energy 'losses':

work done by the crane = work done on the bricks

or:

$$\frac{\text{chemical energy}}{\text{released by fuel}} = \frac{\text{gravitational potential energy}}{\text{gained by load}}$$

Only in a perfect machine, however, would no energy be 'lost'. The chemical energy released by the fuel would be entirely transferred to the load in the form of gravitational potential energy. In reality, some of the energy released as the fuel burns is transferred to the surroundings as heat. Energy is also 'lost' or 'wasted' in overcoming friction between the moving parts of the engine and the crane.

As a result, not all of the energy released by the fuel is transferred to the bricks. Some is 'wasted' (transformed into other, less useful forms):

chemical energy → gravitational potential energy (raising load)
→ heat energy during burning
→ heat energy due to friction

The *total* amount of energy released (in all forms) is equal to the energy released by the fuel.

Quick Questions

1 Complete these energy flow diagrams.
   a) Gas cooker: chemical energy → ....
   b) Loudspeaker: .... → sound energy
   c) Gas camping lamp: chemical energy ⌐→ ....
                                          └→ ....

2 **a)** In any process of energy transfer, energy is conserved. What do we mean when we say 'energy is conserved'?
   b) 100 joules of electrical energy enter a bulb each second. 80 joules are transformed into heat energy. What other form of energy is released, and at what rate?

3 Calculate the work done in each of the following.
   a) A weight lifter raises 100 kg through a height of 2 m.
   b) A train pulls a 15 000 N truck through a horizontal distance of 20 metres against a frictional force of 2000 N.
   c) A person weighing 800 N climbs a hill 1000 m high.

4 Complete the table below.

Device	Useful energy output	Wasted energy output
Lamp		
Petrol engine		
Electric motor		

5.2 Power and efficiency

Power is the rate at which work is done (or a measure of how quickly energy is transferred). The faster work is done (or energy is transferred), the greater the power.

The unit of power is the **watt (W)**. One watt is the equivalent of 1 joule of work being done (or energy being transferred) per second. A larger unit, the **kilowatt (kW)** is also used. 1 kilowatt = 1000 watts.

Power can be calculated using the equation:

$$\text{power (watts)} = \frac{\text{work done (joules)}}{\text{time taken to do the work (seconds)}}$$

Because energy is always transferred when work is done, another way of writing the equation is:

$$\text{power (watts)} = \frac{\text{energy transferred (joules)}}{\text{time taken (seconds)}}$$

Note: the units in these equations are very important.

Worked example

Calculate the power developed by a crane which raises a load of 1000 kg (10 000 N) through 5 metres in 20 seconds.
(Note: In most questions where you need to calculate the power you must first calculate the work done or energy transferred.)

Work done = force × distance
 = 10 000 × 5 = 50 000 joules (or 50 kJ)

Power $= \dfrac{\text{work done}}{\text{time taken}}$

$= \dfrac{50\,000}{20} = 2500$ watts (or 2.5 kW)

This is the same as saying the crane engine transfers 2500 joules of (gravitational potential) energy each second.

Electrical power

Work is done by an electricity supply as it drives current through a circuit. The size of the current will depend on the power requirements of the devices in the circuit. Appliances with a high power rating will need a more powerful supply to deliver the current that is needed.

Household light bulbs may be described as 40 watt, 60 watt or 100 watt. This indicates the power of the bulb – the watt (and kilowatt) are the units of electrical power, as well as mechanical power.

To operate a 40 watt light bulb (effectively) the current must transfer 40 joules of electrical energy each second to the filament of the bulb. A 100 watt (100 W)

bulb, on the other hand, requires a current which can transfer 100 joules of energy per second. A more powerful supply is needed to transfer energy faster.

Calculating the amount of energy used by an electrical appliance

The amount of energy that an electrical appliance dissipates (transfers) will depend on:

- Its power – the greater the power, the more energy it transfers each second.
- The time for which it is used – the longer it is used, the more energy it transfers.

The amount of energy transferred can be calculated using the equation:

$$\text{energy used (joules)} = \text{power (watts)} \times \text{time (seconds)}$$

Worked example

Calculate the amount of energy used by a 1200 watt kettle used for 5 minutes.

Energy used = power × time
 = 1200 × 300 = 360 000 joules

Note: In all questions using this equation check that you have the correct units for power and time – they *must* be watts and seconds. If the questions state any other units you *must* change them before you do the calculation.

The kilowatt (kW) is more often used to describe the power of larger electrical appliances. 1 kilowatt is equal to 1000 watts. A 2 kW electric kettle, for example, transforms 2000 joules of electrical energy (into heat energy) each second when it is used.

The cost of electricity

Electricity supply companies need to measure the energy consumption in our homes. They use a much larger unit than the joule – the **kilowatt-hour**, or a 'unit' of electricity. To calculate the number of units used, the following equation is used:

$$\frac{\text{number of units consumed}}{\text{(or number of kilowatt-hours)}} = \frac{\text{power}}{\text{(kW)}} \times \frac{\text{time}}{\text{(hours)}}$$

Note the similarity between this equation and that shown above – the important difference is the units that are used.

If we know the cost per unit we can then calculate the cost of the energy transferred to the device:

$$\text{cost} = \text{number of units used} \times \text{cost per unit}$$

Worked example

Calculate the cost of using a 7 kilowatt electric shower for 2 hours each week, assuming the cost is 7p per unit.

Number of units of electricity used $= $ power (kilowatts) $\times$ time (hours)

$$= 7 \times 2 = 14$$

Cost $=$ number of units used $\times$ cost per unit

$$= 14 \times 7 = 98\text{p}$$

Efficiency

The **efficiency** of a machine or an electrical appliance is a measure of how much energy it transfers *usefully*. Some devices transfer energy more efficiently than others. Consider two different cranes:

(a) Energy released by engine $= 1000$ joules
Energy gained by load $= 500$ joules

Here half of the energy (50%) released by the engine is usefully transferred to the load. The rest is 'wasted' as heat. We can say that the system is 50% efficient.

(b) Energy released by engine $= 1000$ joules
Energy gained by load $= 750$ joules

Here three quarters (75%) of the energy released by the engine is usefully transferred to the load. We say that the system is 75% efficient. This system is more efficient because more of the energy is transferred in a 'useful' way.

If a lot of energy is wasted the efficiency is low. If most of the energy is changed usefully, with little wasted, the efficiency is high.

The efficiency of a system can be calculated using the equation:

$$\text{efficiency} = \frac{\text{useful energy transferred}}{\text{energy put into the system}} \times 100\%$$

Other equations that can be used to calculate efficiency are:

$$\text{efficiency} = \frac{\text{useful work obtained from the system}}{\text{work put into the system}} \times 100\%$$

and:

$$\text{efficiency} = \frac{\text{power output}}{\text{power input}} \times 100\%$$

Note: efficiency has no units. The use of percentages allows us to see at a glance just how much of the energy is usefully transferred by the device (or how much is wasted).

Worked example

Consider an electric motor, power rating 15 kW, raising a lift of weight 9000 N. The lift rises 20 metres in 15 seconds. What is the efficiency of the motor?

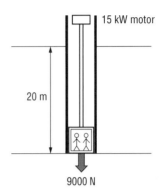

15 kW motor

20 m

9000 N

Figure 5.2.1

Work done by motor $=$ power (W) $\times$ time (s)

$$= 15\,000 \times 15 = 225\,000 \text{ joules}$$

Work done on lift $=$ force (N) $\times$ vertical distance moved (m)

$$= 9000 \times 20 = 180\,000 \text{ joules}$$

$$\text{Efficiency} = \frac{\text{useful energy transferred}}{\text{energy put into the system}} \times 100\%$$

$$= \frac{180\,000}{225\,000} \times 100\% = 80\%$$

Quick Questions

1 How much energy is transformed by a 60 W lamp in 10 minutes?
2 A 2 kW electric fire is used for 4 hours. Calculate:
   a) the number of units used;
   b) the cost, assuming each unit costs 7p.
3 Calculate the total weekly cost at 7p per unit of using all of the following electrical appliances:
   a) a 2 kW electric fire for 4 hours each day;
   b) a 100 W bulb for 5 hours each day;
   c) a 3 kW kettle for 30 minutes each day.
4 An electric motor is used to operate a lift in an office block. When fully loaded, the total mass of the lift and passengers is 2000 kg. It takes the motor 25 seconds to raise the lift through 50 metres. Neglecting energy losses, calculate:
   a) the work done by the motor;
   b) the power developed by the motor.
5 In a quarry, a conveyor belt is used to move the rock. One of the belts lifts 2000 kg of rock to a height of 10 m in 40 s. Calculate:
   a) the work done lifting the rock;
   b) the power used to lift the rock;
   c) the efficiency of the motor if its power rating is 10 kW (10 000 J/s).

5.3 Potential energy and kinetic energy

A hydraulic lift does work when it raises a car. During the process energy is transferred to the car as **gravitational potential energy**.

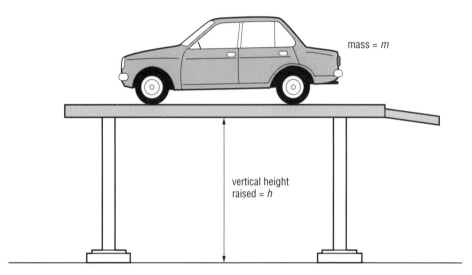

Figure 5.3.1 The work done by the lift raises the car and its gravitational potential energy increases

Work done on car = force × distance moved

= weight of car (*W*) × height raised (*h*)

= *W* × *h* (joules)

Because weight (*W*) = mass (*m*) × gravitational field strength (*g*):

Work done = *m* × *g* × *h* (joules)

But the work done on the car to raise it equals the gravitational potential energy gained, so:

Potential energy gained by the car = *mgh* (joules)

Usually we consider anything at ground level to have zero gravitational potential energy. We can therefore generalise by saying that, for any body that has been raised:

potential energy gained (joules) = *mgh*

where *m* = mass of object (kg)

g = gravitational field strength (N/kg)

h = vertical height raised (m)

Worked example

Calculate the potential energy gained by a cable car of mass 6000 kg if it rises through a vertical height of 300 metres. (*g* = 10 N/kg)

Potential energy gained = *mgh*

= 6000 × 10 × 300

= 18 000 000 joules

Note: In general you should always write answers in the highest possible unit. In the Worked example the potential energy gained could be written as 18 000 kJ or 18 MJ.

Kinetic energy

All moving objects can transfer energy in the form of **kinetic energy**. The kinetic energy of an object depends on its mass and its velocity, and can be calculated using the equation:

kinetic energy (joules) = $\frac{1}{2}mv^2$ where *m* = mass (kg)

v = velocity (m/s)

Worked example

Calculate the kinetic energy of an 8000 kg bus moving at a steady speed of 10 m/s.

Kinetic energy = $\frac{1}{2}mv^2$

= $\frac{1}{2}$ × 8000 × (10)²

= 4000 × 100

= 400 000 joules or 400 kJ

Energy transformation

Many systems, such as the fairground ride shown in Figure 5.3.2, involve changes from potential energy to kinetic energy and vice versa.

Assuming no energy is lost to friction, the *total* amount of kinetic and potential energy in the cars in any part of the system is constant.

Work is done on the car (by an electric motor) which draws it to the top of the slope. Energy is transferred to the car (and the passengers) as gravitational potential energy:

electrical energy ⟶ gravitational potential energy

As the car moves down the slope its gravitational potential energy decreases (because it is losing height). Its kinetic energy increases (because it is gaining speed). Neglecting friction, we can say that the gravitational potential energy lost by the car is equal to the kinetic energy gained by the car:

gravitational potential energy ⟶ kinetic energy

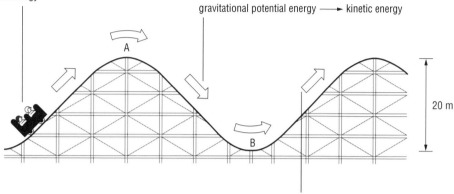

As the car rises, it gains gravitational potential energy. Because it is slowing down it loses kinetic energy. The kinetic energy lost is equal to the gravitational potential energy gained (again assuming we ignore energy 'lost' due to friction):

kinetic energy ⟶ gravitational potential energy

Figure 5.3.2 Energy transformation on a roller-coaster ride

Worked example

Using the information in Figure 5.3.2, calculate the velocity of a car at the bottom of a slope (B). The mass of one car and its riders is 2000 kg.

Gravitational potential energy lost

between A and B (joules) = weight (N) × vertical height (m)

$$= 20\,000 \times 20$$
$$= 400\,000 \text{ J (or 400 kJ)}$$

Assuming no energy is lost, this potential energy will all be transformed into kinetic energy as the car falls down the slope. (Energy is conserved within a system – it is simply changed into some other form.) So:

Kinetic energy of car at point B = 400 000 J

Because kinetic energy $= \frac{1}{2}mv^2$, and mass of car = 2000 kg,

$$\frac{1}{2}mv^2 = 400\,000$$
$$\frac{1}{2} \times 2000 \times v^2 = 400\,000$$

$$\therefore v^2 = \frac{400\,000}{1000} = 400$$

$$v = \sqrt{400} = 20 \text{ m/s}$$

So the velocity of the car at the bottom of the slope will be 20 m/s.

Note that here we have assumed that all of the gravitational potential energy stored in the car at the top of the slope is transformed into kinetic energy as the car accelerates down the slope. In reality, some energy will be transferred to the air and the moving parts as heat (generated in overcoming friction).

Quick Questions

1 Find the work done when a 1000 kg car is lifted a height of 2 m.
2 Calculate the gravitational potential energy gained by a 50 kg person who climbs a 5 metre ladder. (Assume the value of the gravitational field strength to be 10 N/kg.)
3 Calculate the kinetic energy of a 2000 kg car moving at 20 m/s.
4 A 2 kg rock falls from the edge of a cliff. It is exactly 20 m to the sea below.
   a) Calculate the velocity of the rock when it hits the sea. (Hint: assume all of the rock's potential energy is converted into kinetic energy.)
   b) In reality the velocity of the rock will be slightly less than the value you calculated. Explain why.
5 The cars in the roller-coaster in Figure 5.3.2 are replaced by lighter ones. The mass of one car and its riders is now 1500 kg.
   a) What will be the velocity of the car at the bottom of a slope (B)?
   b) Compare your answer with that of the *Worked example*, left, and comment.

5.4 Heat energy

The particles of a substance are always moving – they have kinetic energy. **Temperature** is a measure of the average kinetic energy of the particles. If the substance is heated the particles gain energy so the temperature rises. The more energy they gain, the more the temperature rises. Conversely, if the particles lose energy, then the temperature of the substance falls.

If the substance continues to lose energy the particles will eventually reach a point where they have no energy – they effectively stop moving. The temperature at which this occurs is **absolute zero**. It is equivalent to -273 °C.

Energy transfer and temperature change

A hot drink cools because the surrounding air is cooler than the coffee in the cup. Under these circumstances energy is transferred from the (warmer) coffee to the (cooler) air. We say that heat has been transferred from the hotter object to the cooler object. As a result the air temperature rises slightly (the air has gained extra energy) and the temperature of the coffee falls (the coffee has lost energy). Eventually the temperature of the coffee will be the same as that of the surroundings. Under these conditions no further heat will be transferred in either direction.

The above example demonstrates three general principles:

- When substances gain **heat energy** their temperature rises; when they lose heat energy their temperature falls.
- Energy spreads from warmer regions to cooler regions – the bigger the temperature difference, the faster the energy will be transferred.
- Energy is transferred from the warmer region to the cooler region until they both reach the same temperature.

Specific heat capacity

The **specific heat capacity** of a substance is the energy transferred to or from 1 kilogram of the substance when a temperature change of 1 °C takes place. The units of specific heat capacity are joules/kilogram degree Celsius (J/kg °C).

Water, for example, has a specific heat capacity of 4200 J/kg °C. To raise the temperature of 1 kg of water by 1 °C you would need to transfer 4200 joules of energy to the water.

Copper, on the other hand, has a specific heat capacity of 390 J/kg °C, so to raise the temperature of 1 kg of copper by 1 °C you would need to transfer

390 joules of energy to the copper.

Conversely if the temperature of 1 kg of water were to fall by 1 °C, then 4200 joules of energy would be transferred *from* the water.

The amount of energy transferred to or from anything (solid, liquid or gas) when it undergoes a temperature change can be calculated using the equation:

$$\text{energy transferred (J)} = \text{mass (kg)} \times \text{specific heat capacity (J/kg °C)} \times \text{temperature change (°C)}$$

or, in symbols:

$$E = mc\Delta T$$

Latent heat

When a solid substance is heated its temperature rises. At a specific temperature (the **melting point**) the solid melts, forming a liquid. As the substance changes its state from a solid into a liquid, some of the bonds (forces) between the particles are broken. Energy is required to do this. A heating curve (a graph of temperature against time) shows clearly that, although the substance is being continually heated, no temperature rise takes place during the change of state.

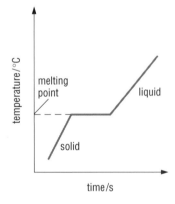

Figure 5.4.1a Change of state from solid to liquid on heating

During this period, the energy supplied is being used to rearrange the particles. The amount of energy needed to do this is known as the **latent heat (of fusion)**. The plateau (flat section of the graph) indicates the temperature at which the change of state occurs (the melting point).

A similar situation arises when a liquid is heated to its **boiling point**. At this temperature the liquid changes state, into a gas. Once again, energy is needed to overcome the intermolecular forces to bring about the change of state. The heat needed to bring about this change is known as the **latent heat**

(of vaporisation). Again, no temperature rise takes place while the substance undergoes the change of state and the heating curve shows a similar plateau, this time at the boiling point.

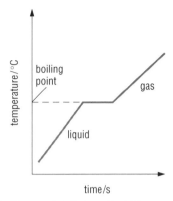

Figure 5.4.1b Change of state from liquid to gas on heating

When a vapour condenses into a liquid the bonds between particles are re-formed and energy is now released. The 'latent heat' which was required for vaporisation is now released during condensation. Although heat continues to be lost to the surroundings, the temperature of the substance does not drop. Only when all of the substance has changed into a liquid does the temperature begin to fall again. A similar situation occurs as a liquid changes into a solid. A graph of temperature against time (in this case a cooling curve because the temperature is falling) again shows 'flat' sections at the boiling point and the melting point.

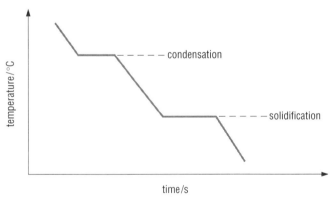

Figure 5.4.2 A cooling curve showing changes of state

Specific latent heat

- The **specific latent heat of fusion** of a substance is the amount of energy needed to change 1 kg of the substance from solid to liquid at its melting point without any change of temperature taking place.
- The **specific latent heat of vaporisation** of a substance is the amount of energy needed to change 1 kg of the substance from liquid to vapour at its boiling point without any change of temperature taking place.

The energy transferred to or from a substance when it undergoes a change of state can be calculated using the equation:

energy transferred (J)	=	specific latent heat (J/kg)	×	mass (kg)

or, in symbols:

$$E = L \times m$$

Quick Questions

1 How much energy must be supplied to raise the temperature of a 0.5 kg block of aluminium from 20 °C to 50 °C? (specific heat capacity of aluminium = 880 J/kg °C)

2 The heater in an electric kettle transfers 1000 joules of energy per second to 1 kilogram of water. If the water is at 20 °C when the kettle is first switched on, how long will it take to heat the water to 100 °C? (specific heat capacity of water = 4200 J/kg °C)

3 The graph shows a cooling curve of a substance as its temperature falls from 300 °C to 20 °C.

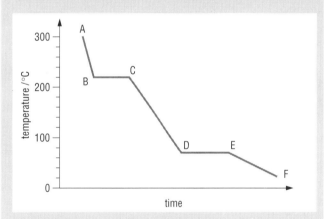

Figure 5.4.3

a) At 250 °C, is the substance solid, liquid or gas?
b) What is the boiling point of the substance?
c) What is the melting point of the substance?
d) Over which sections of the cooling curve is the substance transferring energy to the surroundings, *without* a decrease in temperature?
e) Why does the temperature stay constant over these sections, despite the fact that the substance is losing energy to the surroundings?

4 How much energy would be needed to change 0.2 kg of ice at −5 °C into steam? (specific heat capacity of ice = 2200 J/kg °C; specific heat capacity of water = 4200 J/kg °C; specific latent heat of fusion of ice = 334 000 J/kg; specific latent heat of vaporisation of water = 2 260 000 J/kg)

5.5 Energy transfer

Heat energy may be transferred by **conduction**, **convection**, **radiation** and **evaporation**.

Conduction

The main process by which energy is transferred through solids is **conduction**. It is the particles in a solid which conduct energy. The energy is transferred from warmer regions to cooler regions.

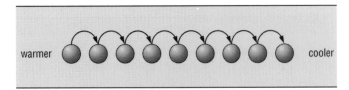

energy is passed from particle to particle

Figure 5.5.1 Conduction in a solid

During conduction, energy passes from particles in the warmer region to their neighbouring particles. They then pass energy to *their* neighbours. This process is repeated throughout the material, so that energy is transferred from the warmer region to the cooler region and the temperature of the cooler region is raised. Note that the particles of the solid do not move through the material – they only serve to transfer energy through the material.

Solid materials do not all conduct heat at the same rate. Some conduct heat much faster than others. The (thermal) *conductivity* of a material is a measure of the rate at which the material transfers heat by conduction.

Conduction through metals

Heat is transferred through metals faster than through non-metals because they contain electrons (normally held tightly within the atoms) that are able to move freely. These are called **free electrons**. At higher temperatures the free electrons move around quickly. As they do so, they collide with other particles, transferring energy to them, and thus raising the temperature of cooler regions.

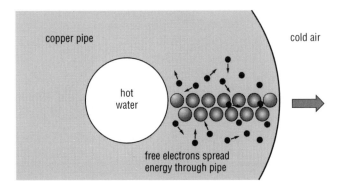

Figure 5.5.2 Conduction in a metal is assisted by free electrons

The free electrons help to conduct heat faster than would take place if it were only passed from particle to particle. Metals are described as good (thermal) **conductors** because heat is conducted rapidly through them – they have a high (thermal) conductivity.

Non-metals have a lower (thermal) conductivity and are described as poor (thermal) conductors, or **insulators**. Gases are good insulators – that's why duvets are so warm – they are largely filled with air 'pockets' which slow down the rate at which heat is transferred (away from your body) by conduction.

Using conductors and insulators

In situations where we need to reduce heat transfer by conduction we use insulators. In other situations, where we need heat to conduct rapidly, we use conductors.

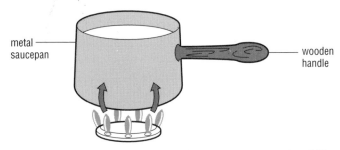

Figure 5.5.3 Metals have a high conductivity so heat spreads quickly through the base of the pan, warming the food rapidly. Heat spreads much more slowly through the wooden handle (an insulator) so it feels cooler when you hold it

Convection

In liquids and gases the particles are free to move, carrying energy with them. The spreading of heat through liquids and gases takes place largely by **convection**. Imagine what happens inside an electric kettle.

Figure 5.5.4 Heat is spread through the water in a kettle by convection

When the kettle is switched on the temperature of the element rises. The metal element immediately becomes hotter than the surrounding water. Energy is transferred from the (hotter) element to the (cooler) water particles, raising the temperature of the water near the element. The heated water expands (the particles move further apart) and becomes less dense than the cooler water around it. The warmed (less dense) water rises, transferring heat away from the element. Cooler, denser water falls to take its place. This, in turn, is heated by the element and begins to rise. As a result energy is spread throughout the water in the kettle. Note that the energy is spread by the movement of the particles themselves (unlike conduction, where the particles remain in fixed positions). The transfer of energy in this way is called convection.

Demonstrating convection

The movement of water particles can be seen if a small coloured crystal is placed in one corner of a beaker containing water. When the water around the crystal is heated, the warmer, coloured water rises and cooler (clearer) water falls from the sides to take its place. Slowly the coloured water can be seen to spread across the surface and fall down the opposite side of the beaker, forming a continuous current. The movement of the water is called a **convection current**.

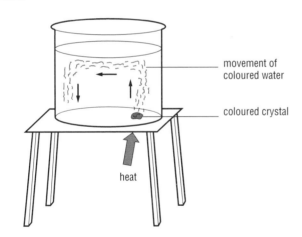

Figure 5.5.5 Demonstrating a convection current

Heat also spreads through gases by convection. Air that is heated by radiators in a closed room is constantly on the move (Figure 5.5.6), although you cannot see it. Air near a radiator will be warmed by contact. The air becomes less dense than the cooler air which surrounds it. The warmer, less dense air rises. Slowly the warmer air will lose energy to the cooler surroundings and it cools, becoming denser. The cooler air falls to be warmed by the radiator once again, and the whole process is repeated. A convection current (a continuous flow of warmed and cooled air) flows around the room.

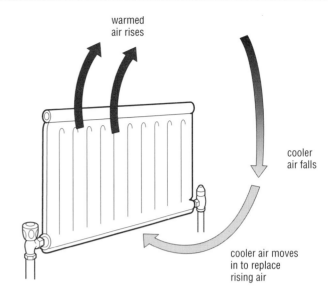

Figure 5.5.6 A convection current in air

Radiation

Radiation is the name given to the transfer of energy by electromagnetic waves (see page 94). Everything emits radiation. In general, the hotter the object the more radiation it emits. At temperatures up to about 300 °C, most of the radiation is emitted in the form of infra-red waves. The infra-red radiation is absorbed by surrounding objects, raising their temperature.

The transfer of energy by radiation is quite different to conduction and convection. In conduction and convection it is the particles of the substance which transfer the energy from place to place. Radiation does not depend on the presence of particles – it can pass through a vacuum. Radiation from the sun, for example, passes through 150 million kilometres of (largely empty) space to reach the earth.

Emitters of radiation

The colour and texture of a material affects how much radiation it emits. This can be shown using Leslie's Cube, a hollow steel cube which is filled with hot water. One side of the cube is painted gloss (shiny) white, another dull (matt) black, a third is dull white, whilst the fourth is a dark gloss colour.

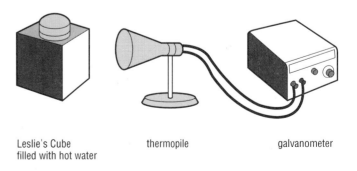

Leslie's Cube filled with hot water   thermopile   galvanometer

Figure 5.5.7 Comparing the radiation emitted by different surfaces

To measure the radiation emitted from the different sides, a thermopile (heat sensing device) is used, connected to a galvanometer. As the thermopile is moved from one side to another, it is found that the dull black surface is the best emitter, whilst the shiny white surface is the worst emitter.

Absorbers of radiation

A similar experiment may be done to find out which colour is the best absorber of radiation. Two conical flasks are used, one of which is covered with dull black paint, whilst the other is covered with aluminium foil or shiny white paint. Both flasks contain the same amount of water, at the same temperature, and are placed at equal distances from a radiant heater.

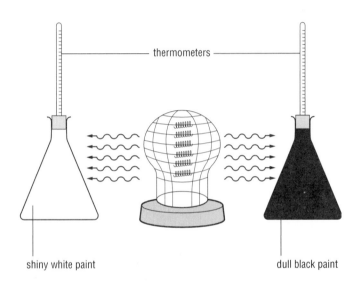

shiny white paint   dull black paint

Figure 5.5.8 Comparing the radiation absorbed by different surfaces

The temperature of the water in the flask with the dull black surface is found to rise significantly more than that in the flask with the light shiny surface, showing that dark, dull surfaces are the best absorbers as well as the best emitters of radiation.

Evaporation

A liquid boils at a specific temperature – its boiling point. Some of the liquid can, however, change into vapour at any temperature due to **evaporation**.

In a liquid the molecules are constantly moving. The temperature of the liquid depends on the average kinetic energy of the molecules in it. As the molecules move they collide with other molecules. As a result of these collisions, at any instant some molecules will be moving faster than the average whilst others will be moving slower than average.

some slower-moving molecules return after leaving the surface   faster-moving molecules escape as vapour

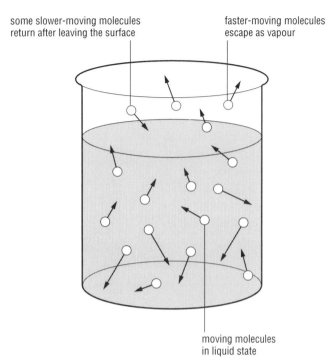

moving molecules in liquid state

Figure 5.5.9 Faster-moving molecules near the liquid surface become vapour

If one of the faster-moving molecules is close to the surface, it may break free and become a vapour molecule. Any movement of the air at the surface, such as a draught, carries the vapour molecule away from the surface so that it cannot return to the liquid.

There may be several thousand molecules leaving the liquid by this process at any time. It follows that the average energy of the molecules left in the liquid state must decrease, and the temperature of the liquid falls.

The rate of evaporation from the surface depends on:

- The temperature of the liquid – hot liquids evaporate faster than cooler liquids.
- The surface area of the liquid – the greater the surface area, the greater the rate of evaporation.
- The surface conditions above the liquid – if the air at the surface is moving (perhaps due to a breeze) then evaporation will take place at a greater rate; also the greater the amount of vapour already in the surroundings, the lower the rate of evaporation from the surface.

Reducing energy losses by conduction and convection

Heat loss by conduction can be reduced using insulating materials such as polystyrene. Heat loss by convection can be reduced by preventing the movement of air around the warmer object, for example by placing a lid on pans or cups. The lid also serves to reduce heat loss due to evaporation.

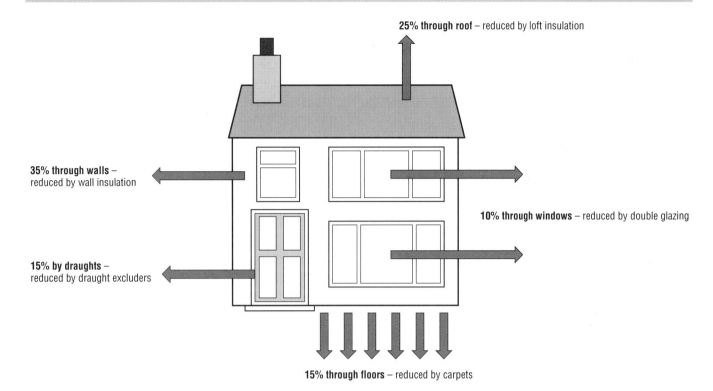

Figure 5.5.10 Heat losses from a typical house

Heat loss from the home

Every home loses heat, although some might lose it more slowly than others. The amount of heat typically lost from different places in a house is shown in Figure 5.5.10.

If you reduce the rate at which energy is lost, then you will use less fuel to keep the temperature at a comfortable level – and that means smaller bills and fuel savings. There are several ways in which the energy losses can be reduced, the main ones being:

* Installing double glazing. Double glazed windows consist of two panes of glass with an air (or a vacuum) gap between them. Double glazing can reduce heat loss through windows by up to 50%.
* Installing cavity wall insulation. Most types of cavity wall insulation consist of fine fibres which are blown into the cavity through holes drilled in the walls. Cavity wall insulation reduces heat loss through the walls and cavity by conduction and convection.
* Installing loft insulation directly above the ceiling. The loft insulation traps air between its fibres. Air is a good insulator, so this reduces heat transfer by conduction.
* Laying fitted carpets in all ground floor rooms. This reduces heat loss through the floor by conduction.
* Installing draught excluders. Fitted around doors and badly fitting windows, these prevent colder air entering the home, thereby lowering the temperature of the air.

Quick Questions

1 Explain why metals are better thermal conductors than non-metals.
2 A spade, with a wooden handle and a metal blade, is left outside on a very cold night. The next morning one part feels much colder than the other.
  a) Which part will feel colder and why?
  b) If the temperature of each part is measured, which, if any, would have the lower temperature?
3 A white car (with white seats) and a black car (with black seats) follow one another on a long journey. They arrive when it is dark and are parked, with all windows shut. The next day, which is warm and sunny, the owners return to their cars. Answer each of the following questions in a sentence which also explains your answer.
  a) 30 minutes after parking, which car bonnet will be hotter?
  b) When the owners return:
    i) which car's seats will be hotter?
    ii) which bonnet will feel hotter?
4 A greenhouse is fitted with a device that automatically opens a roof window as the temperature rises. The hotter it gets, the more the window opens.
  a) Explain, using what you know about convection, why the device helps keep the temperature inside the greenhouse reasonably constant.
  b) The owner finds that the greenhouse gets too cold during the night. She fits bubble plastic (plastic sheets filled with pockets of air) to the glass on the inside. How will this help prevent the greenhouse becoming too cold during the night?

5.6 Electricity supply

Electricity is generated in generating stations (or power stations). All power stations need some source of energy. Most use coal, oil or gas, or nuclear fuels such as uranium or plutonium. Regardless of which fuel is used, they all generate electricity in basically the same way (see Figure 1.13.5, page 31):

- Energy released by the fuel raises the temperature of the water in the boiler. The water boils, forming high pressure steam.
- The high pressure steam is directed onto turbines, making them turn.
- The turbines drive the generator, producing an alternating voltage which drives the current through the cables.
- The National Grid, a network of cables, distributes electricity around the country.

A series of energy transformations takes place inside a fuel-burning power station:

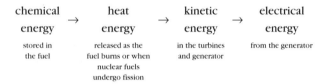

chemical energy	→	heat energy	→	kinetic energy	→	electrical energy
stored in the fuel		released as the fuel burns or when nuclear fuels undergo fission		in the turbines and generator		from the generator

Meeting demand

Occasionally we need more energy than the generating stations can supply. Stand-by generators may be used to generate the extra energy needed. 'Pumped storage' systems, for example, store water in a large reservoir high above a hydro-electric generator (see Figure 5.6.1 and page 142). Vast amounts of potential energy are stored in the trapped water. To cope with additional demands, the water is released and flows downhill, driving the turbine and generator. The electricity is fed into the National Grid. A series of energy transformations takes place:

potential energy → kinetic energy → electrical energy

in the stored water   as the falling water drives turbines and generator   from the generator

At times of low demand, excess electricity is used to pump the water back into the upper reservoir, where it is stored until needed:

electrical energy → potential energy

Although the system is not efficient (more energy is needed to pump the water back into the reservoir than is generated when it is released), it is one of the few ways in which extra energy can be produced 'on demand'.

Fossil fuels

Fuels such as coal, oil and gas are called **fossil fuels** – they were produced from the partly decayed (and fossilised) remains of living things. Coal formed (over a period between 80 and 300 million years ago) from the remains of plants. The stages in the formation of coal are shown in Figure 5.6.2 opposite.

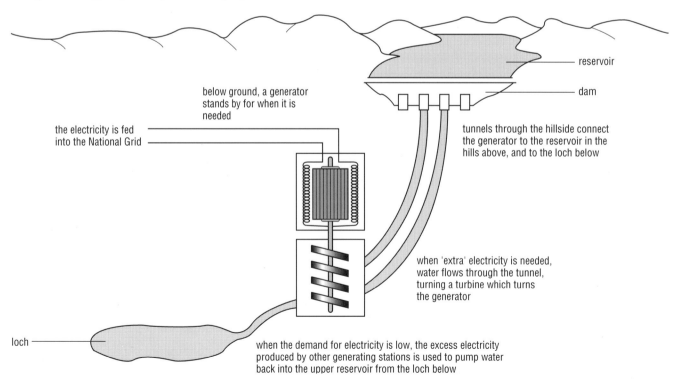

Figure 5.6.1 A typical pumped storage system

1

Between 80 and 300 million years ago plants flourished in the warm, damp climate of swamps

2

As the plants died they formed a layer of decaying matter many metres thick. The plant material did not decay completely due to the absence of oxygen

3
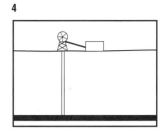
The layer of plant matter was slowly covered and compressed below many metres of sediment. The high pressure changed the partly decayed plant matter into coal (a form of rock)

4

Now the coal is found (often hundreds of metres below ground) in layers called seams

Figure 5.6.2 Stages in the formation of coal

1 Trees and other plants grew quickly in warm, damp climates.
2 Dead plants fell into stagnant water so they only partially decayed (due to the limited supply of oxygen). The decaying plant material formed a dense layer tens of metres thick.
3 Layers of sediment built up on top of the plant remains. Over thousands of years, alternating layers of plant material and sediment were formed which were hundreds of metres thick.
4 The weight of the sediments squashed the partly decayed plant material into fairly thin seams. The layers of sediment formed rock. The chemicals in the decayed plants changed into coal.

Oil and gas were formed in a similar way, from the partially decayed remains of animals that lived in the tropical (warm) seas.

Burning fossil fuels

When fossil fuels are burned in the presence of oxygen, heat energy is released. The original source of this energy (which became trapped in the tissues of the plant) was the sun.

Once used, fossil fuels cannot be used again. They cannot be replaced fast enough to meet demand. They are described as **non-renewable sources** of energy. Eventually we will use up existing supplies of fossil fuels. If we use these fuels more economically (i.e. if we waste less) then:

• Reserves will last longer before they run out.
• We will reduce the atmospheric pollution caused by burning them.

Nuclear fuels

Some electricity generating stations use nuclear fuels such as uranium and plutonium. Uranium-bearing ores are found in the earth's crust, and are mined just like other minerals. Supplies of nuclear fuels are therefore limited and are also non-renewable.

Wood

Wood burns much faster than it grows, so, if it were used as a major source of energy, it would rapidly run out. With careful management, however, supplies can be renewed (in time). Under these circumstances wood can be described as a **renewable source** of energy.

Quick Questions

1 Complete the sentences below.
   a) Coal, oil and gas are described as fossil fuels because ....
   b) Because there is a limited supply of fossil fuels which can only be used once, they are described as .... sources of energy.
   c) .... and .... are nuclear fuels used in power generating stations.
   d) The origin of the energy stored in fossil fuels was the ....
   e) Fossil fuels were formed by the partial decay of plant and animal remains. They only partially decayed due to the absence of ....

2 Complete the following paragraph.

   In a coal-fired power station .... is released as the coal is burned. This heats the water in the boiler, producing .... pressure steam. The steam is directed onto the .... which, in turn, drive the generator. .... energy is transformed by the generator into .... energy. The .... is a network of cables which connect homes and offices to the power generating stations.

3 Every power station (coal, oil, gas, nuclear, hydro-electric, etc.) supplies electricity to the National Grid in this country.
   a) What are the advantages of having them all connected to one system?
   b) What are the advantages of using several different energy sources?

5.7 Renewable sources of energy

Most of the alternatives to fossil fuels are renewable sources of energy. They can be used over and over. Although there are no fuel costs, the cost of equipment and maintenance is high compared with the amount of energy produced.

Some renewable energy resources can be used to drive turbines directly. Therefore the generators are generally more efficient than those driven by non-renewable sources. The major renewable energy sources are outlined on this double-page spread.

Wind energy

Wind turbines are driven by air moving across the surface of the earth (the wind). The blades of the turbine are connected directly to the generator. As the generator turns, electricity is produced.

Advantages: Clean, no atmospheric pollution
Disadvantages: Expensive to install
      May spoil the appearance of the countryside
      Unreliable due to varying wind speeds
Power output: Fairly low

Geothermal energy

In some areas the rock close to the earth's surface is heated by energy released by the decay of radioactive elements in the earth's crust. To capture this 'geothermal' energy, two boreholes are drilled into the rock, and the rock between them is fractured. Cold water is forced, under pressure, down one of the holes. The water is heated as it flows through the cracks in the rock, and then rises through the second borehole.

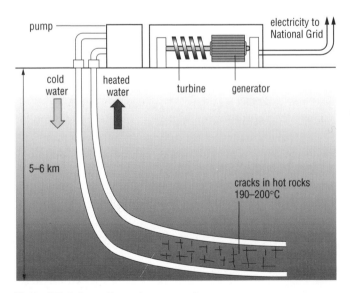

Figure 5.7.1 A geothermal energy system

The heated water can be used to generate electricity, or to warm homes and offices.

Advantages: Clean
Disadvantages: Quite expensive to install and maintain
      Suitable rock found only in a limited number of areas
Power output: Low

Hydro-electricity

Hydro-electricity is generated using water stored in dams. As the water flows down through large pipes in the dam it drives a turbine and generator.

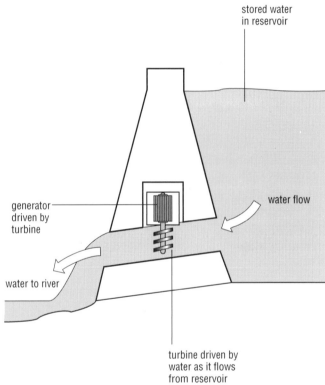

Figure 5.7.2 A hydro-electric dam

Advantages: Clean
      May create leisure facilities
      May provide alternative habitats for animals
      Power output is easily controlled
Disadvantages: Requires relatively high rainfall and mountainous terrain
      May spoil the appearance of the countryside and natural habitats
Power output: Can be fairly high as the same water often flows through several power stations in any one system

Wave power

The up-and-down motion of the waves can provide energy for those countries which have a coastline. Wave generators change the vertical motion of the waves into the rotary motion necessary for electricity generation.

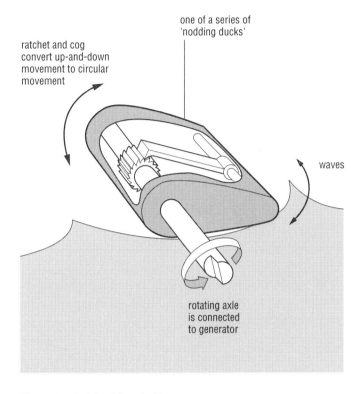

Figure 5.7.3 A 'nodding duck' wave generator

Advantages:	Clean, non-polluting
Disadvantages:	Many miles of coastline needed
	Costs of installation are extremely high
	Maintenance is difficult and expensive
	May spoil the appearance of the coastline
Power output:	Very low compared with cost

Tidal power

Tidal barrages – large dams built across the narrower sections of river estuaries – make use of the ocean tides. As the tides moves in, water flows behind the barrage and the 'gates' are closed. As the tide goes out, the water is trapped, storing potential energy. The water is then allowed to pass through the dam through pipes, turning the turbines which in turn drive generators. The system is similar in construction to a hydro-electric generating station.

Advantages:	Clean, non-polluting
	Reliable – tides rise and fall twice each day
Disadvantages:	Dams are expensive to build
	May damage natural habitats
	Generates energy only at certain times
	May spoil the appearance of the estuary
Power output:	Fairly high

Solar power

Many calculators are now powered by solar cells. Solar cells are electronic devices that convert light energy into electrical energy. In recent years they have been used to power cars, light aircraft, fridges and many other devices.

Advantages:	Clean, non-polluting
	Can be used in remote areas
	Little maintenance needed
	Reliable
Disadvantages:	Cost of manufacture is fairly high
	Needs reasonably clear skies

Solar 'panels' do not produce electricity, but they are designed to absorb radiation, warming water which flows through them. They can be used to supplement heating systems in offices and homes.

Quick Questions

1 Write a sentence describing what is meant by the terms:
   a) renewable energy resource; and
   b) non-renewable energy resource.

2 Which of these energy resources are renewable?

   waves   coal   wind   tidal   solar   nuclear
   hydro-electricity   oil   geothermal

3 Which of the above energy resources drive a generator directly?

4 State one advantage and one disadvantage of each of the following energy resources:
   a) wind;
   b) coal;
   c) hydro-electricity;
   d) solar.

5 a) Explain the difference between solar cells and solar panels.
   b) Draw an energy transformation diagram for a solar cell.
   c) Solar cells are used on satellites. What purpose do they serve?

Section Five: Examination Practice Questions

Foundation Level

1. Currently most of our energy comes from non-renewable energy sources. Scientists believe we should make more use of renewable energy sources.
   (a) Explain the difference between a renewable and a non-renewable energy source.
   (b) Describe **two** advantages of renewable energy sources over non-renewable sources.
   (c) A number of energy sources can be used to generate electricity, such as:

   coal wind tides oil solar waves gas geothermal biomass nuclear

   Which of these energy sources are renewable?
   (d) The diagram below shows a hydro-electric power station.

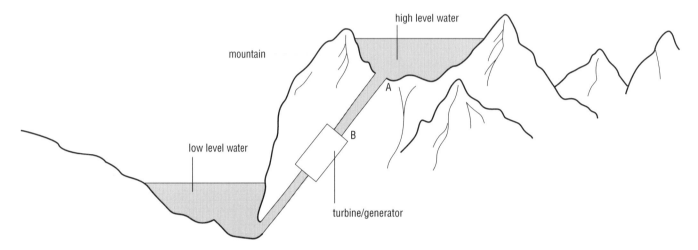

   (i) What form of energy is stored in the water at A?
   (ii) What forms of energy does the water have at B?
   (e) Some hydro-electric power stations are able to pump the water back up to the higher level at night time. This is known as a 'pumped storage system'.
   (i)   Why is the water normally pumped back to the higher level at night?
   (ii) Why is the system not very efficient?
   (iii) Why do we need systems such as this?

2. This modern house makes use of wind energy and solar energy.

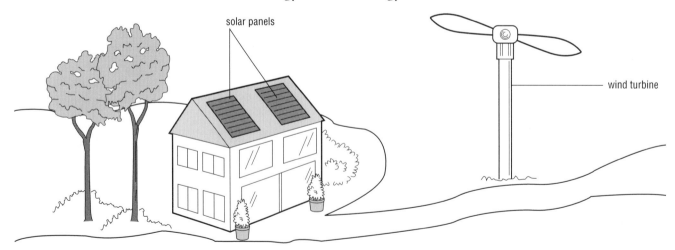

   (a) Explain how the wind turbine generates electricity.
   (b) Batteries are used as a 'back up' system. Why are the batteries needed and when will they be re-charged?
   (c) Even using batteries the house is often without electricity. Under what circumstances do you think that could happen?

(d) The solar panels use solar energy to heat water for the house. What is the disadvantage of this system?

The solar panels are constructed like this:

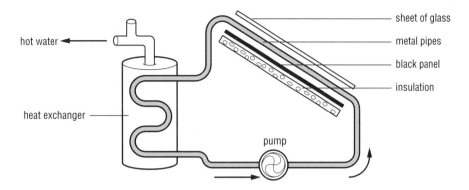

(e) Why are the panels and pipes painted dull black?

(f) By which process is energy transferred through the pipes to the water?

(g) Copper is often used for the pipework. Why is copper suitable for that job?

3. Campers often place a foam rubber mat between their sleeping bag and the ground. Good quality sleeping bags are filled with feathers. The feathers trap air. In really cold weather campers wrap a shiny metal foil blanket around the sleeping bag.

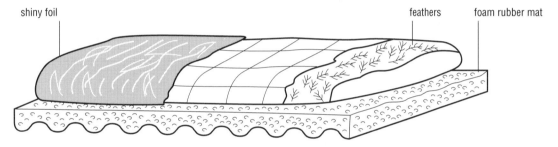

Complete the following sentences using words from this list. Some words may be used more than once.

radiation   convection   insulator   conduction   evaporation   reflected   absorbed

(a) The air between the feathers is an ……… and reduces heat loss from the body by ……… .

(b) The shiny foil helps to reduce heat loss by ……… . Infra-red waves are ……… by the foil and re-absorbed by the body.

(c) If the sleeping bag is wet, heat may also be lost by ……… .

4. (a) Match each of the following statements to the pictures. If, for example, you think statement **1** goes with picture **A**, write **1A**.

A Tennis player dressed in white

B Black solar panel on roof of house

C Hot drink with lid

D Pan with copper bottom

E Oven glove

    1 Reduces heat losses by convection.   **2** Gives good conduction of heat.

    3 Reduces heat gained by conduction.   **4** Absorbs heat radiation.

    5 Reduces heat absorbed by radiation.

(b) This diagram shows milk being heated in a saucepan.

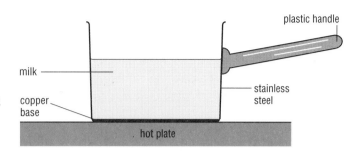

(i) Why is the handle made of plastic?

(ii) Why is the saucepan base made of copper?

(iii) By which process does heat pass through the base of the pan?

(iv) By which process does heat spread through the milk?

5. This diagram shows a living room heated by a radiator.

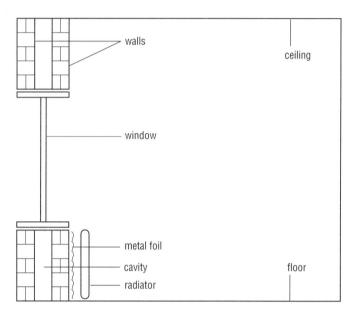

(a) Copy the diagram and draw arrows to show how heat is spread through the room from the radiator.

(b) What is the purpose of the metal foil?

(c) How could energy losses through the walls be reduced?

(d) If this was an upstairs room, what could be done to reduce energy losses through the ceiling?

(e) What could be done with the floor to reduce energy loss?

(f) How could heat loss through the windows be reduced?

(g) How would curtains help reduce heat loss through the windows?

6. **(a)** In 1997 it cost Rafiq £1000 to heat his house. Look at the diagram below. It shows how the £1000 worth of heat energy escaped.

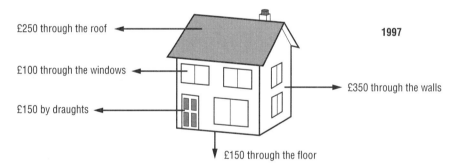

During 1998 he sold his house to Ben who spent a lot of money on different forms of insulation. The diagram below shows how much Ben expected to lose from each part of the house during 1999.

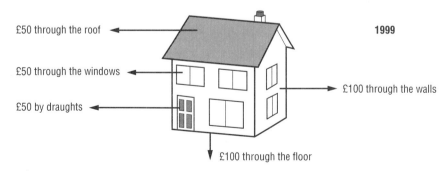

(i) What was the expected heating bill for 1999?

(ii) What was the expected saving over the bill for 1997?

(iii) Which method of insulation saved the most money?

(b) It is important to consider 'pay-back time' when installing insulation.
  (i)   What do we mean by 'pay-back time'?
  (ii) If it cost £4000 to fully double glaze Ben's house, calculate the pay-back time.
  (iii) Ben believes draught-proofing to have been the most cost-effective insulation method. Is this true if it cost £25 to seal off all the draughts?

(c) Complete these sentences by filling in the gaps:

Most insulating materials make use of air. Air is a ……… conductor or it could be called a ……… insulator. The air must be trapped in small pockets to reduce energy being transferred by ……… . In the cavity between walls the air will be warmed from inside the house. This warmer air will ……… and escape. Cavity wall insulation reduces this by trapping air in pockets, with each pocket being surrounded by an ……… material which is a ……… conductor. Some double glazed windows contain a vacuum between the panes of glass. A vacuum is an even better ……… than air because it contains no particles so there will be no energy transfer by ……… or ……… .

(d) The diagram below shows a typical classroom heater.

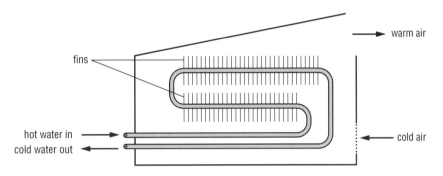

  (i)   Why do the pipes have fins fixed to them?
  (ii) Why are the pipes made of copper?
  (iii) Why are the fins painted black?
  (iv) Explain why the air drawn in at the bottom is cooler than the air at the top of the classroom.
  (v)   Describe how the air spreads heat throughout the room.

7. This water-powered system can be seen lifting people from the beach to the cliff top at Saltburn in Yorkshire.
  (a) Calculate the work done as car A is raised from the beach level to the top of the cliff.
  (b) If the car takes 20 seconds to reach the top, what power is developed by the system?

Both cars contain large water tanks. When both cars are stationary, with A at the bottom and B at the top, water flows into the tank on car B. When sufficient water has been added, car B begins to fall and car A rises.
  (c) What causes car B to move down the slope?
  (d) What form of energy is car B losing?
  (e) What form of energy does car A gain as it rises?
  (f) Someone said 'The energy gained by car A as it rises is equal to the energy lost by car B as it falls'. Why is this not likely to be the case?

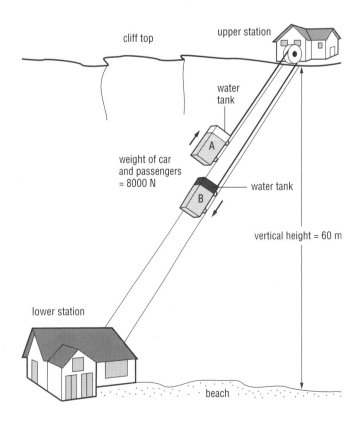

8. **(a)** Mandy and her friend Anna make some sandwiches and wrap them up. They use different wrappings:

black polythene bag

shiny aluminium foil

Mandy's sandwiches

Anna's sandwiches

Their sandwiches are in the sun all morning. Anna's sandwiches stay cooler. Explain why.

(b) Mandy has a drinks cooler, as shown below.
The water soaks through the porous pot and evaporates. Explain, using ideas about particles, how this keeps the bottle of drink cool.

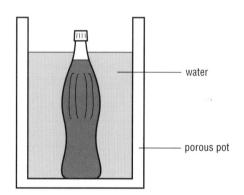

water

porous pot

9. This question is about energy.
   (a) Look at these diagrams.

A

B

C

D

E

(i) Some of the people are NOT doing work. Write down the letters of **two** pictures where work is NOT being done. [2]

(ii) Write down the letter of one picture where work IS being done. [1]

(iii) Write down the letter of a picture where kinetic energy increases. [1]

(iv) Write down the letter of a picture where potential energy increases. [1]

(b) Gillian is carrying out a personal fitness test.
She steps on and off the box 300 times.
She transfers 25 J of energy each time she steps up.

(i) Calculate the energy transferred during this test. [1]

(ii) She takes 5 minutes to do this test.
Calculate her average power. [3]

(MEG, Foundation, 1998 Specimen)

10. The diagram below shows a house which has **not** been insulated. The cost of the energy lost from different parts of the house during one year is shown on the diagram.

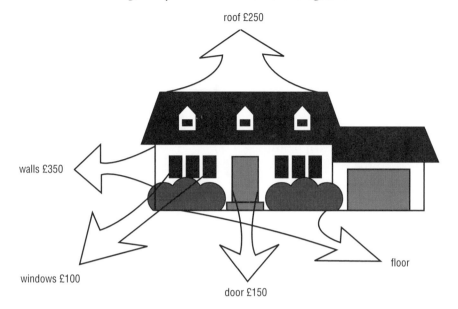

roof £250

walls £350

windows £100

door £150

floor

(a) The total cost of the energy lost during one year is £1000.
  (i) What is the cost of the energy lost through the floor? [1]
  (ii) Suggest one way of reducing this loss. [1]
(b) The table below shows how some parts of the house may be insulated to reduce energy losses. The cost of each method of insulation is also given.

Where lost	Cost of energy lost per year (£)	Method of insulation	Cost of insulation (£)
roof	250	fibre-glass in loft	300
walls	350	foam-filled cavity	800
windows	100	double glazing	4500
doors	150	draught-proofing	5

  (i) Which method of insulation would you install first? Explain why. [3]
  (ii) Which method of insulation would you install last? Explain why. [3]

(NEAB, Foundation, 1997)

Higher Level

1. Kara has a mass of 40 kg and she climbs to the top of a 10 m high water slide. The gravitational field strength is 10 N/kg.
  (a) How much gravitational potential energy does she gain while climbing the slide?

  Her speed at the bottom of the slide is 10 m/s.
  (b) Calculate her kinetic energy at the bottom of the slide.
  (c) Why is there a difference between the answers to parts (a) and (b)?

  Kara's friend Caroline then goes up the slide. She has a mass of 50 kg. Assume Caroline loses the same proportion of energy as Kara.
  (d) Calculate Caroline's speed at the bottom of the slide.
  (e) Comment on your answer.

2. A small ball of mass 0.05 kg is thrown vertically into the air. Its launch velocity was found to be 20 m/s. (Gravitational field strength = 10 N/kg; assume no air resistance.)
  (a) What form of energy will the ball have at its maximum height?
  (b) Calculate the maximum height reached by the ball.
  (c) What will be the velocity of the ball when it reaches the thrower again?

3. (a) The diagram below shows water being pumped from a river into an irrigation channel. The water is lifted a height of 1.5 metres. The pump is able to lift 50 kg of water each second. The gravitational field strength is 10 N/kg.

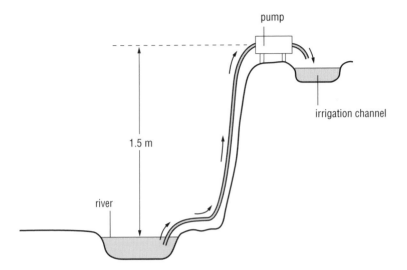

(i) Calculate the work done when 50 kg of water is lifted 1.5 m.

(ii) The electrical energy put into the pump to lift 50 kg of water by 1.5 m is 1200 J. Explain the difference between this number and the answer to part (i).

(iii) Calculate the efficiency of the pump.

(b) The diagram below shows a hydro-electric power scheme. The water flows through the turbines and into the river at 25 m/s. The gravitational field strength is 10 N/kg.

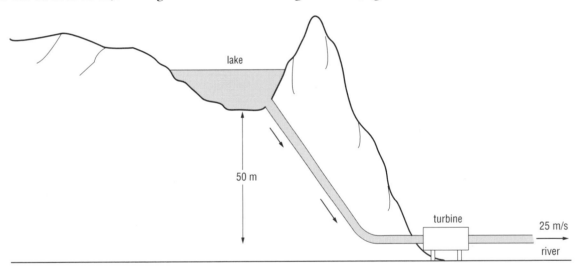

(i) What is the loss of potential energy of 1 kg of water as it falls from the bottom of the lake to the turbine?

(ii) Calculate the kinetic energy of each kg of water after passing through the turbine.

(iii) Use your answers to parts (i) and (ii) to find the energy available for conversion into electricity in the turbine.

(iv) Calculate the efficiency of the system.

(v) Why will the actual efficiency of the turbine be less than the calculated value?

(vi) If the power output is 1 MW and the efficiency is 30%, calculate the power input.

4. A leaflet advertising double glazing contained the following information:

Size of air gap (mm)	0	3	6	12	18
Rate of energy transfer (J/s)	5.6	4.0	3.4	3.0	2.9

(a) What does the leaflet mean by 'air gap'?

(b) Draw a graph of rate of energy transfer against size of gap.

(c) Describe how the rate of energy transfer is related to the gap size.

(d) Which gap size would you think is best? Explain your answer.

(e) Calculate how much energy would be transferred through a single pane in 1 hour.

(f) How does your answer to part (e) compare with the energy lost in 1 hour for a 6 mm gap window?

(g) The leaflet makes no mention of window area. How would the window area affect the rate of energy transfer?

5. Tanveer wants to buy a new electric fire. He is looking at the information provided about three electric fires.

FIRE X	FIRE Y	FIRE Z
5.0 kW input	4.0 kW input	6.0 kW input
3 kW useful room output	3.4 kW useful room output	3 kW useful room output

(a) Calculate the efficiency of each gas fire.

(b) Which gas fire will be the most expensive to use and why?

(c) Which gas fire will heat the room the quickest?

(d) Assuming the cost of all fires is the same, which gas fire should Tanveer choose? Give reasons for your answer.

6. The table below shows the average energy used per person in one year in six different places in the world.

Country	Average number of units of energy used per person per year
North America	340
United Kingdom	180
Japan	150
South America	52
China	26
Africa	17

(a) Why do you think that, on average, people in North America use a lot more energy than those in Africa?

(b) How would you expect the average energy used per person in South America, China and Africa to change over the next few years? Why?

(c) Read the following passage and then answer the questions.

About 40% of the electricity generated in Britain comes from power stations that use coal. A large coal-burning power station called Drax is next to the river Trent and not far from the large cities of Sheffield and Leeds. It was originally built near large coal fields and it is near to motorway and rail links. Drax can produce 240 000 kW of power.

(i) What are the advantages and disadvantages of using coal as the energy source at Drax?

(ii) Why do you think Drax was built next to a river?

(iii) Explain the stages in the production of electrical energy from the coal entering the power station to electricity entering the National Grid.

(iv) Explain how transformers reduce energy losses in electricity distribution.

(d) Modern wind turbines can produce up to 400 kW of electricity.

(i) How many wind turbines would be needed to produce the same power as Drax?

(ii) What are the advantages and disadvantages of using the wind as a power source?

(e) The table below shows how the energy is used in a coal-burning power station.

Energy input per hour	Energy output per hour
6000 MJ from burning coal	100 MJ in operating the power station
	2400 MJ of electricity
	3000 MJ of losses due to heat
	500 MJ of other energy losses

  (i)   What is the useful output of the power station?
  (ii) Calculate the efficiency of the power station.

7. (a) In order to generate electricity we must start with a source of energy. Four possible sources are coal, gas, oil, and wind. The following bar chart shows estimates of how long some of these are expected to last.

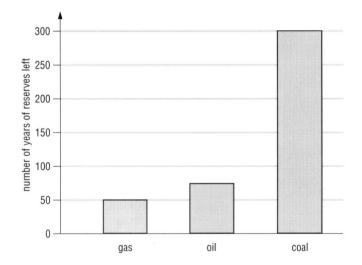

  (i)   How long is oil expected to last?   [1]
  (ii) Suggest **one** reason why coal will last longer than gas.   [1]
  (iii) Why is it **not** possible to show information for wind energy on the bar chart?   [1]
  (iv) A lot of effort has been put into developing the generation of electricity from wind energy. One reason why so much effort has been put into the use of wind energy is that we will eventually run out of coal, gas, and oil.
        Explain **one** other reason.   [2]
  (v)   Wind energy is an example of renewable energy. Give **three** other examples of renewable energy.   [3]
  (b) Most of the energy available to us originated in the Sun. Explain how some of the Sun's energy has become the energy which is now stored in coal. You should name the process and the type of energy involved at each stage.   [6]
  (c) In the United Kingdom about 20% of the electricity is generated in nuclear power stations.
      (i)   From which part of an atom does nuclear energy come?   [1]
      (ii) The following are all parts of a nuclear power station.

            boiler generator reactor turbine

            Put them in their correct order to show how they are used to produce electricity. [1]
      (iii) What useful energy transfer takes place in a generator?   [1]

                                                                      (SEG, Higher, 1998 Specimen)

8. (a) Jane uses a radiator to heat her room. The hot radiator is at one side of her room. Look at the diagram.

radiator

The **whole** room gets warm. Explain why. Use the idea of **convection** in your answer.   [3]

(b) Baked Alaska is a pudding. It is made by covering ice cream with whipped egg white. Whipped egg white contains a lot of air. Look at the diagram.

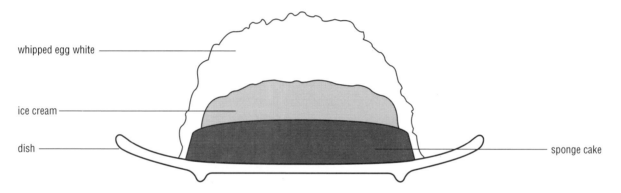

whipped egg white

ice cream

dish

sponge cake

The pudding is baked in a very hot oven for a short time. The ice cream does **not** melt in the oven. Explain why.   [1]

(c) The diagram shows a hot air paint stripper. Air is blown over an electrical heater. Look at the diagram.

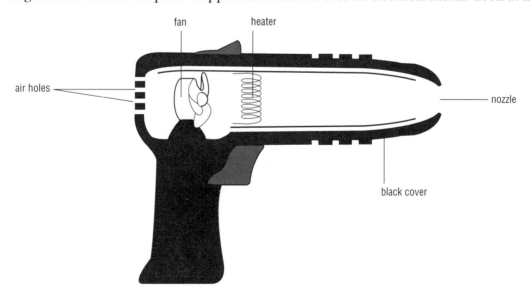

fan   heater

air holes

nozzle

black cover

(i) The cover has a dull black surface. This surface helps to keep the cover cool. Explain how.   [1]
(ii) The cover has ridges. How do these ridges help keep the cover cool?   [1]

(MEG, Higher, 1998 Specimen)

6.1 Radioactivity

Some naturally occurring materials release energy in the form of (nuclear) **radiation**. They are called radioactive materials. The effect is called **radioactivity**. The changes in the radioactive materials are described as radioactive decay – new substances are formed as the original substance changes, or decays.

We are exposed to radiation every day from radioactive sources such as:

- Naturally occurring radon and thoron gas in rocks.
- Medical sources, such as X-rays.
- Fallout from nuclear weapons testing carried out years ago.
- Waste from the nuclear industry, such as nuclear power stations.
- Cosmic rays, from outer space.
- Naturally occurring stone used in (some) buildings.

Radiation from natural sources such as these is described as 'background radiation'. Although it does not produce any noticeable effects on our health, doctors and scientists believe that any exposure, no matter how small, poses some risk.

Ionising radiation

When radiation from radioactive materials strikes neutral atoms or molecules, it can alter their atomic structure leaving them as charged particles or **ions**. This type of radiation is called **ionising radiation**. We say the uncharged molecules or atoms have been ionised. The process is called **ionisation**.

Ionising radiation can be detected using a Geiger counter – a Geiger-Müller tube connected to a ratemeter or a scaler. Each time ionising radiation enters the tube a small pulse of current is produced. Each pulse is 'counted'. The number of counts per second gives a measure of the activity of the radioactive source.

Ionising radiation is particularly dangerous to living cells – it can alter the structure of the cells in such a way that they may become cancerous. The larger the dose of ionising radiation, the greater the risk of cancer.

During **radiotherapy** treatment, cancerous cells are exposed to measured doses of ionising radiation. By carefully focusing the radiation the cancer cells may be killed, leaving normal cells undamaged.

Ionising radiation can be used to sterilise some foods and medical instruments because it kills any micro-organisms which may be present.

Types of ionising radiation

There are three types of ionising radiation:

- **Alpha (α) radiation** is a stream of particles which are released by changes that take place inside the nuclei of atoms. An alpha particle has the same structure as the helium nucleus – two protons and two neutrons.

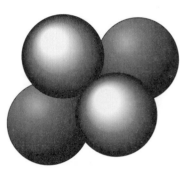

Figure 6.1.1 An alpha particle contains two protons and two neutrons

Alpha particles are fairly heavy and slow. Their energy is easily absorbed by a few centimetres of air or a thin sheet of paper.
- **Beta (β) radiation** is a stream of very fast-moving electrons. The electrons are released from the nucleus of an atom when changes take place inside the nucleus. Beta radiation easily passes through air or thin paper, but is absorbed by a few millimetres of metal.
- **Gamma (γ) radiation** is radiation transferred as an electromagnetic wave with a very short wavelength. Gamma radiation travels at the same speed as light (186 000 miles per second or 300 000 000 metres per second). Gamma radiation is very penetrating and is only absorbed by several centimetres of lead or several metres of concrete.

Figure 6.1.2 summarises the properties of these three types of ionising radiation.

The different properties of alpha, beta and gamma radiation mean that they have markedly different effects on the human body:

- When the sources of radiation are *outside the body*, beta and gamma radiation are the most dangerous because they are able to penetrate the outer layers of the body, reaching cells in the major organs. The cells may become cancerous, and the cancer may spread rapidly through the organs to other parts of the body.
- Alpha radiation is less dangerous under these circumstances because it is easily absorbed by the skin. It is therefore unlikely to reach cells beneath this outer layer.

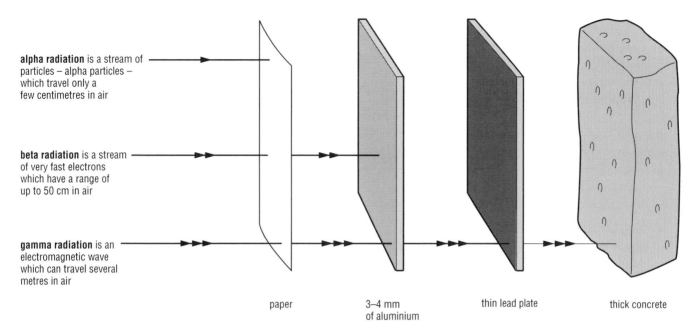

alpha radiation is a stream of particles – alpha particles – which travel only a few centimetres in air

beta radiation is a stream of very fast electrons which have a range of up to 50 cm in air

gamma radiation is an electromagnetic wave which can travel several metres in air

paper

3–4 mm of aluminium

thin lead plate

thick concrete

Figure 6.1.2 The three types of nuclear radiation and a guide to their penetrating powers

- If the radioactive source is *inside the body* (which may happen if the radioactive substance is swallowed or breathed in), alpha radiation is the most dangerous because it is readily absorbed by the cells (in the major organs), causing structural damage.
- Beta and gamma radiation are less dangerous than alpha radiation inside the body, because cells are less likely to absorb (significant amounts of) their radiation.

Quick Questions

1 a) What is meant by the term 'background radiation'?
   b) State three sources of background radiation.
2 Alpha, beta and gamma are all ionising radiations.
   a) Which of these ionising radiations (α, β or γ) is an electromagnetic wave?
   b) Which of the ionising radiations (α, β or γ) consists of particles which are helium nuclei?
   c) Complete this sentence: 'A helium nucleus consists of .... protons and .... neutrons tightly bound together.'
   d) Which radiation has the greatest penetrating power?
   e) Which form of ionising radiation is absorbed by a thin sheet of paper?
   f) Which form of ionising radiation is most dangerous if its source gets inside the body?
   g) How could you protect yourself against the effects of beta radiation?

3 A radioactive source was placed a short distance from a Geiger counter. Various absorbers, shown in the table below, were placed between the source and the counter. The following readings were made using the counter.

Absorber	Activity (counts/minute)
No absorber present	2400
Tissue paper	2000
2 mm thick card	1600
1 cm of lead	20
Background	20

What does this information tell you about the radioactive source?

6.2 Why are some substances radioactive?

Atoms of different elements have different numbers of protons, neutrons and electrons. The number of protons, neutrons and electrons in any atom can be worked out if we know the **atomic number** (the position of the element in the periodic table) and the **mass number** (or **nucleon** number). These numbers can be found from the periodic table of the elements.

mass number (*A*) = atomic number (*Z*) + number of neutrons

This is the **mass number** (or nucleon number) and is given the symbol *A*. It is the total number of protons and neutrons in the nucleus of the atom

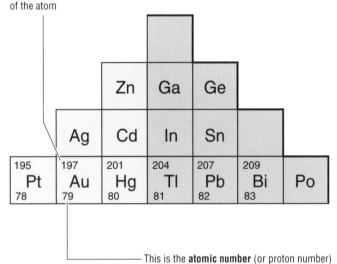

This is the **atomic number** (or proton number) and is given the symbol *Z*. It is the number of protons in the nucleus. No two elements ever have the same atomic number

Figure 6.2.1 A portion of the periodic table

Worked example

The periodic table shows the element uranium as $^{238}_{92}\text{U}$.

The atomic number of uranium is therefore 92, so there are 92 protons in each atom of this particular form of uranium. If there are 92 protons, there will also be 92 electrons. Using

mass number = atomic number + number of neutrons,

then:

number of neutrons = mass number − atomic number
$$= 238 - 92 = 146$$

One atom of uranium will therefore contain:

92 protons
92 electrons
146 neutrons

Isotopes

Isotopes are different forms of the same element which have different mass numbers. They have the same atomic number (and therefore the same position in the periodic table, which is why they do not appear twice). Any isotope of an element that is radioactive is called a radioisotope, or radionuclide.

The element iodine exists in two forms. 'Safe' iodine, found naturally in the thyroid gland in the human body, is iodine-127 – the commonest form. The other form – iodine-131 – is dangerous and can cause cancer of the thyroid gland. Iodine-127 and iodine-131 are isotopes of the same element – iodine.

Table 6.2.1 The isotopes of iodine

Iodine-127	Iodine-131
Atomic number 53	Atomic number 53
Mass number 127	Mass number 131

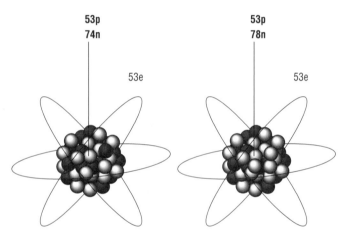

iodine-127
(mass number 127)

iodine-131
(mass number 131)

Figure 6.2.2 Iodine-131 has four extra neutrons and is radioactive

Unstable elements

The nuclei of some atoms, particularly those with atomic numbers above 84, are very unstable and break down (decay) readily, accompanied by the release of energy and other, smaller, particles. These elements are the radioactive elements. During the process of decay, their atomic structure changes and a different material is formed.

When the nucleus of a uranium-238 atom breaks down, an alpha particle (a particle with the same structure as the helium nucleus) leaves the atom. Energy is transferred from the atom by the alpha particle. In the process a new material – thorium – is formed.

In general, when an unstable nucleus disintegrates:

- Ionising radiation is emitted.
- A different atom, with a different number of nucleons is formed.

Some radioactive materials emit only one type of radiation. Others might emit all three types.

Alpha emission

Radium is a radioactive material which emits alpha particles as it decays to form radon gas. An alpha particle is identical to the nucleus of a helium atom, containing two protons and two neutrons. As a result, the original atom changes into a new particle which has a nucleus containing two protons and two neutrons fewer than the original atom.

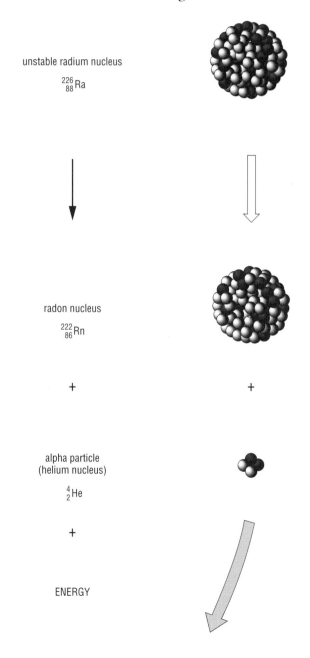

unstable radium nucleus

$^{226}_{88}$Ra

radon nucleus

$^{222}_{86}$Rn

+

alpha particle
(helium nucleus)

$^{4}_{2}$He

+

ENERGY

Figure 6.2.3 The decay of radium by alpha emission

Beta emission

Iodine-131 is a radioisotope which is a beta emitter. It decays to form xenon gas. Beta radiation consists of high energy electrons. The electrons do not come from those which orbit the atom, but are produced in the nucleus as a neutron breaks down. As it does, a proton is formed, the beta particle (electron) is emitted and energy is released. The original atom changes into a new particle with one extra proton in its nucleus, but one less neutron.

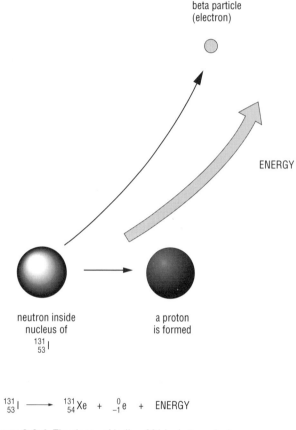

beta particle
(electron)

ENERGY

neutron inside
nucleus of
$^{131}_{53}$I

a proton
is formed

$$^{131}_{53}\text{I} \longrightarrow {}^{131}_{54}\text{Xe} + {}^{0}_{-1}\text{e} + \text{ENERGY}$$

Figure 6.2.4 The decay of iodine-231 by beta emission

Gamma emission

Gamma radiation is a form of electromagnetic radiation similar to X-rays but with a shorter wavelength. It is very penetrating. It is produced as the particles left in the nucleus re-organise themselves after emitting an alpha or a beta particle. Because gamma radiation is not particulate, its emission does not affect the atomic number of the atom in any way – the number of particles in the atom does not change.

Half-life

As the atoms in a radioactive material decay it becomes less radioactive. The rate at which radiation is emitted, measured using a Geiger-Müller tube, decreases.

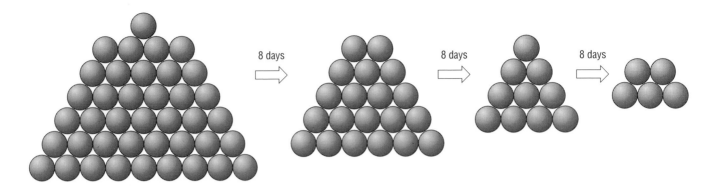

Figure 6.2.5 Imagine looking at just 40 radioactive iodine-131 atoms. After 8 days, 20 would have decayed, leaving only 20 radioactive atoms. After another 8 days, 10 more would have decayed, leaving only 10 radioactive atoms. After a further 8 days, 5 more would have decayed, leaving only 5 radioactive atoms. As a result the activity (the number of particles decaying in a particular time) would decrease

The **half-life** of a radioactive substance is the time taken for half of the nuclei in any sample of the material to decay. It follows that the half-life of a substance is the time taken for the count rate to fall to half of its original value. From the illustration above, you can see that every 8 days the number of radioactive iodine-131 nuclei falls by one half. The half-life of iodine-131 is therefore 8 days.

Although this seems to suggest that the substance decays in a regular manner this is not the case. In fact, the decay is entirely random. There will be times when nuclei decay more rapidly. Only when we consider longer periods of time (significantly longer than the half-life) can we estimate how the radioactive material will change with any degree of accuracy.

Testing the half-life of a radioactive material

The half-life of some radioactive substances can be found experimentally using a Geiger-Müller tube and scaler. The substance is placed in a position where the radiation can be detected by the Geiger-Müller tube. The count rate is noted every minute for, say, 6 minutes. Sample results might look like those in Table 6.2.2.

Table 6.2.2 Experimental results

Time (minutes)	0	1	2	3	4	5	6
Count rate (counts per minute)	490	395	320	258	220	180	140

The count rate will include any background radiation detected during the experiment. A separate experiment is done to find the background count rate, normally by measuring the background count over a period of several minutes and finding an average value. This must then be subtracted from the experimental results shown in Table 6.2.2. A corrected table (showing only the count rate produced by the radioactive source) can then be constructed. Assuming the background count was 30 counts/minute, the corrected values would be as shown in Table 6.2.3.

Table 6.2.3 Results corrected for background radiation

Time (minutes)	0	1	2	3	4	5	6
Count rate (counts per minute)	460	365	290	228	190	150	110

The data can then be plotted on a graph as shown below.

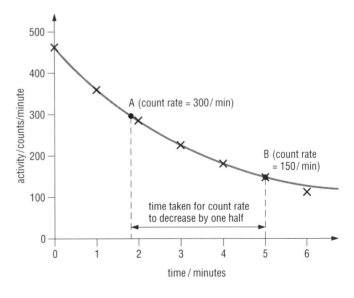

Figure 6.2.6 Finding the half-life of a radioactive substance

To find the half-life:

- Choose any point with a suitable count rate on the graph (A).
- Find a second point where the number of counts per minute is exactly half of the first value chosen (B).
- The half-life is the time taken for the substance to decay from A to B. This can be read from the horizontal axis.

For this substance the half-life would be 3.2 minutes.

Radiotracers

Radioisotopes are often used in hospitals as tracers. When inhaled or injected into the blood stream their progress through the organs can be traced using a special 'camera'.

To ensure that the radiation is able to pass through tissues to reach the 'camera', the radioisotopes are generally gamma emitters. Two common radiotracers are:

- Technetium-99, which, when injected into the body can be used to check the function of the brain, kidneys, lungs and the bones.
- Xenon-133, a gas which can be inhaled, allowing problems in the respiratory system to be identified.

Prolonged exposure to gamma radiation can cause damage to the cells of the body. Radiotracers used in medicine must quickly lose their radioactivity, so those which are used have short half-lives.

Radioactive dating

Carbon-12 is a stable carbon atom found in the atmosphere. In the upper atmosphere, when struck by cosmic radiation, carbon-12 changes into an unstable radioisotope, carbon-14, which has a half-life of 5740 years.

Trees and plants, when living, absorb both forms of carbon from the atmosphere. Once the tree dies, it no longer absorbs carbon. The carbon-14 that is already in the wood decays, forming the more stable

carbon-12. As the amount of carbon-14 in the wood decreases, the wood becomes less and less radioactive. By measuring the amount of radiation given off by a sample of wood, and knowing the half-life of carbon-14, we can deduce the age of the wood (or any materials, such as linen, made from plant materials). The process is known as **carbon dating**.

Similar processes can be used to find the age of rocks in the earth's crust. Uranium isotopes, which have a very long half-life, decay through a series of relatively short-lived radioisotopes to form stable isotopes of lead. The relative proportions of uranium and lead in a sample of igneous rock can be used to determine the age of the rock.

Quick Questions

1. What is meant by the 'half-life' of a substance?
2. A radioactive substance has a half-life of 2 years. How long will it take for the level of radioactivity to fall to one-eighth of its current value?
3. Fill in the missing numbers A, Z in the following equations, which show alpha and beta decay.
   a) $^{238}_{92}U \rightarrow {}^{A}_{Z}Th + {}^{4}_{2}He$
   b) $^{228}_{88}Ra \rightarrow {}^{A}_{Z}Ac + {}^{0}_{-1}e$
4. Name one radioisotope that is used in medicine as a tracer to examine organs in the body.
5. Which properties of radioisotopes make them suitable for use as radiotracers?
6. An experiment was carried out to find the half-life of a radioactive material. The background count was measured at 30 counts/minute before using the radioactive source. The results were:

Time (minutes)	0	1	1.8	3	5	7.5
Count rate (counts/minute)	830	530	380	230	110	55

Draw another table showing the count rate and time after correcting it for background radiation.

Plot a graph of corrected count rate against time and use it to find the half-life of the source.

6.3 Nuclear power

A significant proportion of electricity is now generated in nuclear power stations using nuclear 'fuels' such as uranium or plutonium. The energy released as the nuclei of these materials decay is used to generate electricity.

Fission

The decay process that occurs as heavy, unstable nuclei split into two is called nuclear **fission**. It is the fission process that is used in a nuclear reactor. Large amounts of energy are released. The splitting of the nuclei occurs inside the fuel rods of the reactor.

When the nucleus of an atom splits in two, it emits one or more neutrons at high speed. The ejected neutrons strike neighbouring nuclei, causing them to split in the same way. As they split, they release further neutrons which strike more nuclei, and so on. The process is a 'chain reaction' – nucleus after nucleus is split by neutrons ejected when an earlier nucleus was split (Figure 6.3.1).

The core of a nuclear reactor is designed so that the fission reactions can be carefully controlled (see Figure 6.3.2 opposite).

If uncontrolled, the chain reaction would build up so quickly that huge amounts of energy would be released in a short space of time – a nuclear explosion would occur. This is what happens when a nuclear bomb explodes – the uncontrolled fission reactions produce disastrous results.

Nuclear waste

Each time a nucleus splits, energy is released. In time, the rate at which nuclei are split slows down, because there are fewer and fewer of the original nuclei left. The 'exhausted' fuel rods are then removed and replaced with fresh uranium. The exhausted fuel rods are still highly radioactive, so they must be stored in conditions that do not allow living things, either directly or indirectly (through the food chain) to be exposed to the radiation they emit.

Waste materials from nuclear power plants are classed as either 'high level' or 'low level' waste. The high level waste from the core of the reactor is often embedded in concrete and stored in a sealed environment (often deep underground) for several thousand years before it will be safe. Some low level waste, such as slightly radioactive water, is washed into the sea. Small amounts of radioactive dust and gases may pass into the air.

Do we want nuclear power?

The advantages and disadvantages of nuclear power stations have been much discussed over recent years. They are summarised in Table 6.3.1 opposite.

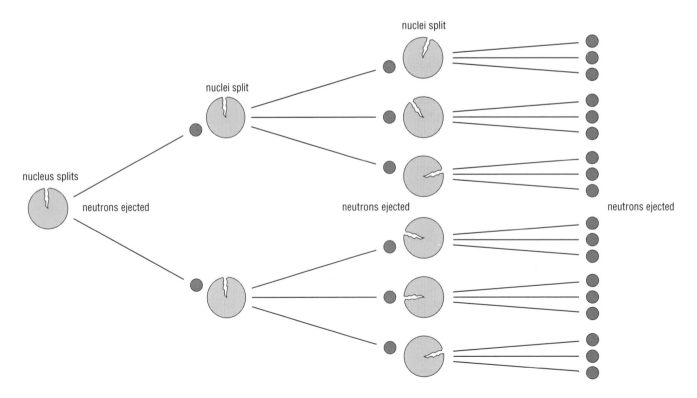

Figure 6.3.1 Fission can develop into a chain reaction

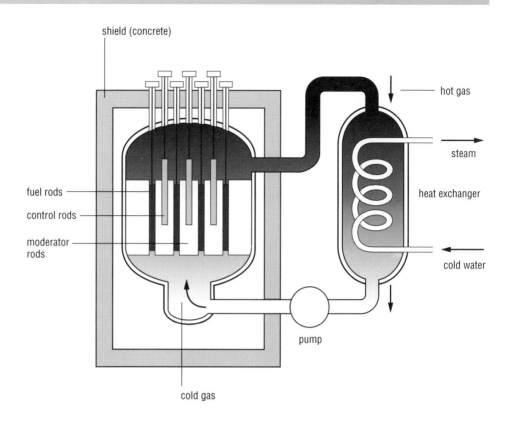

The fuel rods contain pellets of pure uranium-235. 1 kg of uranium-235 produces as much electricity as 60 tonnes of coal. The rods are lowered into the core of the reactor

Boron-steel control rods can be raised or lowered between the fuel rods. Boron-steel absorbs neutrons. Lowering the rods slows the reaction, as more neutrons are absorbed (effectively preventing them from splitting other nuclei). Raising the control rods increases the rate of the reaction

Graphite moderator rods are placed between the fuel rods. Uranium-235 splits best when low speed neutrons strike the nuclei. The graphite moderator slows down the high speed neutrons

High pressure carbon dioxide gas circulates inside the core of the reactor, absorbing the energy released by the fission process. As the gas passes over heat exchangers, it heats the water inside, changing it into high pressure steam which drives the turbines

Figure 6.3.2 The core of a gas-cooled nuclear reactor

Table 6.3.1 Advantages and disadvantages of nuclear power

Advantages	Disadvantages
• Large amounts of energy from small amounts of fuel; 1 kg of uranium produces as much energy as 60 tonnes of coal • Little environmental pollution providing strict precautions are taken • Generally reliable; little maintenance • Relatively low cost of producing energy • High power output from single power station	• Non-renewable fuel • Potentially highly dangerous; strict safeguards are needed to prevent dangers to all living things • Very expensive to build power stations • Very expensive to dismantle and clean up power stations at the end of their useful life; land beneath may be contaminated for thousands of years afterwards • Waste materials need to be stored for several thousand years and are highly dangerous; many unknown factors about waste disposal

Quick Questions
● ●

1 Name two materials that are used as fuel in nuclear power stations.

2 Radioactive materials undergo *fission* in nuclear power stations. What is meant by the word *fission*?

3 In a nuclear reactor, what is the purpose of
   a) the fuel rods;
   b) the control rods;
   c) the moderator?

4 Why is the reaction that takes place inside the core of a nuclear reactor described as a 'chain' reaction?

5 Used fuel rods contain materials with extremely long half-lives. What steps need to be taken to ensure that they are stored so that they pose no risk to the public or the environment?

Section Six: Examination Practice Questions

1. **(a)** The symbol below is shown outside a storeroom.

      (i)   What does it tell you about the materials in the store?
      (ii)   Why would the storeroom normally be well away from where people regularly work?
      (iii) Outside which hospital department might you see the same symbol?
      (iv) At what type of power station would you see the symbol?

   (b) The dangerous materials are stored in a wooden box which is lined with metal.
      (i)   Why is the box lined with metal?
      (ii)   Which type of metal is normally used?
      (iii) Suggest **two** safety precautions which should be taken when using the dangerous materials.

2. The diagram below shows how a radioactive source and sensor automatically control the filling of soap powder packets.

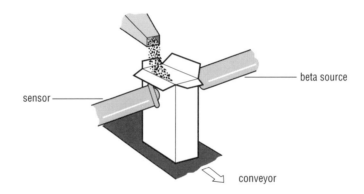

When the packet is empty, beta radiation passes from the source to the sensor. When the packet is filled, the beta radiation is absorbed. The sensor detects that the radiation has been blocked and switches off the flow of powder until the next packet arrives.

   (a) Why would an alpha source be of little use here?
   (b) Why could a gamma source not be used?
   (c) Why is a beta source such a good choice?
   (d) Why does the presence of the radiation source pose little risk to workers?

3. This diagram shows a model of the atom.

   (a) What is the name for the central part of the atom (A)?
   (b) What is the name of the uncharged particles found inside the atom?
   (c) Which particles are positively charged?
   (d) Which particles are negatively charged?
   (e) Where is nearly all the mass concentrated in an atom?
   (f) Some atoms emit radiation. What is the source of the radiation?

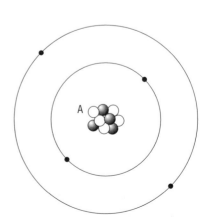

4. There are three types of nuclear radiation, known as alpha, beta and gamma.
  (a) (i)   Which form of radiation is an electromagnetic wave?
      (ii) Which form consists of particles which have the same structure as a helium nucleus?
      (iii) Which form consists of high energy electrons?
      (iv) Which form is used to sterilise hospital equipment?
  (b) A Geiger counter is left working in Mr Walker's laboratory after all the radioactive sources have been taken away to the storeroom. He notices that radiation is still being detected.
      (i)   What is this radiation called?
      (ii) Name **two** sources of the radiation.
  (c) A radioactive source which emits alpha, beta and gamma radiation is placed in front of a Geiger counter. Three absorbers are placed in turn between the source and the counter and the following results are obtained.

Material	Corrected counts/min
none (air)	600
thin sheet of paper	450
3 mm of aluminium	300
30 mm of lead	100

      (i)   What is meant by **corrected counts/min**?
      (ii) Which type of radiation would be absorbed by the paper?
      (iii) Which type(s) of radiation would be absorbed by the aluminium?
      (iv) Why is a count still obtained even when 30 mm of lead is used?
  (d) Describe **two** ways in which radioactive sources are used.

5. **(a)** Here are some words which will help you in this section. Each word may be used once, more than once or not at all.

  electron   cathode   nucleus   electrode

      (i)   What is the centre of the atom called?   [1]
      (ii) Radioactivity happens when part of an atom breaks up. Which part?   [1]
  (b) A radioactivity detector is placed near a radioactive source. The detector is used to take measurements. It is moved further away for each reading. Look at the diagram.

source   detector

  The detector can detect three kinds of radiation:

  alpha   beta   gamma

      (i)   Which kind of radiation is stopped by 5 cm of air?   [1]
      (ii) Which radiation will pass through paper but not 3 mm of aluminium?   [1]
      (iii) Which kind of radiation is most penetrative?   [1]

(c) Nirvisha tries a different experiment with the radioactivity detector. She uses a different radiation source. She takes readings from the detector every 10 s.
Look at the graph of her results.

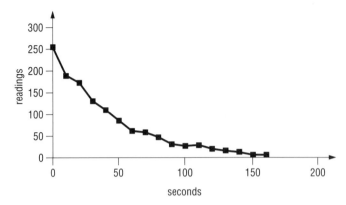

(i) The detector starts reading at a value of 250. How long did it take for the detector reading to fall to a value of 100? [2]

(ii) At the end of the experiment Nirvisha puts the radioactive source away. The detector still gives a small reading even though the radioactive source is not there. Explain why. [1]

(d) Write down one use of radioactivity. [1]

(MEG, Foundation, 1998 Specimen)

6. Radioactive isotopes can be used to locate internal bleeding in the body. A commonly used radioactive isotope is ^{131}I. This emits gamma radiation and has a half-life of 8 days.

(a) Describe what is meant by **radioactive isotope**. [3]

(b) Describe what is meant by **half-life**. [2]

(c) The activity of a sample of ^{131}I was measured over a period of 20 minutes on three separate occasions. The readings obtained were:

338 Bq,   356 Bq   and   326 Bq

(i) Explain why the readings were **not** all the same. [1]

(ii) Calculate the average count rate for the radioactive isotope. [1]

(d) A patient has internal bleeding from a blood vessel in her leg. A small quantity of the isotope ^{131}I is injected into her blood stream. A detector is used to find the internal bleeding. The diagram below shows the arrangement and the results of the test.

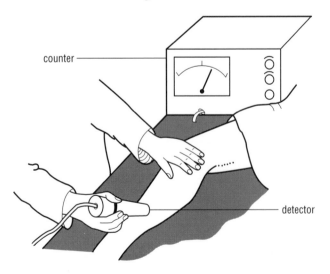

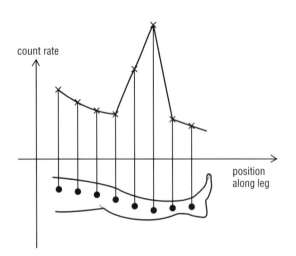

(i) State the name of a suitable detector. [1]

(ii) The radioactive isotope used for this purpose is a gamma emitter and not an alpha emitter. Why is a gamma emitter used? [3]

(iii) How will the doctor tell from the results where internal bleeding is taking place? [2]

(London, Foundation, 1998 Specimen)

Higher Level

1. (a) Radium has an atomic number of 88 and a mass number of 226 – $^{226}_{88}$Ra.
  (i) How many protons are there in the radium nucleus?
  (ii) How many neutrons are there in the radium nucleus?
(b) The reaction in a nuclear reactor can be represented by the equation:

$$^{235}_{92}U + ^{1}_{0}n \rightarrow aX + cY + 3^{1}_{0}n + energy$$

where X and Y are substances formed by the breakdown of the uranium.
  (i) What is the name given to the process whereby the uranium breaks down to form two other substances?
  (ii) *b* and *d* represent the atomic numbers of substances X and Y. What will be the numerical value of (*b* + *d*)?
  (iii) *a* and *c* represent the mass numbers of substances X and Y. What will be the numerical value of (*a* + *c*)?
  (iv) How many neutrons are emitted from the uranium-235 as it breaks down?

2. (a) These results were obtained by measuring the activity of a radioactive sample over a period of 6 minutes.
  (i) Draw another table showing the corrected count rate (taking into account the effects of background radiation).
  (ii) Draw a graph and estimate the half-life of the sample being tested.

Background count = 25 counts/minute

Time (minutes)	Activity (counts/min)
1	485
2	390
3	315
4	215
5	175
6	135

(b) Radioactive carbon-14 is formed in the upper atmosphere and mixes with the (non-radioactive) carbon-12 in the lower atmosphere. Both types of carbon are absorbed by the leaves of trees during photosynthesis. As a result, one gram of living wood emits 16 beta particles per minute, on average. When the tree dies the carbon-14 begins to decay (forming carbon-12). The carbon-14 has a half-life of 5700 years.
  (i) Draw a graph showing how the number of beta emissions from one gram of wood will change over a period of 30 000 years following the death of the tree.
  (ii) Some small wooden bowls were found on an archaeological site. When tested, they were found to be emitting 7 beta particles per minute per gram. Use your graph to estimate their age.

3. (a) In an experiment a Geiger counter was started at zero and five minutes later showed a count of 420. Calculate the background radiation in counts per second during this experiment. Show clearly how you get to your answer. [3]
(b) (i) Radioactive substances may give off alpha (α), beta (β) or gamma (γ) radiation. Complete the **two** spaces in the following sentences with the correct type of radiation.
  .... radiation is at the high-frequency end of the electromagnetic spectrum.
  .... radiation consists of high speed electrons. [2]
  (ii) Complete the **two** spaces in the following sentence.
  Particles of .... radiation are the same as the nuclei of .... atoms. [2]
(c) The table gives information about four radioactive isotopes.

Isotope	Half-life	Type of radiation given out
thorium-231	1 day	beta (β)
protactinium-231	32 000 years	alpha (α)
actinium-227	22 years	beta (β)
thorium-227	18 days	alpha (α)

A radioactive source can be used to control the thickness of cardboard as it is manufactured. The following diagram shows how this is done.

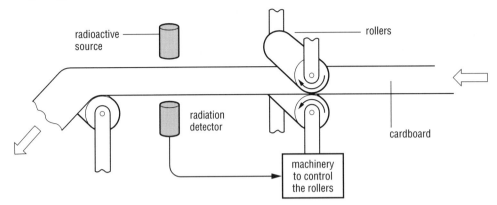

(i) Which **one** of the four isotopes in the table (on the previous page) would be the best choice for this radioactive source? Explain your answer. [3]

(ii) If the same rollers were used to produce steel none of the isotopes in the table would be suitable. Explain why and state the type of radioactive source that would be used. [2]

(SEG, Higher, 1998 Specimen, part)

4. Atomic nuclei contain both protons and neutrons. $^{11}_{6}C$, $^{12}_{6}C$ and $^{14}_{6}C$ are all forms of carbon. The nucleus of $^{11}_{6}C$ consists of 6 protons and 5 neutrons.

(a) (i) Write down the number of protons and neutrons in $^{12}_{6}C$. [2]

(ii) Explain why $^{14}_{6}C$ is described as 'neutron-rich'. [1]

(iii) What do the nuclei of $^{11}_{6}C$, $^{12}_{6}C$ and $^{14}_{6}C$ all have in common? [1]

(b) The graph below can be used to show the numbers of neutrons and protons in the lighter nuclei. The crosses represent the nuclei of $^{12}_{6}C$ and $^{14}_{6}C$.

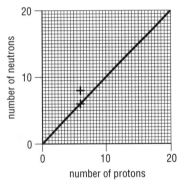

For a nucleus to be stable, a plot of its number of neutrons against its number of protons must lie on or close to the diagonal line.

(i) Sketch the graph and mark **X** to show the position of $^{11}_{6}C$. [1]

(ii) What is the condition for a nucleus with less than 10 protons to be stable? [1]

(iii) Which form of carbon is the most stable? Explain your answer. [2]

(c) The diagram below represents the decay of a nucleus of $^{14}_{6}C$.

(i) Use the diagram to write down what happens to the numbers of protons and neutrons when $^{14}_{6}C$ decays. [2]

key
○ proton
● neutron

(ii) What particle is missing from the right hand side of the diagram? [1]

(London, Higher, 1998 Specimen)

Glossary

Absolute zero   The lowest temperature ($-273\ °C$) that any substance can reach. At this temperature the molecules or atoms of the substance have no heat energy.

Acceleration   The rate of change of velocity of a body.

Acceleration due to gravity   The acceleration of a freely falling body within a gravitational field. Close to the surface of the earth its value is $10\ m/s^2$.

Alpha radiation   Particulate radiation emitted by the decay of some radioactive substances which consists of a stream of (relatively) slow moving helium nuclei.

Alternating current (a.c.)   Electric current whose direction alternates (changes) at regular intervals.

Ammeter   An instrument used to measure electric current.

Ampere   The unit used to measure electric current.

Amplitude   The maximum displacement of an oscillation from its mean position.

Asteroid belt   A region between the orbits of Mars and Jupiter which contains much rock debris.

Atmospheric pressure   The pressure exerted on a body by the atmosphere, due to the weight of the atmosphere. At the surface of the earth atmospheric pressure is $100\ kPa/m^2$.

Atomic number   The position of an element in the periodic table of the elements. The atomic number is equivalent to the number of protons in the nucleus of the atom.

Beta radiation   Particulate radiation emitted by some radioactive substances which consists of a stream of high energy electrons.

Boiling point   The temperature at which a substance undergoes a change of state between liquid and gas (vapour).

Capacitor   A component of electronic systems which can be charged and discharged, and which may be used to create time delays.

Carbon dating   A process in which relative amounts of carbon-12 and radioactive carbon-14 are measured to date the remains of living material.

Centre of gravity   The single point on a body at which the weight appears to act.

Centripetal force   The force that acts towards the centre of the circle in which a body is moving, which keeps the body in circular motion.

Compression   The state of any object that is subject to inward-acting (squashing) forces. Also, a region of a medium within which the particles are at above mean pressure, due to the passing of a sound wave.

Concave lens   A curved section of a refracting material which causes parallel light to diverge after refraction.

Conduction (thermal)   The process of transferring heat through a material without any visible change in the motion of the particles of the material.

Conductors   Materials that allow the ready transfer of heat by conduction, or of electricity by current flow.

Convection   The process of transferring heat by the movement of the fluid (liquid or gas) through which heat is being transferred.

Convection current   The continuous transfer of heat by circulation in a fluid. Convection currents are created by changes in the density of the fluid – the warmed fluid expands, and therefore has a lower density than the surrounding fluid. The less dense fluid rises through the denser, cooler fluid, carrying heat with it.

Convex lens   A curved section of refracting material which causes parallel rays of light to converge after refraction.

Coulomb   The unit representing the amount of charge passing any point in a circuit when a current of 1 ampere flows past that point for 1 second.

Critical angle   The angle of incidence at which light undergoes total internal reflection at a boundary between a dense and a less dense substance.

Diffraction   The spreading of waves as they pass by the edge of an obstacle or through a narrow slit.

Direct current (d.c.)   The flow of charge through a circuit in one direction only.

Dispersion   The phenomenon in which radiation is separated into its constituent wavelengths. Dispersion causes white light to separate into seven colours – red, orange, yellow, green, blue, indigo and violet – which collectively form the spectrum of white light.

Echo   A sound that has undergone reflection.

Efficiency   The ratio of the useful energy obtained from a device compared with the amount of energy put into the device to operate it.

Elastic (behaviour)   The property of a material that regains its original shape after some deforming force has been removed, providing the elastic limit of the material has not been exceeded. Also, a type of collision between bodies in which the total kinetic energy is conserved.

Elastic limit   The load beyond which a material ceases to show elastic properties and exhibits plastic behaviour.

Electric charge   A quantity of unbalanced (positive or negative) electricity.

Electric current   The rate at which charge flows through a conductor.

Electrical energy   Energy associated with the flow of charge through any part of a conducting circuit.

Electromagnet   A soft iron core surrounded by a coil of wire, which acts as a magnet when current flows through the coil.

Electromagnetic induction   The generation of an induced electric current when a conductor is moved through a magnetic field. The transfer of electrical power from one circuit to another (as in the case of transformers).

Electromagnetic spectrum   A continuous arrangement that displays electromagnetic waves in order of increasing frequency or wavelength.

Electromagnetic waves   Transverse waves that consist of electric and magnetic oscillations at right angles to one another and to the direction of travel.

Electrons   Negatively charged particles found orbiting the nucleus of an atom, also emitted from a radioactive nucleus in beta decay.

Equilibrium   The situation in which the effects of several forces cancel one another in terms of both magnitude and direction, producing zero resultant force. The state of a body at rest, or moving with constant velocity.

Evaporation   A process by which liquid molecules may become vapour molecules at a temperature other than the boiling point.

Fission   The process whereby large unstable atomic nuclei split into two smaller nuclei, releasing energy.

Force multiplier   Any machine that during operation converts a small force into a larger force.

Fossil fuels   Fuels formed over millions of years by the partial decay of the remains of living things.

Free electrons   Electrons that are able to move freely from atom to atom within a material.

Frequency   The rate at which some regular disturbance takes place. For a wave this represents the number of complete oscillations per second.

Friction   A force caused by contact between two uneven surfaces moving past one another, or between the surface of a body and the fluid in which it moves, which resists the motion of a body.

Galaxy   A group of millions of stars, held together by gravity.

Gamma radiation   Electromagnetic (non-particulate) radiation emitted by the decay of particles inside the nucleus of atoms of some radioactive substances.

Gravitational field strength   The gravitational force exerted on a 1 kg mass placed within any gravitational field.

Gravitational potential energy   The energy stored in a body that has been raised within the earth's gravitational field.

Gravity   An 'action at a distance' force of attraction between two bodies.

Half-life   The time taken for half of the nuclei of a radioactive substance to undergo disintegration (decay).

Heat   Thermal energy in the process of being transferred in some way.

Hertz   A unit of frequency of vibrations. 1 hertz is equivalent to one oscillation per second.

Hooke's Law   Relates to the elastic behaviour of materials: *the extension of a material is proportional to the applied load, provided the elastic limit is not exceeded.*

Hydraulic system   A system that transfers force from place to place using fluids.

Ideal gas equation   The relationship between pressure, volume and temperature of a fixed mass of gas under conditions of change.

Induced current   A current that is induced in a conductor due to the relative motion of the conductor and a magnetic field.

Insulators   Materials that prevent, or significantly inhibit, the flow of heat, or electricity, through them.

Internal reflection   The phenomenon in which light undergoes reflection at the boundary between two surfaces which have different optical densities.

Ions   Particles that have excess negative or positive charge.

Ionisation   The process in which an uncharged atom or molecule becomes charged.

Ionising radiation   Radiation that causes the ionisation of atoms or molecules, leaving them with excess positive or negative charge.

Isotopes   Forms of the same element with the same atomic number but different mass numbers. Some elements have only one natural isotope but all have artificially created isotopes.

Joule   The unit of energy. 1 joule is the work done when a force of 1 newton moves its point of application through a distance of 1 metre in the direction of the force.

Kilowatt   A unit of power equal to 1000 watts, or a rate of energy transfer of 1000 joules per second.

Kilowatt-hour   A unit used by electricity supply companies, representing the energy dissipated in one hour by a device with a power of 1 kilowatt.

Kinetic energy   Energy associated with the movement of a body.

Latent heat   The heat exchanged when a substance undergoes some change of state (with no accompanying change in temperature).

Lever   An appliance which is pivoted about some point, and which generates a turning effect when a force is applied at some point other than the pivot.

Light dependent resistor (LDR)   An electronic component whose resistance varies with light intensity.

Logic gates   A group of digital systems in which the state of the output depends on a particular combination of input conditions being met.

Longitudinal wave   An energy-carrying wave in which the movement of the particles is in line with the direction in which the energy is being transferred.

Machine   An appliance that enables work to be done.

Magnetic field   A space in which forces would act on magnetic poles placed within it.

Mass   The property of a body that resists attempts to change its motion.

Mass number   The number of particles (protons and neutrons) inside the nucleus of an atom.

Melting point   The temperature at which a substance undergoes a change of state between solid and liquid.

Moment   The turning effect created by a force acting on a lever.

Momentum   A property associated with the mass and velocity of a body.

Neutrons   Uncharged particles found in the nuclei of atoms.

Newton   The unit of force. 1 newton is the force that gives a 1 kg mass an acceleration of 1 m/s^2.

Non-renewable source   A source of energy that is used up faster than it can be replaced.

Nucleon   A general term used to describe a particle (proton or neutron) found in the nucleus of an atom.

Ohm   The unit of electrical resistance. 1 ohm is the resistance of a sample of conducting material across which a potential difference of 1 volt causes a current of 1 ampere to flow.

Ohm's Law   A relationship between the current flowing through a conductor and the potential difference across the ends of the conductor: *the current through a conductor is proportional to the potential difference across the ends of that conductor, provided the temperature of the conductor is constant.*

Optical fibres   Very thin strands of pure optical glass through which light undergoes total internal reflection.

Oscillation   One complete to-and-fro motion of a vibrating object.

Parallel circuit   A circuit in which the current passes through two or more paths, or loops, before rejoining.

Pascal   A unit of pressure equivalent to a force of 1 newton acting on 1 m^2.

Pitch   The property of a note that determines how 'high' or 'low' it sounds to the listener.

Plastic (behaviour)   A property of a material which, when subjected to some distorting force, remains deformed when the distorting force is removed.

Potential difference   The difference in electrical potential between two points through which a current is flowing. A potential difference of 1 volt exists between two points if 1 joule of electrical energy is changed into other forms when 1 coulomb of charge passes between the two points.

Potential energy   The energy stored in a body due to its position.

Power   The rate at which work is done or energy is transferred by a device.

Pressure   The force per unit area acting on a surface in such a way that it is tending to change the dimensions of the surface.

Primary light colours   Red, blue, green. By mixing these colours of light any other colour can be produced. Combining them equally produces white light.

Protons   Positively charged particles found in the nuclei of all atoms.

Radiation   The process of transferring energy by electromagnetic waves. Also (nuclear radiation) emissions of alpha particles, beta particles and gamma rays from radioactive nuclei.

Radioactivity   The physical changes (decays) that take place inside the nuclei of atoms of radioactive elements, and that result in the emission of (nuclear) radiation.

Radiotherapy   A medical procedure in which living tissue is exposed to controlled amounts of (nuclear) radiation.

Rarefaction   A region of a medium within which the particles are at below mean pressure, due to the passing of a sound wave.

Real image   An image formed by the convergence of real rays of light and which can be displayed on a screen.

Refraction   The phenomenon that occurs when a wave passes from one medium into another, causing a change in speed, and, possibly, direction.

Relay   A device operated by a low current that may be used to control a second circuit through which a larger current flows.

Renewable source   A source of energy that may be used repeatedly.

Resistance   A property of materials which resist the flow of electric current through them to some greater or lesser degree.

Resistivity   The resistance per unit length of unit cross-section of a material.

Resultant force   The effective force on a body on which several forces, of different magnitudes, may be acting in different directions.

Secondary light colours   Magenta, yellow, cyan. Produced by mixing two primary colours.

Series circuit   A circuit in which all devices are connected in one continuous loop through which a common current flows.

Sound energy   Energy that has been transformed into an audible form.

Sound wave   A longitudinal wave that transfers sound vibrations from place to place.

Specific heat capacity   The heat exchanged when 1 kg of a substance undergoes a change of temperature of 1 °C.

Specific latent heat of fusion   The heat exchanged when 1 kg of a substance undergoes a change of state between solid and liquid.

Specific latent heat of vaporisation   The heat exchanged when 1 kg of a substance undergoes a change of state between liquid and vapour.

Spectrum   An orderly arrangement of, for example, waves, in which the frequency (or wavelength) changes progressively.

Speed   The rate of change of distance with time for a moving body.

Structure   A framework of rigid parts that are integrally designed to resist forces that act within the framework.

Strut   Part of a structure that is resisting opposing forces that are tending to compress it.

Supernova   An exploding star.

Temperature   A measure of the relative 'hotness' of bodies; it depends on the average kinetic energy of the particles of a body.

Tension   The state of anything that is subject to outward-acting (stretching) forces.

Terminal velocity   The maximum velocity of a freely falling body in a fluid when the opposing forces are equal in magnitude and opposite in direction.

Thermal energy   Energy associated with heating effects.

Thermistor   An electronic component whose resistance varies with temperature.

Tie   Part of a structure that is resisting opposing forces that place it under tension.

Total internal reflection   A phenomenon that occurs when light travelling from a dense medium to a less dense medium strikes the boundary at an angle equal to or exceeding the critical angle for the material. The light is completely reflected into the denser medium.

Transformer   A device that transfers the energy of an alternating current in the primary coil to a secondary coil through electromagnetic induction. Transformers may be step-up transformers, producing a higher output voltage than that which is input, or step-down transformers, which convert a higher input voltage to a lower output voltage.

Transistor   A component of electronic systems which may act as a voltage dependent switch or an amplifier.

Transverse wave   A wave in which the oscillations are at right angles to the direction in which the wave transfers energy.

Truth table   A matrix that displays the output of a digital system for all possible input conditions.

Ultrasound   Sound waves with frequencies beyond the upper limit of human hearing.

Velocity   The rate of change of displacement of a moving body (in terms of both distance and direction) with time.

Virtual image   An image formed by the apparent convergence of virtual (non-real) rays of light and which cannot be displayed on a screen.

Volt   The unit of potential difference. A potential difference of 1 volt exists between two points when 1 joule of work is done in transferring 1 coulomb of charge between the two points. Alternatively, a potential difference of 1 volt exists between two points when 1 ampere of current dissipates 1 watt of power on passing between the two points.

Voltage   The value of the potential difference between two points (e.g. the terminals of a cell).

Voltmeter   An instrument used to measure potential difference (voltage).

Watt   The unit of power, equal to a rate of energy transfer (or work done) of 1 joule per second.

Wave equation   The relation *speed = frequency × wavelength* which applies to all forms of wave motion.

Wavelength   The distance between two successive points on a wave that are at the same stage of oscillation, i.e. in terms of their direction and displacement from their mean position.

Weight   The gravitational force acting on a body.

Work   The energy transferred in any system where a force causes movement. The work done is the product of the force and the distance moved by its point of application along the line in which the force acts.

Answers to questions

Section One: Quick Questions

1.1
1 a) Repulsion (they repel one another).
b) Attraction of polystyrene pieces.
c) Attraction (they attract one another).
2 a) Electrons pass from the perspex to the cloth. The perspex loses negatively charged electrons so it has a net positive charge.
b) Negative. The cloth gains electrons from the perspex (because of friction) and so gains negative charge.

1.2
1 The conductor becomes charged, ionising the surrounding air; these ions stream upwards, cancelling some of the charge in the cloud, and this makes a lightning strike less likely. If lightning does strike, charge flows to earth through the conductor rather than the building.
2 a) i) Friction between the rubber belt and the air and plastic roller.
(ii) Friction between moving particles in the cloud and upward-moving air.
b)

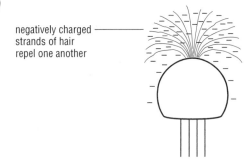

negatively charged strands of hair repel one another

3 a) Copper, iron, carbon, aluminium, steel are conductors.
b) Glass, polythene, plastic are insulators.
4 a) Like (the same) charges repel.
b) Negative.
5 a) Friction between fuel and pipe produces charge which could produce a spark which may well ignite the fuel vapour.
b) Tanker and aircraft are at the same potential, so no spark. Conductor provides a path for the charge, so no spark.

1.3
1 a) The fuse has been replaced with inappropriate material; remove and put in correct fuse.
b) There is too much bare wire between the cables and connections; re-wire so that no bare wire is visible.
c) The live and neutral wires are wrongly connected and the cable grip is loose; re-wire correctly and tighten the cable grip.
2 a) 0.3 A, 3 A; **b)** 2.8 A, 3 A; **c)** 8.7 A, 13 A;
d) 0.1 A, 3 A.

3 The fuse wire melts and breaks, creating a break in the circuit.
4 a) They are insulating materials.
b) Steel and brass are conducting materials.
c) Water may conduct electricity so you are more likely to get a shock as current passes through you to earth.

1.4
1 a) Switch; **b)** ammeter; **c)** light dependent resistor;
d) thermistor; **e)** variable resistor.
2 If one component fails the others still work. Each component can be independently controlled.
3 a) i) 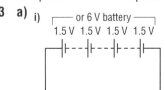 ii)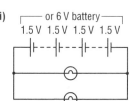

b) Circuit (ii). There is a bigger potential across/higher current through each bulb.
c)

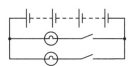

1.5
1 a) 3 A; **b)** $A_1 = 1.5$ A, $A_2 = 2$ A.
2 40 C.
3 6 A.
4 86 400 C.
5 a) i) Dimmer; ii) brighter; iii) brighter.
b) i) Lower reading; ii) higher reading; iii) higher reading.
6 a) 10 Ω; **b)** 40 Ω.
7 a) Combined resistance = 20 Ω.
b) Combined resistance = 23 Ω.

1.6
1 a) 1.5 V; **b)** 6 V.
2 a) 1.5 V; **b)** $V_1 = 1.5$ V, $V_2 = 1.5$ V; **c)** 3 V.
3 Electric current, series, parallel, potential.
4 12 V.

1.7
1 a) i) 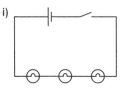 ii)

b) i) 0.6 A; ii) 0.2 A.
2 6 Ω.
3 a) Line (iii); **b)** Line (i).
c) i) and iii) Temperature appears constant;
ii) temperature has changed resulting in a change in resistance.
d) Graph (ii).

4 a) The filament has become so hot it has melted and broken.

b) The filament is cold so it has a low resistance, resulting in a high current which overheats it. When the bulb has been on for a while the filament will be hotter, giving a higher resistance and a lower current.

1.8

1 Potential difference or voltage (volts), current (amps), time (seconds).

2 23 Ω.

3 0.43 A.

4 a) 12 W: 0.052 A; 60 W: 0.26 A.

b) A greater proportion of the electrical energy is converted to light energy, and less to heat energy.

5 a) Device (i); **b)** device (ii); **c)** device (ii).

d) Device (ii) has a higher resistance than device (i).

e) 24 Ω.

6 450 000 J, 216 000 J, 2 minutes, 1100 W.

1.9

1

Input	Processor	Output
LDR thermistor pressure switch etc.	NOT gate AND gate OR gate etc.	lamp motor buzzer etc.

2 a) Its resistance decreases.

b) Its resistance decreases.

3

A	B	C
0	0	1
1	0	1
0	1	1
1	1	0

4 a) Base, emitter, collector.

b) Switch, amplifier.

c) A device that only allows current to pass in one direction. Prevents current flowing between collector and emitter of the transistor.

5

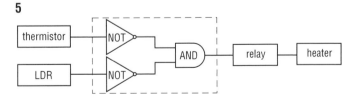

1.10

1 Iron, nickel, cobalt.

2 Repel, attract, north pole.

3 See Figure 1.10.6 (page 25); note field pattern for two south poles is as for two north poles but the arrows point towards the south poles.

4 Magnet can be repelled and attracted, both ends of iron are attracted, non-magnetic material is not affected.

1.11

1 a)

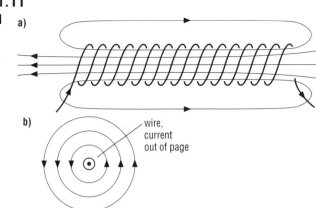

b)

wire, current out of page

2 Increasing the number of coils, increasing the current.

3 Magnetic field lines pass through the solenoid.

4 a) Breaks circuit if current exceeds a pre-set value.

b) Current flowing through coil around soft iron core will magnetise it. If current is large enough the iron rocker will be attracted, creating a gap in the circuit at the switch contacts, so protecting the power pack by stopping the flow of high currents.

1.12

1 More turns on coil, stronger magnets, greater current.

2 Reversing current, reversing magnetic field.

3 (Fleming's) left hand motor rule; outwards (away from) the magnet.

4 a) Softer so 'beds' into the commutator shape to make good contact. The carbon (or phosphor bronze) brushes suffer wear rather than the copper commutator.

b) Current reversed each half revolution to keep the armature rotating.

1.13

1 Moving the magnet faster, stronger magnet, increasing number of coils on solenoid.

2

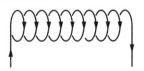

3 Waves, tides, wind, falling water, coal, oil, gas, uranium, hot rocks beneath the earth's surface.

1.14

1 a) For a given power output a higher voltage means a lower current, so energy losses due to heating of the cables are reduced; **b)** transformer.

2 If there are fewer turns on the secondary coil than the primary coil then the primary voltage would be decreased, and vice versa.

3 The primary alternating current induces an alternating magnetic field in the soft iron core. This then induces an alternating current in the secondary coil.

4 No alternating (moving) magnetic field in the core, so no induced secondary current.

5 9.6 V (assuming no energy losses).

6 630.

Section One: Exam Practice Questions

Foundation Level

1 a) i) Iron, nickel, cobalt; ii) steel; iii) plastic; iv) carbon; v) copper; vi) iron.

  b) Attract, repel, repel, attract.

2 a) It will move – into the paper.

  b) It will move – out of the paper.

  c) It will move – into the paper.

3 a) Hair will be attracted to the comb.

  b) The pieces of paper will stick to the comb.

  c) i) Positive, negative; ii) electrons; iii) negative.

  d) They will repel each other.

  e) It will be attracted.

  f) i)   As the spray passes through the nozzle.
  ii) Each droplet has the same charge and the same charges repel.
  iii) Attracts the paint droplets, especially to difficult/hidden spots (as opposite charges attract).

4 a) i) A and B on; ii) A off, B on; iii) A on, B off.

  b)

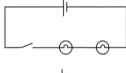

  c)

  d) Independent switching of components; if one component fails the others still work.

5 a) The ammeter is connected in parallel and it should be in series.

  b) and c)

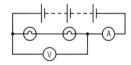

  d) X; X, Z; X, Y, Z; X.

6 a) i) C; ii) B; iii) A.

  b) To stop the metal case of an appliance becoming live if a fault occurs (by conducting the current to earth).

  c) To melt and break, creating a gap in a circuit if a fault occurs.

  d) i)   Y = cable grip, Z = fuse.
  ii) Plastic/rubber.
  iii) Live = brown, neutral = blue, earth = green/yellow.
  iv) Earth.

7 a) i) P, S; ii) P, R, S; iii) Q, S; iv) Q, R, S.

  b) i)   A thin piece of wire which melts if 5 A of current flows through it.
  ii) The fuse melts and breaks, creating a gap in the circuit so switching off the current.

8 a) Amps, volts, watts.

  b) Cooker.

  c) Television.

  d) Hairdrier.

  e) Cooker.

  f) Would only use 20 A if all parts (oven, hot plates, grill) were switched on and set at the maximum value, and this is rarely the case.

  g) High current user, so needs thicker cable.

  h) 5.65 A

  i) 13 A

  j) 6 A fuses are not readily available, so the next highest available one is used.

  k) i) 7.7p; ii) 6.44p; iii) 2.275p.

  l) 3.04 A

  m) i)   Alternating current.
  ii) Direct current.
  iii) A = a.c., B = d.c.
  iv) d.c. always flows the same way through a circuit; a.c. alternates, i.e. changes direction of flow (100 times per second).

9 a) It would slow down.

  b)

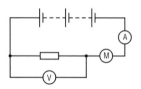

  c) i) volts; ii) amps.

  d) 2.5 ohms.

  e) Decreases, decreases, reduce, increase, increase.

  f) She has created a short circuit. The route via the switch will have (almost) zero resistance so all the current will go through the switch, missing the bulb.

10 a) D, E.

  b) B 0.25 A, C 0.17 A, D 1 A, E 1.5 A.

11 a) Deflection.

  b) Zero.

  c) Deflection but in opposite direction to (a).

  d) Faster movement of the magnet, more turns on the coil, stronger magnet.

  e) Turn magnet round (i.e. reverse poles) and push in the same end of the coil; pull magnet from the other end of the coil, without reversing poles.

12 a) Coal, oil, gas, energy released from uranium or plutonium (any 3).

  b) i)

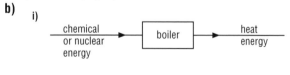

  ii)

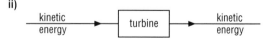

  iii)

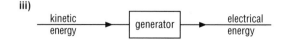

c) National Grid.

d) From the cables as heat.

e) Reduces current, which reduces the heat generated in the cables.

13 a) 2.17 A; **b)** 8.70 A; **c)** 0.26 A.

14 a) A 3 units, B 2.5 units.

b) 36p.

c) 70p.

d) i) 189p (£1.89).
ii) 157.5p + 892.5p = 1050p (£10.50).
iii) To prevent the water in the pipes freezing.

15 a) i) Brown; ii) blue; iii) green/yellow.

b) i) Resistance decreases and current increases.
ii) The fuse melts and breaks.

c) i) It becomes live.
ii) The large current would flow to earth, the fuse would melt.

d) All internal electrical parts are completely insulated from outer parts (which may be touched). Also all outer parts are normally made of an insulating material (e.g. plastic).

16 a) i) 40 Ω; ii) 3 Ω.

b) i) 6 V; ii) 1.5 V; iii) 0 V.

c) 0.6 A.

d) Current would reduce (to 0.4 A) as the circuit resistance has been increased (by 5 Ω or 50%).

e) X 0.3 A, Y 0.4 A.

17 a) 0.2 A; **b)** 3 V.

c) Zero. There is a gap in the circuit so no current can flow. The very small current that would flow via voltmeter S is negligible because voltmeters have a very high resistance.

18 a) Fuse

b) The brown (live) wire should connect to L. The green and yellow (earth) wire should connect to E.

c) Live (brown) and neutral (blue) wires are used. It is safe because the hairdrier is double insulated, meaning the case is made of an insulator and no metal parts can be touched.

d) Units used = 0.5 kW × 5 h = 2.5 kWh or units.
Cost = 2.5 × 8p = 20p.

19 a) i) Direct current (d.c.)
ii) Alternating current (a.c.)

b) i) x = off, y = on.
ii) x = on, y = on, z = on.

c) i) A, C; ii) B, D, E.

d) i) W; ii) U; iii) volts.

e) The longer the wire, the greater the resistance to current flow. The greater the resistance, the lower the current in the circuit and the dimmer the bulb. The results show the current and the brightness both decreasing as the wire's length increases.

Higher Level

1 a) and **b)**

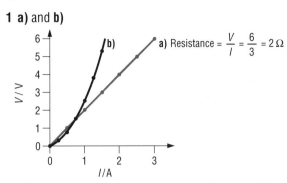

a) Resistance $= \dfrac{V}{I} = \dfrac{6}{3} = 2\,\Omega$

c) Both have zero current for zero voltage; straight line graph shows a fixed resistance; lamp graph curves, showing resistance increases as current increases.

d) Temperature of the filament increases, causing resistance of the filament to increase.

2 a) 144 000 C.

b) 0.26 A, 15.65 C.

c) 200 s.

3 a) 0.6 A; **b)** 1 A.

4 a) Dampness completes circuit inside the sensor, causing a current flow through the transistor which operates the relay, switching on the buzzer.

b) Prevents current flowing back through the transistor, collector/emitter circuit.

c) i) 2; ii) 1; iii) 3.

d) 0.5 mA.

5 a) i) The same charges repel.
ii) Opposite charges attract.
iii) The polythene and the duster both have opposite charge to the perspex, i.e. negative.
iv) The polythene and the duster both have an excess of electrons, transferred from the perspex.

b) Conductors have 'free' electrons which are able to move through the material when a potential difference is applied to the ends; insulators have no 'free' electrons.

6 a) To keep the charge on the spheres/prevent charge flowing to earth.

b) Electrons travel to the right-hand side of Y.

c) X positive, Y negative.

d) X becomes neutral (equal numbers of positive and negative charges); Y is still negative.

7 a) Transformer (iii); **b)** transformers (i) and (ii).

c) 4000.

d) i) 120 V; ii) 750.

e) The a.c. in the primary coil causes an alternating magnetic field in the core; this field induces an alternating voltage at the secondary terminals.

8 a) i) X is a voltmeter; Y is an ammeter.
ii) Variable resistor/rheostat.
iii) Resistance = voltage/current = 1/gradient.

b) i)

 or

ii)

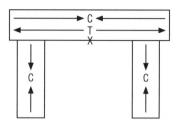

c) i) Very high melting point – above 2500 °C.

ii)

iii) When first switched on the filament will be cold, so have a low resistance. This will allow a large current to flow, producing rapid heating and expansion of the filament, so causing it damage.

9 a) $\dfrac{V_s}{V_p} = \dfrac{T_s}{T_p}$ $\quad \therefore \dfrac{V_s}{10} = \dfrac{30\ 000}{1000}$

$$\therefore V_s = \frac{30\ 000}{1000} \times 10 = 300 \text{ volts.}$$

b) i) Power = voltage × current
= 25 000 × 16 = 400 000 W.

ii) 400 000 W.

c) i) Low currents produce less heat so less energy is lost, thinner (cheaper) cables can be used to carry low currents.

ii) It is more difficult to insulate the high voltages – ceramic insulation is needed between cables and pylon to stop conduction through the pylon.

d) i) More material is needed.

ii) The cable is heavier and more difficult to handle; stronger pylons are needed and they need to be closer together, resulting in more pylons.

iii) Thicker cables have a lower resistance, resulting in a smaller heating effect.

Section Two: Quick Questions

2.1

1 a) Accelerates forward, maintains a steady height.
b) Falls at a steady speed.
c) Accelerates in reverse direction.
d) Slows down/decelerates/speed decreases.

2

Earth	10	20	**200**
Moon	1.66	**1**	1.66
Venus	**9**	2	18
Mars	4	**4**	16
Jupiter	26	**4**	104
Neptune	14	10	**140**

2.2

1 a) Stretch (extend), squash (compress), bend, twist.
b) The elastic material would regain its original shape after being deformed (providing the elastic limit had not been exceeded); the plastic material would not.

2 a)

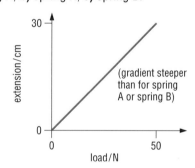

b) The closer the pillars, the greater the strength.

3 a) Cheap, easy to mould to shape, prepared on site, strong in compression (any 3).
b) In tension.
c) Reinforced with steel rods.

2.3

1 Elastic limit, directly proportional, original length, elastic, plastic.

2 a) Returns to original shape and size, when force removed.
b) Does not return to original shape and size, when force removed.
c) As one quantity doubles so does the other, etc.

3 12.5 cm.

4 a) Spring A; **b)** spring A; **c)** spring B.

d)

(gradient steeper than for spring A or spring B)

2.4

1 a) Weight of solid, area on which it rests.
b) Depth, density, gravitational field strength.

2 a) 20 000 Pa (N/m^2); **b)** 500 Pa (N/m^2).

3 a) 3 075 000 Pa (N/m^2) or 3075 kPa.
b) To withstand greater pressures due to increased depth of water.

4 a) Snow shoes, tractor tyres, wide bag strap.
b) Knife, ice skates, nail, cheese cutter, tigers' teeth.

5 a) 10 N/cm^2 (0.001 Pa); **b)** 50 N.

2.5

1 a) More molecules so the rate of collisions with the tyre wall will increase, so increasing the pressure.
b) Squashing and stretching of the rubber of the tyre and friction between the tyre and road have heated the tyre and air, increasing the speed of the air molecules. This

increases the rate at which molecules collide with the tyre, increasing the pressure. Air should not be let out because pressure will return to normal when the tyre cools down.

2 **a)** 543 K, 2273 K, 43 K.
   b) −146 °C, 327 °C, 100 °C.
3 **a)** Heated air molecules travel faster, increasing the pressure in the ball which pushes the sides of the ball out.
   b) The heat would produce great pressure inside the can and it could explode.
   c) Allows air (and vapour) to escape as the temperature rises, preventing a dangerous increase in internal pressure.
4 1200 K or 927 °C.
5 13.33 m^3.

2.6

2 **a)** 200 N m.
   b) Door edge furthest from the hinges, 200 N.
3 **a)** A; **b)** C; **c)** B.
4 **a)** The force exerted by his arm (downwards).
   b) The weight of the ladder.
   c) 400 N.
   d) 0.5 m behind his shoulder.

2.7

1 **a)** Less grip/friction so car skids easily/takes longer to stop when the brakes are applied.
   b) Air resistance is reduced so they travel faster.
   c) Friction reduced/more streamlined, uses less fuel, travels faster.
   d) Air resistance produces heat which raises the temperature of the rocks.
2 **a)** Accelerates/speeds up to the right.
   b) Decelerates/slows down.
   c) Accelerates to the left.

2.8

1 $x = 5$ m/s, $y = 100$ km, $z = 10$ s.
2 **a)** Velocity is a speed in a particular direction.
   b) i) 38.67 km/h; ii) 10.74 m/s.
3 **a)** 33.33 m/s; **b)** 0.09 s.
4 **a)**

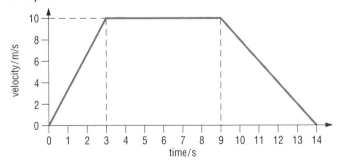

   b) Distance = area under graph = 100 m.
5 OA – accelerating, AB – steady speed, BC – accelerating, CD – decelerating. Acceleration for BC is smaller than for OA.

2.9

1 **a)** 3 m/s^2; **b)** 6 m/s; **c)** 24 m; **d)** 10.33 s (4 s + 6.33 s).
2 **a)** 8 m/s^2; **b)** 12 000 N.
3 **a)** Decelerating; **b)** constant velocity; **c)** accelerating; **d)** accelerating; **e)** accelerating.
4 **a)** 8 s; **b)** 45 m.

2.10

1 150 N. At the top of the circle the weight of the water acts as part of the centripetal force required to keep it moving in a circle so it causes no downward motion. (If the speed were lower – less than 4.5 m/s – the weight would be greater than the centripetal force required so the weight would cause the water to move downwards, i.e. fall out.)
2 As the drum spins, water is forced against it. The water passes through holes in the drum because here there is nothing to provide the centripetal force needed to keep it moving around.
3 Between the tyres and the road, towards the centre of the circle of which the corner forms a part. Car would continue in a straight line.
4 **a)** Mass of earth, mass of moon/satellite, distance apart.
   b) Orbit closer and faster.
5 **a)** The spinning would force the astronauts against the rim and the rim would apply a centripetal force on the astronauts; this would give the impression of weight.
   b) 20 m/s.

2.11

1 **a)** 24 000 kg m/s; **b)** 48 000 kg m/s; **c)** 0.6 kg m/s; **d)** 1 000 000 kg m/s.
2 $x = 20$, $y = 15$, $z = 1800$.
3 **a)** 50 kg m/s ; **b)** 40 000 kg m/s; **c)** 1200 kg m/s.
4 5.56 m/s.
5 180 m/s.
6 6000 N.
7 5 m/s.

Section Two: Exam Practice Questions

Foundation Level

1 **a)** C; **b)** A, B; **c)** D, E, F, G; **d)** none.
   e) Larger area of contact.
   f) Racing car 80; ordinary car 40.
   g) Racing tyre unsuitable because layer of water between road and tyre gives less grip/friction. Tyres with tread are better because water between tyre and road is removed, giving more grip/friction.
2 **a)** i) BC; ii) AB, DE; iii) OA, CD.
   b) i) 15 s; ii) 30 s; iii) 1.67 m/s^2.
   c) i) 16 m/s; ii) it reaches the bottom of the hill; iii) at 18 s; iv) increases.
   v) Stays constant (assuming no energy loss due to heat or sound) – as KE increases, PE decreases, but total KE + PE will remain the same.

3 a) Straight line graph.

   b) Increases with speed.

   c) 12.5 m.

   d) 25 m.

   e) Twice as far.

4 a) 5 m/s.

   b) Her speed varies and is higher in some places than others, e.g. she starts from rest then accelerates.

   c) i) Chris; ii) 80 m; iii) 9.5 s; iv) 15 s.

5 a) Heather. She has least mass, and acceleration = force/mass.

   b) 20 m; **c)** 100 m.

6 a) Reduce pressure/spread the force over a greater area.

   b) 9 N/cm^2; **c)** 3.6 N/cm^2.

   d) Pressure is transmitted by the hydraulic fluid.

   e) Friction.

   f) Reduces it as the brakes respond more slowly/less evenly (air bubbles are compressible).

   g) Pressure constant throughout system, so a larger area means a larger force on the slave piston and hence brake pad.

7 a) Alan. Greatest force, and acceleration = force/mass.

   b) i) 100 g. Least mass, and acceleration = force/mass.

      ii) Hit 100 g with 50 N force or hit 200 g with 200 N force.

   c) It will move to the left.

   d) Puck will move slower because of greater friction between the puck and road (compared with ice) so she will need to hit it harder.

8 a) i) C; ii) A; iii) B.

   b) i) It will move with constant speed.

      ii) It will accelerate.

      iii) It will decelerate.

9 a) Up to the elastic limit the spring will return to its original length when any stretching force is removed. Beyond the elastic limit the spring will be permanently stretched.

   b) The spring will be longer than its original length when the 110 N load is removed.

   c)

1	20
5	20
more than 15	more than 20

   d) i) 1.5 N; ii) 6.6 cm; iii) 21.6 cm.

10 a) i) Between 3 and 7 metres.

      ii) Between 0 and 3 metres.

      iii) Between 7 and 10 metres.

      iv) Between 3 and 7 metres and between 10 and 16 metres.

   b) i) Gravity.

      ii) Air resistance.

      iii) Increases.

      iv) Horizontal line at 40 m/s.

      v) Force of gravity balanced by force of air resistance.

      vi) Parachute opens.

      vii) 8 m/s.

11 a) B, 110 s; **b)** 80 s; **c)** A; **d)** 225 m; **e)** C; **f)** 50 m;

   g) 7.27 m/s, 6.15 m/s.

12 a)

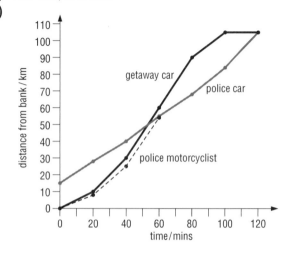

   b) Car.

   c) 52 minutes.

   d) After 60 minutes.

   e) 20 minutes.

   f) Getaway car 52.5 km/h, police car 45 km/h.

13 a) 4 s; **b)** 7.5 m/s^2; **c)** 6 s; **d)** -15 m/s^2; **e)** 270 m.

14 a) i) Accelerating; ii) constant speed.

   b) 10 s; **c)** 2 m/s; **d)** 0.2 m/s^2.

15 a) Gravity.

   b) Air resistance.

   c) F_1 is greater than F_2.

   d) It will increase.

   e) It will fall with constant speed.

16 a) 60 kg; **b)** 100 N.

   c) i) 720 N; ii) 72 kg; iii) 72 kg.

      iv) He was 'weightless' during space travel.

17 a) 6 000 000 N.

   b) Force of 6 000 000 N is greater than its weight of 5 000 000 N.

   c) 2 m/s^2.

   d) i) 2.5 m/s^2; ii) 4 m/s^2.

   e) Rocket has less weight as fuel is used; force of gravity decreases with height.

18 a) i) Alex increases his speed from 0 m/s to 7 m/s in 4 s. The acceleration is greatest (the curve has its steepest slope) in the first second and decreases to zero after 4 s.

      ii) He is running with a constant speed of 7 m/s.

   b) *Section A–B:* A straight line from A to B would give a distance of 14 m ($\frac{1}{2} \times 4 \times 7$). The curve gives a distance of more than 14 m but less than 28 m: estimate 21 m.

   Section B–C: 11 s at 7 m/s = 77 m.

   Therefore total = 77 + 21 = 98 m (allow 95 $\pm$ 6 m).

19 a) Rivka.

  b) i) The speed is increasing with time.
  ii) $20 - 6 = 14$ m/s.
  iii) The kinetic energy increases as the car's speed increases. The potential energy decreases as the car goes down the hill. The total energy (kinetic and potential) remains the same (if no energy is lost as heat, sound, etc.)

Higher Level

1 a) 2.5 cm.

  b) There will be 500 N tension in the other rope, which is greater than its elastic limit of 450 N, so this rope will stretch by more than 5 cm, stay permanently stretched and may even break.

  c) 3000 N.

  d) 500 N upwards.

  e) 1.67 m/s^2.

  f) It will expand, becoming less dense.

  g) The air in the balloon is less dense than the surrounding air, giving an upthrust.

  h) The air cools and becomes more dense, reducing the upthrust.

2 a) Molecular collisions with the walls of the tyre.

  b) More molecular collisions per second with the tyre wall because the rise in temperature gives the molecules more kinetic energy, so they travel faster.

  c) 301 205 Pa.

3 a) 1500 N; **b)** 1000 N/cm^2; **c)** 1000 N/cm^2; **d)** 4500 N;

  e) 110 m; **f)** 30 m/s; **g)** 0.67 s.

  h) i) A = van, B = car; ii) car, smallest mass; iii) 0.1 s; iv) 80 m/s^2; v) 1 m.

4 a) Gravity acting downwards, air resistance acting upwards.

  b) It will increase.

  c) Air resistance increases, gravity almost constant (slight increase as altitude decreases).

  d) Air resistance, by changing her shape (streamlining).

  e) She will have constant velocity.

  f) Constant velocity of a falling object, achieved when force of gravity is balanced by upward resistance.

  g) There will be greater air resistance, causing her to slow down (until the air resistance again equals the force of gravity).

5 a) 20 000 kg m/s; **b)** 20 000 kg m/s; **c)** 11.11 m/s;

  d) 1778 N.

  e) They increase the 'collision time', so reducing the force of impact.

6 a) S; **b)** S.

  c) Always above the same place on the earth. (It is not stationary but moving at the same rotational speed as the earth.)

  d) Satellite receiving dishes need not be moved and transmission systems can be pointed at the known satellite position.

  e) The force of gravity equals the required centripetal force.

7 a) i) 1: B; 2: C.
  ii) Less than, less than.

  b) i) 70 kg $\times$ 10 N/kg = 700 N.
  ii) Work done = force $\times$ distance = 700×0.5
    = 350 J.

  c) i) Efficiency $= \dfrac{\text{work out}}{\text{work in}} \times 100\%$

    $= \dfrac{350}{1400} \times 100\% = 25\%.$

  ii) Work is done against friction between the crate and the plank.
  iii) It is easier than lifting, i.e. the pushing force **F** is less than the weight of the crate.

8 a) i) Average speed = distance/time = 25/10 = 2.5 m/s.
  ii) Acceleration = gradient of graph = 5/10 = 0.5 m/s^2.
  iii) $F = ma$ $\therefore m = F/a = 3500/0.5 = 7000$ kg.

  b) It might have a greater load, or there may be a head wind.

  c) Wet or icy roads/worn brakes or tyres.

  d) $\dfrac{P_1 V_1}{T_1} = \dfrac{P_2 V_2}{T_2}$

    Assume the temperature remains constant, so $T_1 = T_2$.
    $P_1 V_1 = P_2 V_2$ $\therefore 100\,000 \times 200 = 250\,000 \times V_2$
    $\therefore V_2 = 80$ cm^3.

Section Three: Quick Questions

3.1

1 Vibrations from the source of sound cause layers of particles in the carrier medium (e.g. air) to vibrate, creating areas of compression and rarefaction. These transfer sound energy through the medium away from the source.

2 a) The higher the frequency, the higher the pitch.

  b) The greater the amplitude, the louder the sound.

  c) *Compression:* area of high pressure; particles closer together than normal. *Rarefaction:* area of low pressure; particles further apart than normal.

3 300 m/s (30 000 cm/s).

4 a) 320 m/s.

  b) Do it in the same direction as the wind, then against the wind and calculate the average of the two answers.

  c) To avoid echoes.

  d) Light travels (much) faster than sound.

5 3300 m (3.3 km).

3.2

1 *Hard:* nearly all reflected; angle of incidence = angle of reflection; echo. *Soft:* little reflected; most energy absorbed.

2 70 m.

3 **a)** Furniture etc. absorbs sound energy so little is reflected around the room.
   b) Tiles are hard and reflect sound energy.
   c) i) Double glaze.
      ii) High fence or wall, plant trees/shrubs.

4 Sounds with frequency above the human range of hearing. Between 20 kHz and 10 MHz.

5 **a)** By different reflection (detection and computer analysis) of the ultrasound from the boundaries between tissue, muscle, bone, etc.
   b) Safer to patient and operator; detects tissue and muscle as well as bone; operator can be with the probe and control it by hand.
   c) See page 91.

6 0.2 s

3.3

1 Light travels faster than sound, is a transverse wave and not a longitudinal wave, can travel across a vacuum but sound cannot.

2 **a)** E; **b)** C; **c)** A–F; **d)** B–C; **e)** 100 Hz.

3 **a)** Trace (iii); **b)** Trace (i).

4
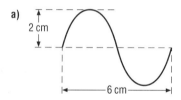
a)

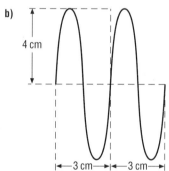
b)

Wave (b) has highest frequency.

5 **a)** 300 000 000 m/s.
   b) Velocity = frequency × wavelength ($v = f\lambda$).
   c) i) 3.41 m; ii) 432 900 Hz (432.9 kHz).

3.4

1 Cells in the retina (in the eye) respond to these wavelengths only.

2 Gamma, X-rays, ultra-violet, visible light, infra-red, microwaves, radio waves.

3 Travel at the same speed, transfer energy, travel through a vacuum, transverse waves, raise temperature when absorbed.

4 **a)** X-rays; **b)** gamma rays; **c)** (longer wavelength) radio waves; **d)** ultra-violet; **e)** microwaves; **f)** infra-red.

5 **a)** red; **b)** violet.

6 **a)** There are likely to be more and more cases of skin cancer.
   b) UV cannot penetrate glass.
   c) Certain fluorescent chemicals used in security paints emit light when illuminated by UV.

7 **a)** Gamma – radiotherapy; X-rays – fracture detection; ultra-violet – killing food-poisoning microbes; visible light – seeing things; infra-red – cooking; microwaves – cooking; radio waves – communications.
   b) Gamma, X-rays – ionisation of living cells; ultra-violet – sunburn; visible light – none; infra-red – burning; microwaves – burning; radio waves – none known.

3.5

1 *Rough:* diffused or scattered reflection. *Smooth:* regular reflection ($i = r$).

2 **a)** i) CI; ii) IG; iii) IE; iv) D; v) F.
   b) Angle of incidence and angle of reflection are equal.

3 See page 99.

4

Eye	Camera
The retina acts as light-sensitive film	The film is coated with light-sensitive chemicals
The shape of the lens is changed (by the ciliary muscles) to ensure the image is focused on the retina	The lens is moved closer to/further away from the film (using the screw thread) to ensure the image is focused on the film
The iris opens/closes to control the amount of light entering the eye	The iris diaphragm is opened/closed to control the amount of light entering the camera

3.6

1 **a)** See pages 100–101.
   b)

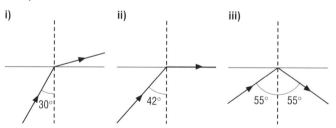
i)   ii)   iii)

2 **a)** Light undergoes successive internal reflections through the optical fibres, known as total internal reflection.
   b) Keyhole surgery, telecommunications.

3 Refraction of light (away from the normal) as it leaves the (more dense) water and enters the (less dense) air).

rod

air
water

B
A

Eye (and brain) 'believes' light can only travel in straight lines, so it believes A is at B.

4 a) Prisms do not deteriorate as quickly as mirrors and they reflect a higher proportion of the incident light.

b)

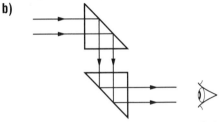

5 a) i) Reflect light from the car's headlights back to the driver, giving an indication of position.

ii)

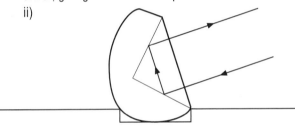

b) They reflect light, so the vehicle is more easily seen. The back of the reflector is covered with small plastic prisms, which reflect the light (from the following vehicle's lights) by total internal reflection.

3.7

1 i) Convex; ii) concave; iii) convex; iv) convex; v) convex; vi) concave.

2 *Short-sighted:* cannot see distant objects, such as road signs, clearly; glasses have concave lenses; light is refracted too much by the cornea/eye lens, or the eye ball is too long.
Long-sighted: cannot see close objects, such as the words in a book, clearly; glasses have convex lenses; light is not refracted enough by the cornea/eye lens, or the eye ball is too short.

3 a) i) J; ii) C; iii) CJ; iv) D, E; v) F, G; vi) A, B.

b)

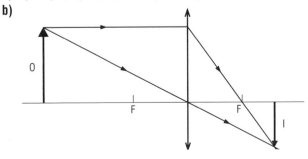

O

F

F

I

The image is 4.8 cm from the lens, 2.4 cm tall, diminished, inverted, real.

3.8

1 a) Red, orange, yellow, green, blue, indigo, violet.
b) Red, blue, green.
c) Cyan, magenta, yellow.

2 a) Violet has a shorter wavelength.
b) *Dispersion:* splitting of white light into its spectral colours by passing the light through a material with a different refractive index.
Refraction: the change in velocity of light when it passes into, or out of, a material with a different density, which may lead to a change in direction.

3 a) Magenta; **b)** yellow; **c)** white; **d)** white; **e)** green; **f)** yellow.

3.9

1 a) The spreading out of waves after passing through a gap (of similar size to the wavelength) or around the side of an obstacle.
b) *Water:* ripple tank, harbour wall. *Sound:* doorway. *Light:* when objects are viewed through a fine mesh (net) curtain. *Radio:* over hills and mountains.

2 See Figure 3.9.5, page 111.

3 The amount of diffraction by hills etc. depends upon the signal wavelength. Shorter wavelengths may not be diffracted at all, passing directly over the hills. Aerials are erected in regions with a stronger signal, and then the signal can be relayed to other regions.

3.10

1 Crust, mantle, outer core, inner core. All but the outer core are, for the most part, solid (although parts of the mantle have the constituency of thick, warmed toffee).

2 a) Primary and secondary waves.
b) P longitudinal, S transverse.
c) *Longitudinal:* vibration is parallel to the direction of wave travel/energy transfer.
Transverse: vibration is at 90° to the direction of wave travel/energy transfer.

3 a) P; **b)** the distance from the focus of the earthquake to the seismic station.

4 S waves cannot be detected on the opposite side of the earth (but P waves can be) and it is known that S waves cannot pass through a liquid.

Section Three: Exam Practice Questions

Foundation Level

1 a) Longitudinal, 340, decrease, be constant, rarefactions, energy, does not.
b) i) Light travels faster than sound; ii) 136 m.
c) 150 m.
d) i) Frequency above human hearing range.
ii) Reflect from boundaries between tissue, muscle, bone, etc.

iii) Safer for baby, mother and operator. Shows tissue as well as bone.

2 a) i) Dispersion; ii) red; iii) violet; iv) orange, yellow, green, blue, indigo.

b) i) Just beyond visible red; ii) infra-red radiation; iii) black is a good absorber of infra-red so produces a significant rise in the temperature of the mercury.

3 a) Ultra-violet; **b)** X-rays; **c)** microwaves, infra-red; **d)** ultra-violet, infra-red, microwaves; **e)** radio; **f)** gamma.

4 a) Up and down/vertically; **b)** A; **c)** B; **d)** 0.4 cm; **e)** 1.4 cm; **f)** 20; **g)** same height, waves further apart; **h)** smaller vertically, waves same distance apart; **i)** hertz; **j)** 200; **k)** decrease (to 0.27 cm).

5 a) Visible light; **b)** infra-red; **c)** radio waves; **d)** ultra-violet; **e)** X-rays; **f)** gamma waves.

6 a) Longitudinal; **b)** transverse.

7 a)

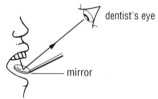

b) Magnifies the image of a tooth, i.e. tooth looks larger.

c)

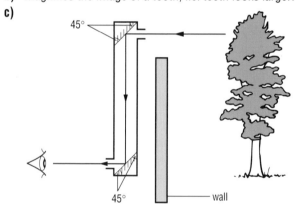

d)

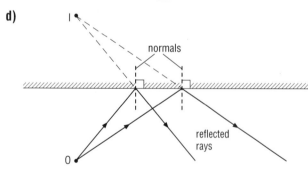

e) i) A concave, B convex.

ii)

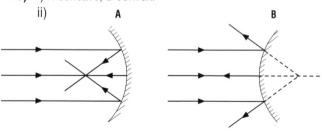

iii) A. The rays meet (converge) after reflection.

iv) B. Greater field of view.

8 a) i) a; ii) e; iii) f; iv) c; v) d; vi) b.

b) i) A convex, B concave.

ii)

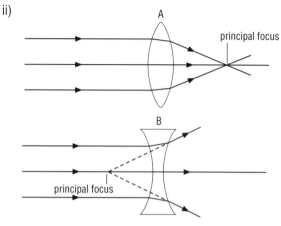

iii) A. The rays meet (converge) after refraction.

iv) A.

c) The one that has the greatest curvature/fattest in the middle (if same diameter).

d) i) B

ii)

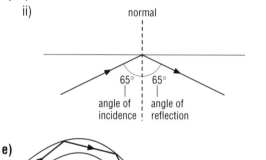

e)

9 a) i) Dots randomly spaced with no points of concentration.

ii) Sound will not travel across a vacuum – it needs a carrier material (medium). There is no carrier material between the earth and the moon.

b) i) Light travels faster than sound.

ii) Speed = distance/time

∴ distance = speed × time = 340 × 5 = 1700 m.

10 a) Any 2 of:

Method of communication	Sense involved
semaphore (signalling with flags)	sight
Morse Code with lights	sight
siren	hearing
loud hailer	hearing

b) Cannot see each other because of curvature of earth; cannot hear as sound would not travel that far.

c) i) C.

ii) Speed = distance/time.

iii) Distance = speed × time = 1.5 × 80 = 120 m.

Higher Level

1 a) i) Visible light and short wavelength infra-red will pass through the glass and into the greenhouse; the ultra-violet and the remainder of the infra-red will not pass through the glass – they are absorbed or reflected.

ii) It absorbs the short wavelength infra-red radiation.

iii) Longer wavelength infra-red. Its wavelength has increased.

iv) It reflects back in or is absorbed. It does not leave the greenhouse.

v) Heat energy emitted from the warm soil remains in the greenhouse.

vi) Warm air is convected to glass; heat is conducted to outside where it warms air which is then convected away.

vii) Ultra-violet (which is responsible for sun tanning) cannot penetrate the glass.

b) Reflection from the layer of the atmosphere called the ionosphere.

c) i) Number of complete waves to pass a point in 1 second.

ii) Same velocity, transverse, can travel across a vacuum, carry energy (any 3).

iii) 3.75 m.

2 a) i) 3.

ii) Vertically up and down only (no sideways movement as it is a transverse wave).

iii) Unchanged.

iv) Reduced.

v) Reduced. From $v = f\lambda$, f is constant so if λ is reduced so is v.

vi) 6 cm/s.

b) i) 1.0 cm.

ii) Spread out, diffract. Wavelength unchanged.

iii) Diffraction.

iv) Less diffraction.

v) Sounds we can hear have much greater wavelengths (16 mm → 16 m) than light (10^{-4} mm). Diffraction occurs when the gap the sound or light is passing through is about the same size as the wavelength. We more often experience sound passing through gaps in the mm/m range than light passing through gaps of the order of 10^{-4} mm.

vi) 5×10^{14} Hz.

3 a) i) 0.5 m; **ii)** 0.3 m.

b) i) Conduction. The particles at the surface of the food gain energy from the infra-red waves, causing them to vibrate more. They collide with neighbouring particles, so making them vibrate more, and the energy is thus passed through the food.

ii) Microwaves are able to penetrate into the bread. Their energy is absorbed by frozen water molecules, giving them more vibrational energy. Energy is then conducted throughout the bread. Infra-red only warms the surface and not the inside, leaving the outside burned and the inside still frozen.

iii) The aluminium foil will conduct heat in a conventional gas or electric oven, but it will reflect microwaves.

4 a) Frequency = number of waves per second = 5/10
                                                            = 0.5 Hz.

b) Velocity = frequency × wavelength
∴ wavelength = velocity/frequency = 8/0.5 = 16 km.

Section Four: Quick Questions

4.1

1 Mercury, Venus, Earth, Mars, Jupiter, Saturn, Uranus, Neptune, Pluto.

2 See Figure 4.1.2, page 122.

3 a) $365\frac{1}{4}$ days (1 year); **b)** almost 28 days; **c)** 24 hours (1 day).

4 Elliptical, greater, lower, frozen gases, dust, elliptical.

4.2

1 a) An explosion of a mixture of particles and electromagnetic radiation which is thought to indicate the origin of the universe.

b) Between 15 000 and 20 000 million years ago.

2 Radiation detected from faraway galaxies is shifted towards the red end of the spectrum, indicating they are moving away from the earth and one another.

3 a) Protostar → main sequence star → red giant → white dwarf → black dwarf.

b) Protostar → main sequence star → red supergiant → supernova → neutron star or black hole.

4 The light we see from stars has taken many years (hundreds or thousands in many cases) to reach us. In that time the star could have progressed to another stage but the light has yet to reach us.

Section Four: Exam Practice Questions

Foundation Level

1 a) Our moon, earth, Jupiter, sun, solar system, galaxy, universe.

b) i) Gravity; **ii)** they reflect light from the sun; **iii)** stars emit light and planets do not/planets orbit stars.

c) i)

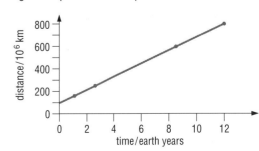

ii) 5.2 years.

iii) C. Only C has a temperature close to the earth's average surface temperature of 20 °C. A and B are too cold and D is too hot for humans to survive.

iv) Oxygen, water.

2 a) i) 1 day.

ii) The earth rotates on its axis so that sometimes Britain is facing the sun and at other times it is facing away from it.

b) i) Star.

ii) Fusion of hydrogen into helium.

c) i) The lenses in the telescope produce a magnified image of Mars.

ii) Gravity.

iii) Communications/TV/weather observations.

3 a) Earth is made up of mainly water and rock, so contains elements heavier than hydrogen and helium. Density = mass/volume. Jupiter has a much greater volume and its materials have lower mass.

b) i) Very strong magnetic field.

ii) Its orbital speed is less; it is further from the sun so it has to travel a greater distance to complete one orbit.

iii) Because it is further from the sun less radiation will reach the surface of Jupiter; also, the earth's surface of water and rock is better at retaining heat energy (higher specific heat capacity).

c) Active volcanoes; colder.

d) i) Its temperature was raised due to the heating effect of friction between the probe and the gases in the atmosphere.

ii) The parachute slowed the probe's fall, so reducing the friction with the gases and reducing the heating effect.

Higher Level

1 a) It emits light and heat energy and becomes visible; it becomes stable and stops collapsing.

b) Fusion.

c) They are balanced.

d) Its core will collapse and the outer layers will expand, becoming cooler and redder, forming a red giant.

e) They are moving away from each other (i.e. the universe is expanding).

f) It will contract, or it will remain at its current size.

2 a) i) Planet; ii) universe.

b) It is too far from the earth.

c) C, D, B, A.

3 a) Velocity = frequency × wavelength

∴ frequency = velocity/wavelength = $3 \times 10^8/0.3$

= 10^9 Hz.

b) i)

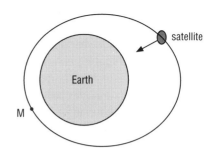

ii) The force will be greatest when the satellite is closest to earth and least when it is furthest from earth.

iii) See diagram above.

Section Five: Quick Questions

5.1

1 a) Heat energy; **b)** electrical energy; **c)** heat energy, light energy.

2 a) In any process the total amount of energy is constant, although the energy may exist in several different forms. The total energy before any transfer equals the total energy (in all forms) after the transfer.

b) Light energy, 20 J/s.

3 a) 2000 J; **b)** 40 000 J; **c)** 800 000 J.

4

light	heat
kinetic	heat + sound
kinetic	heat + sound

5.2

1 36 000 J.

2 a) 8; **b)** 56p.

3 a) 56 units × 7p = £3.92.

b) 3.5 units × 7p = 24.5p.

c) 10.5 units × 7p = 73.5p.

Total = £4.90.

4 a) 1 000 000 J; **b)** 40 000 J/s (40 000 W or 40 kW).

5 a) 200 000 J; **b)** 5000 J/s; **c)** 50%.

5.3

1 20 000 J.

2 2500 J.

3 400 000 J.

4 a) 20 m/s.

b) Energy is 'lost' because of air resistance (energy is transformed into heat) so kinetic energy at sea level is slightly less than potential energy at top of cliff.

5 a) 20 m/s.

b) The velocity at the bottom does not depend on the mass, only on the height.

5.4

1 13 200 J.

2 336 s or 5 min 36 s.

3 a) Gas; **b)** 220 °C; **c)** 70 °C; **d)** BC, DE.

e) The particles are rearranging themselves into a state of lower (potential) energy; their kinetic energy (and hence temperature) does not decrease.

4 605 000 J.

5.5

1 Metals have 'free' electrons which are able to move through the material, colliding with other particles and so helping to transfer the energy more quickly.

2 a) Metal blade. Metal is a better conductor than wood so it will conduct heat away from the hand faster.

b) Same temperature.

3 a) White because the black bonnet will have radiated more heat – black surfaces are better emitters of radiation.

b) i) Black (better absorber of radiation).
ii) Black (better absorber of radiation).

4 a) Hot air rises in the greenhouse by convection and escapes through the window. As hot air leaves, cooler air replaces it and is in turn warmed.

b) Air in the bubble plastic is a good insulator so heat escapes more slowly by conduction.

5.6

1 a) They are produced from partly decayed (and fossilised) remains of living things; **b)** non-renewable; **c)** uranium, plutonium; **d)** sun; **e)** oxygen.

2 Heat energy, high, turbines, kinetic, electrical, National Grid.

3 a) Allows closure of power stations for maintenance; some power stations can be taken 'off-line' during periods of low demand; generally allows for fluctuations in demand in different parts of the country.

b) Greatest use can be made of the cheapest source at the time; supply problems (e.g. due to low rainfall) reduced; competition between suppliers helps to keep costs down.

5.7

1 a) It will not run out/be used up; it can easily be used over and over.

b) It can only be used once; supplies will run out.

2 Waves, wind, tidal, solar, hydro-electricity, geothermal.

3 Waves, wind, tidal, hydro-electric.

4

	Advantage	Disadvantage
a)	no pollution	low output
b)	high output	pollution/significant inefficiencies
c)	no pollution	needs high rainfall/ environmental concerns
d)	useful in remote areas/ no pollution	needs reasonably clear skies

5 a) Solar cells produce electricity. Solar panels warm water.

b)

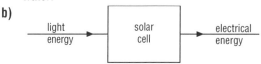

c) Generate electricity to power the equipment.

Section Five: Exam Practice Questions

Foundation Level

1 a) Non-renewable energy sources can only be used once (e.g. one piece of coal can only be burned once). Eventually all non-renewable sources of energy will run out. Renewable sources of energy will not run out and will always be available for use, although not all the time every day (e.g. we know there will always be solar energy available but not 24 hours each day). Renewable energy sources can be used over and over.

b) Less pollution as they do not involve any burning; energy source can be used repeatedly.

c) Wind, tides, solar, waves, geothermal, biomass.

d) i) Potential; ii) potential and kinetic.

e) i) It uses surplus electrical energy available from the National Grid as the demand is lower at night time.
ii) More energy is required to pump the water up than it generates as it falls.
iii) To cope with sudden increases in demand.

2 a) The wind rotates the blades (turbines) which are connected directly to a generator.

b) When there is no wind the batteries are needed as no generation will be taking place. The batteries will be re-charged when it is windy, using surplus electricity generated.

c) Long windless spells.

d) They only work effectively in bright sunlight.

e) Best colour to obtain maximum absorption of infra-red radiation.

f) Conduction.

g) Good conductor, does not rust, bends easily.

3 a) Insulator, conduction; **b)** radiation, reflected; **c)** evaporation.

4 a) 1C, 2D, 3E, 4B, 5A.

b) i) Insulator, so handle does not get too hot to hold (heat transferred more slowly).
ii) Good conductor, so milk is heated quickly (heat transferred more rapidly through the base).
iii) Conduction.
iv) Convection.

5 a)

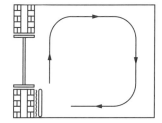

b) To reflect radiant heat back into the room.

c) Cavity wall insulation.

d) Loft insulation.

e) Carpets/underlay.

f) Double glazing.

g) They would keep the warm convected air away from the cold window, thus reducing heat loss through the window by conduction – curtain fabric is an insulating material.

6 a) i) £350; ii) £650; iii) wall insulation.

b) i) The time it takes for the savings to match the initial cost of insulating the house.

ii) 80 years.

iii) Yes, as the pay-back time is only 3 months. All the other methods will cost a lot more than £25 and will have longer pay-back times.

c) Poor, good, convection, rise, insulating, poor, insulator, conduction, convection.

d) i) Greater warm area, so higher rate of heat radiation.

ii) Copper is a good conductor.

iii) Black surfaces are good emitters of radiation.

iv) Cooler, denser air sinks to the floor.

v) Hot air rises as it is less dense than cooler air. As it rises it will cool, becoming more dense so it sinks back towards the floor. This creates a convection current which circulates heat around the room.

7 a) 480 000 J; **b)** 24 000 W; **c)** gravity; **d)** potential;

e) potential; **f)** some energy will be 'lost' due to friction in moving parts and between the wheels and the rails.

8 a) Shiny aluminium foil is a poor absorber of infra-red radiation – it reflects a lot of the energy; black polythene is a good absorber of radiation and hence the temperature of those sandwiches is raised more quickly.

b) Of the particles of water that soak through the pot, those with higher energy evaporate, leaving the remainder with lower average energy and hence a lower temperature. There will be energy transfer (by conduction) from the pot and its water, thus cooling the pot water and the drink.

9 a) i) A (no force being applied), B, D (no movement) (any 2); ii) C, E; iii) E; iv) C.

b) i) $300 \times 25 = 7500$ J.

ii) 5 minutes = 300 s;

$$\text{average power} = \frac{\text{energy transferred}}{\text{time}} = \frac{7500}{300}$$
$$= 25 \text{ J/s (25 W)}.$$

10 a) i) £150; ii) fitted carpets/better carpet underlay.

b) i) Draught-proofing; for the low installation cost of £5, £150 might be saved in a year; the pay-back time would be only 5/150 = 0.033 years.

ii) Double glazing; of the four methods listed it has the highest installation cost (£4500) and the lowest possible savings (£100); the pay-back time would be 4500/100 = 45 years.

Higher Level

1 a) 4000 J; **b)** 2000 J; **c)** heat – friction between Kara and the slide; **d)** 10 m/s; **e)** the same as Kara's, as the velocity is independent of the mass.

2 a) Potential; **b)** 20 m; **c)** 20 m/s.

3 a) i) 750 J.

ii) The system is not 100% efficient – not all of the electrical (pump) energy is used for lifting the water, e.g. energy is 'lost' as heat due to friction between moving parts in the pump and resistance to water flow along the pipe, sound from the pump, etc.

iii) 62.5%.

b) i) 500 J; ii) 312.5 J; iii) 187.5 J; iv) 37.5%; v) energy losses; vi) 3.33 MW.

4 a) The width of the space between the two panes of glass.

b)

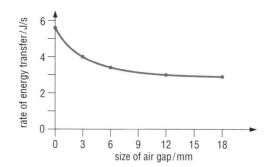

c) The larger the gap, the lower the rate of energy transfer through the window.

d) Initially each 3 mm increase in the air gap produces a significant change (decrease) in the rate of energy transfer. At 12 mm, any increase in the air gap produces insignificant changes in the rate of energy transfer. 12 mm may be the best gap to use.

e) 20 160 J (a single pane is equivalent to having zero gap).

f) 6 mm window transfers 12 240 J in 1 hour, which is 7920 J less (or 39.3% less) than for a single pane.

g) The greater the area of the windows, the greater the rate of energy transfer.

5 a) X 60%, Y 85%, Z 50%.

b) Z (highest power rating and least efficient).

c) Y (highest output).

d) Y. It is the most efficient and it has the lowest power rating, making it the cheapest to use. Also it has the highest output so it will heat a room faster than the others.

6 a) North America is more developed with more industry requiring energy; there is much greater fuel consumption by vehicles and aircraft, and greater energy use for entertainment and leisure; less energy is used on heating in Africa because of its climate.

b) Likely to increase because these countries will develop more uses in industry, homes and transport.

c) i) *Advantages:* coal field nearby, good transport links. *Disadvantages:* pollution, coal is non-renewable, expensive to mine.

ii) Available water for cooling.

iii) Coal is burned producing heat energy from chemical energy. The heat energy boils water to produce steam (under pressure). The steam turns a turbine which turns a generator which produces electrical energy.

iv) Energy losses in electricity distribution increase with an increase in current. Transformers step-up the voltage, which reduces the current, before distribution.

d) i) 600.

ii) *Advantages:* no pollution, renewable source, free source.

Disadvantages: not always windy, each turbine produces small amounts of power, may spoil landscape.

e) i) 2400 MJ; ii) 40%.

7 a) i) 75 years.

ii) More coal reserves than gas reserves and coal is being used at a slower rate.

iii) Wind energy is renewable; it will not run out.

iv) Wind energy requires no expensive raw materials; it is free. It produces no atmospheric pollution.

v) Solar, waves, tidal, hydro-electric, geothermal, biomass (any 3).

b) *Heat* energy released in sun from *nuclear fusion* of hydrogen to helium; *radiation* of *heat/light* energy from sun to earth; absorbed by green plants and trees during *photosynthesis* and stored as *chemical* energy; the *partial decay* of these plants buried under sedimentary material in the absence of oxygen, and with the effects of *pressure* from the rock above over many thousands of years, has produced coal which contains the trapped *chemical* energy.

c) i) Nucleus.

ii) Reactor → boiler → turbine → generator.

iii) Kinetic energy → electrical energy.

8 a) The air near the radiator is warmed. The air particles move about faster and the warm air expands and becomes less dense. It rises towards the ceiling. Cooler, denser air falls and is in turn warmed by the radiator. This rising and falling of air sets up a convection current which circulates the heat energy around the room.

b) The whipped egg white is a poor conductor of heat (an insulator) because of the air trapped in it. Heat is conducted through it very slowly. The sponge is also a poor conductor as it contains air bubbles. In the time that the pudding is in the oven, insufficient heat energy reaches the ice cream to melt it.

c) i) Dull black surfaces are good emitters of infra-red radiation.

ii) The ridges increase the surface area from which energy can be radiated.

Section Six: Quick Questions

6.1

1 a) Nuclear radiation from natural sources.

b) Radon or thoron gas in rocks, medical uses, nuclear waste, cosmic rays, weapon testing fall-out, some rocks (any 3).

2 a) Gamma; **b)** alpha; **c)** two, two; **d)** gamma; **e)** alpha; **f)** alpha; **g)** few mm of metal/keep at a distance.

3 There is some alpha present as tissue paper reduces the count rate, some beta present as thick card further reduces the count, and gamma present as 1 cm of lead further reduces the count down to background levels – no gamma penetrates the lead.

6.2

1 The time taken for half of the nuclei in a radioactive sample to decay.

2 6 years.

3 a) $A = 234$, $Z = 90$; **b)** $A = 228$, $Z = 89$.

4 Technetium-99/xenon-133.

5 Short half-lives (minimum activity), gamma emitters (penetrate tissue).

6

Time (minutes)	0	1	1.8	3	5	–
Count rate (counts/minute)	800	500	350	200	80	25

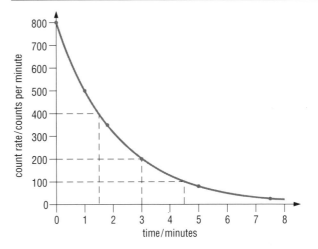

The half-life is 1.5 minutes.

6.3

1 Uranium, plutonium.

2 A nuclear reaction in which nuclei split, releasing energy.

3 a) Energy producer, via nuclear fission (and the release of fission neutrons).

b) Controls the number of neutrons available to cause further fission.

c) Reduces the speed of fission neutrons (slow neutrons are more likely to cause nuclei to split).

4 When a nucleus splits the released neutrons can cause more nuclei to split. The process continues, releasing more neutrons and causing even more fission.

5 Need to be stored in a sealed environment for several thousand years.

Section Six: Exam Practice Questions

Foundation Level

1 **a)** i) They are radioactive.

ii) To protect them from the radioactive emissions.

iii) Radiotherapy.

iv) Nuclear.

b) i) To reduce radioactive emissions.

ii) Lead.

iii) Keep them away from the body (especially eyes and reproductive organs), hold with tongs, always point away from people (any 2).

2 **a)** It would not penetrate the packet material.

b) The soap powder would not reduce gamma penetration.

c) The quantity of powder affects the amount of beta radiation that penetrates and reaches the detector.

d) Beta has a short range in air of up to 0.5 m, so provided the workers keep a greater distance away they will receive no beta radiation. The packet and soap powder will not become radioactive.

3 **a)** Nucleus; **b)** neutrons; **c)** protons; **d)** electrons; **e)** nucleus; **f)** nucleus.

4 **a)** i) Gamma; ii) alpha; iii) beta; iv) gamma.

b) i) Background; ii) cosmic rays, radioactive gas (radon, thoron) from rocks, nuclear waste, nuclear weapon tests, (some) rocks, medical use (any 2).

c) i) Background radiation count has been subtracted; ii) alpha; iii) alpha, beta; iv) some gamma radiation is still penetrating.

d) See page 154.

5 **a)** i) Nucleus; ii) nucleus.

b) i) Alpha; ii) beta; iii) gamma.

c) i) Between 40 and 50 s.

ii) It is detecting background radiation.

d) Dating rocks, sterilisation of instruments, radiotherapy, radiotracers, smoke detectors (any 1).

6 **a)** Isotopes of the same element have the same number of protons in the nucleus but a different number of neutrons. Some isotopes – radioactive isotopes – are unstable and decay, releasing energy and particles.

b) The half-life is the time taken for half the radioactive isotopes present in a sample to decay.

c) i) Radioactive decay is a random process; ii) 340 Bq.

d) i) Geiger-Müller tube/Geiger counter.

ii) Alpha radiation would cause damage to the cells in the body by ionisation; it would not penetrate through to the skin and so would not be detected. Gamma radiation is much more penetrating.

iii) A higher concentration of blood would produce a higher count rate.

Higher Level

1 **a)** i) 88; ii) 138.

b) i) Fission; ii) 92; iii) 233; iv) 3.

2 **a)** i) Activity (counts/min): 460, 365, 290, 190, 150, 110.

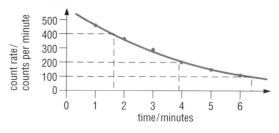

ii) The half-life from the graph is about 2.3 minutes.

b) i)

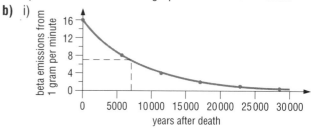

ii) 7500 (±250) years.

3 **a)** 5 minutes = 300 s; 420 counts/300 s = 1.4 counts/second.

b) i) Gamma, beta; ii) alpha, helium.

c) i) Actinium-227; it is a beta emitter with a long half-life. Alpha radiation would not penetrate the cardboard. A beta emitter with a short half-life would emit unnecessary amounts of radiation, potentially causing harm to workers, and it would need to be replaced too frequently.

ii) Neither alpha nor beta radiation would penetrate steel. A gamma emitter would be required.

4 **a)** i) 6 protons, 6 neutrons.

ii) It has 6 protons and 8 neutrons, i.e. 2 extra neutrons.

iii) They all have 6 protons.

b) i)

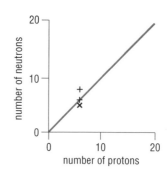

ii) The number of neutrons should equal the number of protons.

iii) $^{12}_{6}$C is the most stable; other forms have too few or too many neutrons.

c) i) Number of protons increases by 1; number of neutrons decreases by 1.

ii) Beta particle (electron).

Index